# Multiple Factors:
# Classroom Mathematics for
# Equality and Justice

# Multiple Factors: Classroom Mathematics for Equality and Justice

*Sharan-Jeet Shan*
*and Peter Bailey*

*tb*

Trentham Books

First published 1991

Reprinted 1994

Trentham Books Limited
Westview House
734 London Road
Oakhill
Stoke-on-Trent
Staffordshire
England ST4 5NP

**British Cataloguing in Publication Data**
A catalogue record for this book is available from the
British Library.

ISBN: 0 948080 30 2

Cover acknowledgements:
Pupils from George Dixon Senior School, Birmingham.
Photographer: John Lawler, Joseph Chamberlain Group.


Designed and typeset by Trentham Print Design Limited, Chester
and printed in Great Britain by Bemrose Shafron limited, Chester

# Preface

Freedom from systematic oppression releases a huge amount of energy. The first instinct is to use this energy to tell one's own story and thereafter to find one's own mode of existence. At least that's how it has been with me. Having written my autobiography *In My Own Name,* I was thrown into a whirlwind of critical dialogue with young people about the tools and paths of freedom; how to take control of one's own life? what to do with the control thus gained? and so on. This book was conceived during such a time, stirring an irrepressible desire to see changes in the context and delivery of the school curriculum, so patently conceived and structured for an élite. As a mathematics teacher, I could see clearly how many of my students could never find the slightest relationship between their lives and classroom mathematics, nor see how mathematics was and is so powerful in the decision-making process about their future careers.

While working on *antiracist approaches to the teaching of mathematics* with a group of Birmingham colleagues, I met Peter Bailey, then Head of Mathematics at a Birmingham school. He had been looking to develop classroom examples in mathematics that would alert his pupils to issues of race and class. It was rare to meet someone on a similar wavelength about such contentious issues. I had found many colleagues willing to 'multiculturalise' mathematics but none wanting to explore issues of equality and justice in a mathematics classroom. Together we decided to work on a book offering practical support for all colleagues, from those wishing only to dip their toes to those who would want to revolutionise their teaching of mathematics.

We have used other people's work throughout the book as illustrative or/and supportive material. They are too numerous to thank individually but all are listed in the Bibliography. We owe them a considerable debt and thank them for their permission, given generously. We did not receive replies to all the letters we sent out requesting permission so would like to note here our grateful thanks to all. It is only fair to state that the way in which we have used the material demonstrates the basis of our philosophy of equality and justice in mathematics. The responsibility for this interpretation is absolutely ours.

We give our warmest and most grateful thanks to Gillian Klein whose unfailing patience, meticulous editing, encouragement and faith in our book made it possible to get to the final preparation of the manuscript and John Stipling whose artwork for illustrations has made many examples come alive.

## by Sharan-Jeet Shan
*General Advisor (National Curriculum Assessment) Sandwell Education Authority*

I have been teaching maths in secondary schools for 24 years. For many years I had been feeling that, although I was considered to be a good teacher, it was only the bright academic students who were really motivated. There was something about the maths syllabuses and my classroom practice which were preventing the majority of students from really getting involved in maths lessons.

A few years ago I had the privilege of teaching in Botswana, where I became to appreciate the delight and the responsibilities of teaching students from a variety of cultural backgrounds. On my return to England I became Head of Maths at an inner-city school in Birmingham. The Cockcroft Report was published. Members of the department spent much time reviewing their approaches to the teaching of maths.

Much thinking about multicultural education had been going on before my arrival at Golden Hillcock School. Birmingham was preparing new policies and I became involved in a number of working groups concerned with matters such as 'under-achievement', culture and relations between home and school. Sharan-Jeet Shan was the leader of one of these groups. She was most encouraging and most persistent. I brought to these meetings many years of experience in the teaching of maths. She brought some clear radical thinking on issues concerning culture, racism and justice, together with a wide understanding of students and schools. Even when she was moved to a different position in the education support service and the working group came to an end, we continued to discuss, argue and try out new ideas. We wrote down some suggestions for colleagues to trial and amended them in the light of feedback. Eventually we took them along to the conferences of

The Mathematical Association and the Association of Teachers of Mathematics for further discussion.

We also attended the sixth International Congress on Mathematical Education in Budapest and were amazed and saddened to find that many international maths educationalists had not yet moved their thinking as far as we had. This gave us the motivation to put our ideas down in book form. With encouragement from Trentham Books (and Gillian Klein in particular) we offer our current thinking for debate.

Education will never stand still, and I am very much aware that much more will be said and written on maths and culture. I hope that many other maths teachers will follow the exciting path that Sharan-Jeet and I have discovered over the recent years.

**by Peter Bailey**
*Deputy Head Teacher, Park View School, Birmingham Education Authority*

# Contents

*Chapter 1*

# Mathematics for Equality and Justice — An Introduction

> *If only I had known, I would have become a watch maker.*
> — Albert Einstein.

Mathematics, English and science are core subjects in the National Curriculum for England and Wales. Mathematics and science occupy the highest position on educational agendas the world over, but mathematics has a unique position. It is used by all societies in everyday living, for work and for leisure (as in games). Yet no other subject inspires such controversial views and debate, not only among teachers and teacher-educators, but also among students, parents and society at large. This chapter looks at some possible explanations for this controversy and sets the context in which our ideas developed. Our arguments are supported with evidence from research in the teaching of mathematics and also science, because the two subjects are closely related.

The chapter is divided into 3 sections. The rationale examines the myth that mathematics as a body of knowledge is neutral. We show how the eurocentrism of mathematics text books and its pedagogical implications are being challenged worldwide. Ideas of enculturation, placing mathematics in its historical, social, political and economic context, are being developed. Though the theoretical orientations behind this evolution are not the subject of this book, it is important to note that these new developments are backed by academic theories.

*The history* of the development of mathematics curriculum is not separate from other areas of the curriculum nor from other political and institutional developments in society. We look briefly at the perception, definition and response of policy makers in the UK to issues of 'race' and 'racism' in education from the 60s to the 80s.

The last section of the introduction outlines a holistic approach to the culture of school mathematics, placing teacher and student at the centre of developments. One aspect of the classroom is little influenced by educational changes: the interpersonal exchange between student and teacher, for which they alone are responsible.

## The Rationale.

It is distressing that so many students all over the world achieve low levels in mathematics examinations. This sad fact has inspired mathematics educators to examine the cultural context of mathematics in the hope of improving the quality of mathematical education by embedding it in the reality of the students lives. Their analysis has shown that mathematics takes its values from, and gives value to, a particular culture, and that western mathematics is the product of much that went before. This relatively new approach is variously termed: *multicultural mathematics, ethnomathematics, antiracist mathematics.* Our rationale draws upon these developments as well as suggesting some new ideas. We have not concerned ourselves with absolute, definitive, or clearly identifiable meanings to these terms. We are aware that disagreements exist about definitions amongst the mathematicians whose work we have drawn upon. However, for clarity, we use a consistent set of definitions, which are given at the end of this chapter.

## The Neutrality Myth and Eurocentrism in mathematics.

*The Concise Oxford Dictionary* defines mathematics as a 'pure, abstract science of space and quantity'. This fosters the notion that mathematical ideas develop in a neutral context, free of social or political influences. Yet mathematics is the basis of the world of commerce, science, technology, and the countless everyday transactions that we all perform. How then has this activity of daily life come to be regarded as abstract? The answer has two independent parts.

The first lies in the mystique that has been accorded to the study of mathematics in all civilisations, and the result of this is that mathematics, like many other areas of knowledge such as science and music, comes across in history as the domain of the learned male.

Secondly, the European dominance of the past 400 years suppressed the high achievements in science and mathematics of pre-colonial times in all countries colonised. (*Aborted Discovery,* Goonatilake, S. 1984)

Hogben, in his book *Mathematics for the Million,* traces the development of the mystique tendency to the time of Pythagoras:

> they formed themselves into secret societies and invested mathematics with the august and awful mystery which it has had ever since. Mathematical discoveries were communicated under oath — Hippasus, a member of one of these societies, is said to have been drowned in his bath for giving away mathematical truths for nothing.

In ancient Hindu society, mathematics was regarded as sacrosanct, awesome and the purest of all disciplines. Ancient Hindus went to great lengths to disguise and conceal their discoveries of calculus. The sacred Vedas hold a testimony to this. The mathematical developments were hidden into the Vedic text in the form of Sutras-threads, which even today baffle world scholars. (*Vedic Mathematics.* By Tirathji. 1966)

Hindu Brahmins saw mathematics as holding the key not only to the universal mysteries of stars and planets, but also to the timeless truths of the gods, heaven and hell. Though modern scholars have now attained some understanding of how ancient Brahmins mastered abstract number, in AD 595, you would have had to be a male child in a high caste household to get a look in at this sacred knowledge. The development of mathematics and science in every age and society reflects the values and needs of the times. Every development of mathematics in the Greek and Roman world related to the kind of societies they were. Pythagoras theorem, the Plumb line, and Euclidian geometry were born out of a direct necessity to solve contemporary problems in building in Greece, Rome, and Egypt. (*Egypt is in Africa and not a part of Saudi Arabia, a common misconception amongst children and many adults, along with the idea that all the Egyptians were white*).

Applied mathematics is rationally developed to suit the economic, social and political needs of a particular society. Both science and mathematics are products as well as creators of the social order. The greatest mathematicians of India in mediaeval times, Brahmagupta (7th century), Mahavira (9th century), and Bhaskara (12th century), were not housewives, warriors or poor farmers. They were members of the highest caste — the Brahmins. This elite caste had the privilege of bestowing labouring positions to the rest of society. This meant that the members of the Brahmin caste could afford the luxury of spending their lives studying and advancing this single cause of human knowledge.

In modern times, the all powerful computer was born out of calculating machines used to speed up addition and other calculations for simple accounting. It would be interesting for our students to find out who puts the money into the developments of modern micros and the variety of uses to which they are put in industry and commerce. The so called 'pure' research into such technology is made possible only by funding from the Ministry of Defence and the multinationals. In *Anti-Racist Science Teaching* (1987), Robert Young suggests that 80% of this country's research budget goes on improving the efficiency and accuracy of targeting nuclear devices.

The myth of neutrality pervades the scientific and mathematical organisations and structures, which in turn perpetuate the myth-upholding curriculum. Examinations, the curriculum materials and the teaching techniques designed to meet their demands, perpetuate the role of mathematics as a stabiliser of the power of the elite. Success in examinations is considered the key factor in the selection of society's 'best brains'. A good pass in mathematics is often a key requirement for university and polytechnic entrance, particularly to courses relating to industry. Success in mathematics determines access to power, thus perpetuating the belief that mathematical understanding is a privilege of a select few who have some special innate ability.

The eurocentric bias in the perception, development, dissemination and evaluation of all science and mathematics is evident from the recording of the history of mathematics and science. Even the Open University, our standard bearer in progressive education, gives no special recognition to Hindu and Arab mathematics in their course books for the history of mathematics. There is no acknowledgment of the Vedic mathematics which covered all aspects including calculus, and which is the oldest written record of mathematics. This omission is due to an outdated colonial perspective and it distorts or entirely obliterates the contribution of some of the world's great mathematicians. In their book, *Schooling in Capitalist America*, 1976, Bowles and Gintis argue that:-

> One result of colonialism and imperialism has been the suppression of the culture and science of the 'third world' peoples and the creation of the myth of European science as a seamless body of truth. In this way it promotes an inferiority notion of black peoples and encourages white male chauvinism. Too much of the way we teach mathematics shares in this. We do little to show that mathematics is the product of the thinking and achievements of all the peoples in the world. We must not allow the universality of mathematics to be lost.

If we truly believe that mathematics is a universal activity, then we must acknowledge its universal origins. A range of formulations of the same basic concepts should strengthen the commonality of human beings.In his book, *History of Mathematics* (1990), G.G.Joseph raises an important question:

If one is imprisoned within the ethnocentricity of a particular place/time location, then non-European reality may only impinge marginally either as an unchanging residual experience to be contrasted with the dynamism and creativity of Europe or as a rationale for the creation of disciplines concealed in subjects such as Development studies, Anthropology, Orientalism, Indology and Sinology.

Given the symbiotic relationship of the writing of European history of mathematics and science, with the scramble for Africa and the subjugation of Asia, it is no wonder that all mathematical origins are eurocentrically located in the lap of Greeks. A substantial body of research has revealed evidence of references by the Greeks themselves to visits by their great mathematicians such as Thales and Pythagoras, to Egypt, Babylon and India to study mathematics. A few such pieces of evidence, from the oldest Indian, Chinese and Arab books on mathematics and science expose the racist imperialist ideology of dominance.

— The earliest known proof of the Pythagoras theorem appears in *Sulbasutras* (c600-800 BC), an ancient Indian text. The earliest known Greek proof was given by Euclid. There is no recorded evidence that Pythagoras ever stated or proved this theorem.

— The first known statement of the law of gravity, later attributed to Newton, was by an Arab scientist, Ibn-al-Haytham.

— The first example of the rationale underlying the 'scientific method' usually attributed to Francis Bacon, is found in the works of Arab scientists Ibn Sina, Ibn-al-Haytham and al- Biruni.

— The first clear statement of the theory of evolution, usually attributed to Darwin, is by Ibn Miskawayah.

These examples have barely touched the tip of the iceberg, but I hope that colleagues will be intrigued enough to explore further, to look beyond and behind the mathematical formulae, to what this fascinating world of numbers, lines and shapes tells us about our world and ourselves.

## Maths in a Social and Cultural Context

Here is an enthralling example of mathematics being used as a means of observation of human history. These are opening lines from: *Mathematics: A vehicle for better global understanding,* by Frank Swetz, USA.

Jacob Bronowski, in his magnificent television series *The Ascent of Man* (1973) relates his experience of the debate on the question of Australopithecus being a true predecessor to the human species — in 1924, the oldest

5

humanoid fossil skull, over 2 million years old, was uncovered at Taung in Southern Africa.

I was asked to do a piece of mathematics. Could I combine a measure of the size of the Taung child's teeth with their shape, so as to discriminate them from the teeth of apes? I had never held a fossil skull in my hands, and I was by no means an expert on teeth. But it worked pretty well: and it transmitted to me a sense of excitement which I remember at this instant. I, at over forty, having spent a lifetime doing abstract mathematics about the shapes of things, suddenly saw my knowledge reach back 2 million years and shine a searchlight into the history of man. That was phenomenal.

University mathematicians world wide have begun to accept the relationship between mathematics, its social context and construction and cultural influences. (Bishop, 1988; Bishop and Nixon, 1983.) Teachers in England and Wales have also begun to take up the challenge that mathematics should be used to impart a variety of information about everyday life as affirmed in the *Cockroft Report* (1982).

Recognition of these societal connections led the sixth International Congress of Mathematical Education in Budapest, 1988, to explore connection between mathematics, education and society. Issues raised ranged from challenges to institutionalized mathematics education, the image of mathematics in society, worldwide developments in ethnomathematics, social construction of mathematical meaning and the societal determinants of learning. The conference, attended by some 2000 of the world's leading educators in mathematics, raised the following questions::

- Which interests are served by mathematics education?
- Whose interests are served by mathematics education?
- How does mathematics education relate to destructive technological developments?
- Are girls around the world underprivileged in mathematics education?
- Do mathematics educators know what they are doing?
- What are the challenges to mathematical instruction in the next decade?
- What can we expect from 'ethnomathematics'?

All this may be dismissed by those hiding behind the neutrality myth as politicisation. They argue, we should not bring politics into the classroom. Our response is that politics is always present in our teaching, but is not perceived as political when supportive to the dominant ideology. Chandler Davis, a mathematician from the University of Toronto, asks why, if physicists, chemists, engineers and even historians can talk about their social responsibility, can't mathematicians? In his paper at ICME-6 in Hungary (August 1988), Davis gave examples of the pledges that were made by several scientists at international level, banning the use of their research for military purposes. He proposed a similar qualifying commitment to that taken by Medical Doctors:

> They call World War 1 the chemist's war, World War 2 the physicist's and World War 3 the mathematician's. — isn't it time that there was an ethical statement, a pledge for mathematicians, analogous to the Hippocratic oath in medicine?

There are many reasons why the nature of mathematics makes it one of the most important connections between political, economic and social aspects of an individual's life. Ole Skovsmose, from Aalborg University Centre, Denmark, also a well-known artist, picks up this argument for examining popular attitudes to mathematics and expands it further. He would like his students to develop a critical attitude to the applications of mathematics and associated social functions. He sees the need to increase the interaction between critical education and mathematical education:-

> if mathematics education is not to degenerate into one of the most important ways of socialising students into the technological society and at the same time destroying the possibilities of developing a critical attitude towards precisely this technological society. —

Arguing for developing such mathematical materials as would constitute a basis for reflective knowledge. i.e, knowledge about how to evaluate and criticise, not just to build a mathematical model, he warns that mathematical education at present implants a servile attitude towards technological questions in many of our students. In his opinion:

> The fundamental structuring principles of the curriculum are derived from or are in accordance with the dominant power relations of the society. Critical mathematical education would develop the content and form of mathematical education in such a way that it will serve as a tool of democratization and see to it that dominant power relations are not passively reproduced.

## Ethnomathematics.

Ethnomathematics is a relatively new concept, researched and published primarily by two mathematicians — Ubiratan d'Ambrosio from Brazil and Paules Gerdes from Mozambique. It explores cultural specific mathematical practices and is substantially different from the formalised ways of mathematical knowledge, particularly in ciphering, counting, classifying, measuring, ordering, inferring and modelling.

Gerdes (1982) bases his case for using mathematical education as the means for emancipation in ex-colonised countries on the history of Mozambique. We should not assume that these mathematicians consider all mathematics based on western ideas of wealth as bad. They are talking about redressing the balance by taking cognizance of the historical influence in shaping the present economy of their countries. Gerdes identifies a change in the nature of mathematical education from colonial rule to independence:

> During the Portuguese domination, mathematics was taught, in the interests of colonial capitalism, only to a small minority of African children. And those Mozambicans were taught mathematics to be able to calculate better the hut tax to be paid and the compulsory quota of cotton every family had to produce. They were taught mathematics to be more lucrative 'boss boys' in South African mines. Post-independence objectives of mathematics education is to 'serve the liberation and peaceful progress of the people'. Mathematics is taught to place its applications within the reach of the worker and the peasant masses, to stimulate them to take an interest in general mathematical creation.

Gerdes employs cultural strategies by which mathematics can be learnt, and a pride fostered by locating mathematical concepts in the capabilities of people to develop mathematics themselves. For example:

- Fishermen learning to dry fish by placing them in a circle around a fire, constructing the circle with two sticks and a rope.
- Constructing houses using the shape concepts.
- Traditional mats and containers that use the concept of spirals, volume, maximisation, capacity etc.
- Historical evidence that people all over the world developed mathematics for everyday use.

Social initiatives have been established, such as special awards and scholarships for children and young people of both sexes and all social classes. Also individual/collective strategies that encourage students to work in groups and reflect together on processes and concepts, and to work creatively. These examples illustrate how functional mathematics is used to foster an integrated approach, taking in the social context as well as appealing to the aesthetic sense of students.

Our chapter on multicultural mathematics gives some examples of how Gerdes has used cultural practices to teach traditional mathematics.

Ubiratan d'Ambrosio, in his book, *Ethnomathematics and its place in the History and Pedagogy of Mathematics* (1985b) seeks to get at the underlying structure of the process by which many ad hoc mathematical practices around the world — develop into methods which — develop into theories — finally developing into scientific inventions. Considering the long period and the power of colonisation which determined who would receive professional accreditation, it is no wonder that western scientists and mathematicians became the models for the rest of the world. D'Ambrosio quotes from Bellatone's book on a second scientific revolution:

> There is a temptation hidden in the pages of history of science — the temptation to derive the birth and death of theories, the formalization and growth of concepts, from a scheme (either logical or philosophical) always valid and everywhere applicable.
>
> —Instead of dealing with real problems, history would then become a learned view of edifying tales for the benefit of one philosophical school or another.

Mathematics such as ethnomathematics may not be usable as 'revolutionary mathematics' or recognisable as a traditional scientific discipline but it strongly challenges western theory based, structurally and systematically organised mathematics. It highlights a fact in which the tribal peoples of the world can take justifiable pride: that despite the oppression of colonialism and slavery, they did not let their sound traditional practices in any 'knowledge' area die and that they have much to teach us.

There are many examples of the western model of mathematical education being challenged by mathematics educators from the East. In his study of *Mathematics, Culture and Authority* (ICME-6 1988) Munir Fasheh asserts:

> The main objective of teaching mathematics and for that matter any other subject should be to doubt, to enquire, to discover, to see alternatives, to enhance a critical attitude of one's self, society and culture, and most of all to be an instrument in changing attitudes, convictions and perspectives.

His experience is located in teaching Palestinian Arabs at Birzeit University on the West Bank, under different political constructs and authorities. (The region had been under British rule since 1948, Jordanian rule from 1967, and Israeli occupation from 1972.) Through examples of everyday events, students learn that 'axioms are not God-given', but are rather statements that evolve with time and through a long hard process. They learn how the meanings of words and concepts evolve, and that there are vast differences in *facts* and their interpretations. Working in a strife-torn country, he challenges the western notion of mathematics being absolute and detached:

> In spite of the claim by educational institutions that they encourage free and critical thinking, in general one finds that they discourage original, free thinking and expression, especially when that touches upon the *important* issues in society. Such students everywhere in the world are considered a threat to existing and established institutions... The world is heading to a peak of cultural changes and cultural awareness. Mathematics can be used to stress one's own culture with its special and beautiful characteristics, as well as making oneself aware of the drawbacks and how to overcome them. I have always read, for example, that the Arabs contributed a lot to mathematics and science — they invented the solution to the general cubic equation. The school curriculum never showed me how they did it. Western historians in general have denied this. Teaching maths in a purely abstract, symbolic and meaningless way is not simply useless and boring, it is positively harmful to our students, to society, to mathematics itself, and to the future generations.

## Our approach: Problematisation of Reality

We have combined the rationale above with Friere's principle of problematisation of reality in classroom situations. Teachers are the makers of that unique classroom experience for their students. We believe that this rationale will lead to a critical understanding of reality.

Only a holistic awareness of the political, social, economic and cultural will lead our students to use mathematics as a tool to work out real solutions to real problems. This is explained in greater detail later in this chapter.

## The History

The curriculum is not developed in a vacuum. One reason why progress in the multiculturalisation of mathematics has been so slow, is the attitude of successive governments to antiracist/ multicultural education — indeed to education itself. While models of the curriculum have see-sawed between student-centred learning and the core curriculum, common curriculum and the national curriculum (Lawton,1978), contradictions abound in policies on multicultural education. From Rhodes Boyson to Kenneth Baker, they may have shifted their focus, but never their ideological ground. From assimilation to integration to multiculturalism — all reflect the institutional racism which was the basis of:

> racially explicit policies in immigration housing and employment issues as opposed to racially inexplicit policies in educational orientations. (Troyna and Williams,1986)

It is not long — 1962 — since an overt colour bar operated in Britain's cities (Daniels,1968). During the *assimilationist phase,* the 60s, bussing of black children, withdrawal classes and some separate RE provision was the sum total of curriculum development for multicultural Britain. DES circular 7/65 sums up the contradiction between educational and political rhetoric:

> the culture, language and religion of the immigrant children not only impedes their progress, it also has a negative effect on their white schoolmates.

Educational documents from the DES during the *integrationist* phase, 70s show no signs that policy makers had begun to acknowledge structural inequalities and to stop locating the underachievement of black children in their home backgrounds and culture.

During the *multiculturalist* phase in the early 80s while there were some exciting developments in the curriculum, such as challenging bias in textbooks, white students studying 'other' cultures, black students studying the history of their parental countries etc., there was very little debate on the racism experienced by black people.

*Antiracist education,* which asks for a change in the institutional orientation (Mullard, 1984), has generated wide spread debate amongst teachers, teacher educators and educational theorists. Though the attitude of the central government has remained unchanged in terms of policy making and implementation, there have thankfully been regional variations on the theme. Almost invariably, these initiatives have been in those inner city authorities where ethnic minority communities had settled in large numbers. Several authorities have begun to scrutinise the dynamics of classroom pedagogy in order to eliminate factors which disadvantage black and white working class students and girls — particularly Asian girls. Problem posing, participatory strategies involving students in their own learning, have been actively followed by many teachers, particularly in areas of geography, history and mathematics, though not always from an antiracist point of view.

11

The notion of 'education for all', the main tenet of the Swann Report (1985), sees multicultural education as central to the entire curriculum of all schools. It seeks to challenge racism and attack inherited myths and stereotypes embedded in institutional practices. Even so, many feel that Swann does not go far enough in challenging racist institutional practices within the state or the educational system.

Before the advent of the Education Reform Act, Local Education Authorities (LEAs) were asked to declare their policies on countering the influence of racism, including in the examination systems.'Education for all' was to permeate throughout teacher education as a central and compulsory core. The policy statement from Birmingham District Council hoped to achieve:-

reorientation of perspectives by underlining the ways in which attitudes and structural practices lead to racist outcomes. In an all white school a deliberate effort has to be made towards this reorientation lest education of the white pupil be anachronistic and unfit for the real world.

The National Curriculum and the fate of antiracist education are considered in a later chapter.

It is important to recognise that while there has been progress, the policies for multicultural/antiracist education have been constantly under threat. The sensational elements in the press have taken every opportunity to attack. Their treatment of the tragic killing of a 12 year old Muslim boy in a Manchester school in 1984 is typical. The MacDonald enquiry report stated that the school's antiracist policy was kept in the filing cabinet and that there was no structure in the school for its implementation. And yet the press blamed the school's antiracist policy for causing overt tensions which lead to the death of Abdul Iqbal Ullah at the hands of his white classmate. Because Manchester City Council withheld the report for a long time, full information on events and staff attitudes before and after the death were difficult to establish at the time. The long delay in publishing the enquiry findings suppressed serious debate and allowed the popular press to promote the erroneous belief that antiracist polices inevitably lead to confrontation. The crucial issue is: what was at fault: the policy or its implementation — or both?

Helped by and helping the adverse press coverage, antiracist education is under fierce attack from the new right. This has influenced some major changes by the government such as the dismantling of the Inner London Education Authority (ILEA). The speed of its execution and the total disregard of the parents' votes for ILEA to continue suggests that the motives were ideological rather than educational. This book will be criticised by the right, but there is greater awareness of the many cultures in this country and at least some black men and women are in senior positions in the country's institutions. We hope that the more active, challenging and experiential way of learning mathematics set out here will contribute towards change.

A commonly held notion is that antiracist education is to do with helping black people. But antiracism is in fact the critical rationale whereby racist attitudes can be reviewed in the light of oppression in race, class and also in terms of gender and special needs issues. It brings the hidden agenda into view and goes deeper than the skin. The labels 'antiracist education' or 'education for emancipation' may have threatening connotations for some colleagues. Examining and challenging the *status quo* is bound to cause discomfort and even personal and interpersonal conflict.

Antiracist education compels us to examine the total dimension of our professionalism. Enhancing the life chances of all our pupils demands a critical review of the following:

- organisations — structures and related politics.
- self-assessment of one's professional knowledge.
- an awareness of oneself as a person and one's interpersonal relationships with other colleagues — as human beings not just as competitors.
- attitudes to pupils, parents & their expectations. attitudes to community organisations.
- attitudes to technology and class, race and gender oppressions world wide.

Before, during, and after the empire, the lives of ordinary people were, and still are caught in the control phenomenon. Mahatma Gandhi, on visiting the cotton mill workers in Lancashire, expressed his grief at taking cotton cloth production away from them and placing it in the hands of Indian farmers who had grown the crop.

Many students are still being fed the anachronistic idea that the British still rule the world. The National Curriculum could become the institutional enforcement of the study of 'Englishness', as opposed to 'other cultures', if the following statement from the former Secretary of State for Education were to be followed.

Next to our people, the English language is our greatest asset as a nation, it is essential for the Englishness of England. — It is the people of England who fashion the shape, create the flavour and determine the direction of our changing national consciousness.

13

Mr. Baker seems to have overlooked certain aspects of British life, such as the brutish football fans who terrorise Europe. The rationale that we would have hoped for from the Secretary of State for Education would strive towards a new identity for all British children, a new pride in working collectively to eradicate discrimination and to create equal access to opportunities for enhancing life chances for all pupils. This is the rationale that should have come from the Secretary of State for Education.

## What this book does.

This book indicates some new ways of looking at teaching mathematics, more truly educational and more satisfying. In the past, many students became anxious about mathematics, disliking it for not relating to their world. The exercises that we have devised are located in contemporary issues and in local, national and international scenes.

We look at our own experience in teaching mathematics in Britain and ask:

— Why are so many of our students and their parents afraid of mathematics?

— Which aspects of classroom practice lead to such an active dislike and fear of mathematics?

— Why do students feel bad about themselves if they aren't good at classroom mathematics?

— How is our mathematics teaching *really* received by students?

— Why is mathematics considered a key to success?

We echo the challenge of Paolo Friere (1972): that the 'banking concept of education is a tool used for the oppression of people'. Students are not little vessels that you fill with contents of your own choice. Most modern mathematics teaching, despite Cockroft's plea (1982) for a problem solving, participatory approach, is based on the 'banking' concept. Its followers would inevitably view antiracist education as a subversive ideology, because it makes people aware of how the state purposely constructs limitations on their life chances and uses education as a major system of control for maintaining the subordination of the majority. Antiracist education threatens the dominant ideology and social order. It engages people in the active process of their own liberation, enabling them to recognise and combat discriminatory practices by the state. In Friere's critical praxis of problem-posing education, the teacher/student model takes a new shape:

Liberation education consists of acts of cognition, not transferrals of information. It is a learning situation in which the cognizable object (far from being the end of the cognitive act) intermediates the cognitive actors, teachers on the one hand and students on the other... Through dialogue, the teacher of the students and the students of the teacher cease to exist and a new term emerges: teacher students with student teachers... Whereas banking education anaesthetises and inhibits creative power, problem posing education involves a constant unveiling of reality. The former attempts to maintain the submersion of consciousness: the latter strives for the emergence of consciousness and critical intervention in reality.

If we as adults do not challenge the basis of the knowledge presented to us, do not locate the reality of progress in its totality, into the context in which it is born, how can we inspire our pupils to think and act critically? When one area of knowledge has been elevated to a pure form of logic, culture free and abstract, for thousands of years, it will be resistant to the antiracist approach. And as the debate moves on from using mathematical education for celebration of difference to using it as a vehicle for combating discriminatory practices, resistance will grow.

Sharan-Jeet, one of the authors of this book, writes:

> When I started to train as a teacher here in England, back in 1968, freshly arrived from India, I was constantly being exposed to most derisory and derogatory images of my mother country in the science, maths, geography and history textbooks used in British schools. Later, as a teacher, I soon came to realise that education is not politically free. I had a proud childhood as the daughter of an Indian Army officer and a rich education in an ordinary state school in Delhi, gaining mastery over three languages... so it is true that I come from a relatively privileged background .
>
> It was an amazing discovery for me that the country which sings 'Land of Hope and Glory' so proudly, has so rigid a class system and that the poor are trapped just as in the country of my birth. The old 'rulers' of the world have many thousands of homeless, and millions unemployed and living below the poverty line.
>
> I hesitate to call them rulers because they were really exploiters and oppressors. I could name some true rulers in the history of India such as Moghul Emperor Akbar, Ashoka the Great, and Jhansi ki Rani.
>
> And yet all I have seen on British television and in British textbooks are statistics that keep telling me and my students what a primitive, overpopulated and poor country my India is. It is no wonder that often my students

> have asked: Did you live in a mud hut, Miss? This awareness of falsification of information and belittling and humiliation of black people by clever use of statistics, was my first step to looking into the teaching of mathematics as a liberating form of education, a personal cause.

The antiracist approach is not about patronising 'other' cultures nor merely appreciating a variety of languages and customs. It is about enabling our pupils to understand how the imbalance of economic power is created, so challenges racism directly. Statistics can be used to reflect the social reality of our world and can be a tool for students to explore inequality and injustice. Antiracist mathematics issues a challenge to the one third of the world which exploits the other two-thirds purely for profit. (George,1976)

Many studies have identified the underachievement of black children, in particular children of West Indian origin. Reports have also highlighted the manner in which girls and children from the working classes in general come to be disadvantaged in the system. The research indicates that one of the largest factors which erodes the creative energies of very young children is the social and economic deprivation caused by discriminatory practices in government policies, particularly housing, employment and education. (For example see: 'School process — An ethnographic study' by Cecile Wright in *Education for Some,* the Eggleston report. 1986 and Bernard Coard: *How the West Indian Child is made Subnormal in the British School System,* 1971).

Black children and their origins have been devalued by labels like 'first generation immigrants, Asian, West Indian, coloured, ethnic minority, and finally Black British'. Always the white community has been referred to as 'hosts' in relation to the black — as if we are guests who will one day leave! And can there be such a person as a 'second generation immigrant?'.In line with this thinking, there have been immigrant units, remedial classes, the humiliating system of bussing for black children, and multicultural education promoting 'other cultures' — the sarees, samosas and steel pans syndrome, all of them at best token measures and at worst positively divisive and damaging.

The problem is this: Whenever single factors such as self concept, language, culture are used to explain poor achievement by black pupils, the *status quo* of institutional discrimination and exclusion of black people from power structures becomes entrenched even further.

Milner's conclusions on identity and self-esteem, which formed the backbone of many initiatives in multicultural education, have been effectively challenged by Maureen Stone in her book: *The Education of the Black*

*Child in Britain.* Milner shows how ideas confirming racial attitudes are inculcated in very young children and this is valuable. However, Stone demonstrates how the identity and the self-esteem model is used to place the causes for underachievement in the black child him/herself, so establishing a blame-the-victim model, which is both unjust and incorrect. Thus institutional racism goes unchallenged and teachers continue to applaud themselves for doing something for the poor black children.

While supporting our rationale with current theoretical and academic debate, the main aim of this book is to provide colleagues with classroom material. We looked at the published mathematics resources available — the pejoratively biased, the multiculturalised, with a range of names from different backgrounds, images of various lifestyles, positive role models. We particulary noted the materials produced by the ILEA, such as *Everyone Counts* and the other LEAs, at Brian Hudson's project at York University, especially their data base. There are five chapters on classroom examples, to be used in a variety of ways. We suggest ways of implementing a policy in your department and provide checklists for monitoring implementation. We have examined the National Curriculum requirements and used them as helping factors rather than hindrance. We invite you to come with an open mind on your journey with us, developing new ideas on mathematics teaching and sharpening the edges of professionalism. We have tried to take cognizance of how certain attitudes are developed and engaged in critical dialogue. We have raised many questions and hope to have answered a few.

We look also at published materials available in England. Some publishers have sought to multiculturalise textbooks, and we list those who are most forthcoming in including names from different backgrounds, images of various lifestyles, positive role models in terms of gender and jobs. We welcome such attempts unless they are overtly tokenistic. The ILEA publication Everyone Counts actively challenges mathematics text books. Teachers of mathematics in ILEA have also produced materials that use statistics from South Africa, from the Community Relations Council, from Tate and Lyle's sugar empire and from aid and trade situations from around the world, particularly in the clothing industry. Other local education authorities are also beginning to re-evaluate mathematics, as is evidenced by a number of small booklets, some in draft.

Dr. Brian Hudson and his team at the University of York, have developed a package of materials on issues relating to world development, military technology, the arms race and human rights. Their data base containing data on 127 countries includes life- expectancy, infant mortality rates, levels of military expenditure etc. Students can use the data to learn mathematics, while learning of the power mathematics can provide for analysing our world. They can explore how mathematics is used to help perpetuate the political and social structures that control countries. We wish to extend and develop this approach so that students analysing such data learn that human beings are not only interdependent but that the majority are exploited for the benefit of the few. Students need to understand how inequality is systematically created and how people are trapped. This book suggests ways in which mathematics teachers can enable students to do so.

This book challenges racist myths and related stereotypes and seeks to expose some of the systematic exploitation that has so effectively institutionalised racism by using three, often interwoven, strategies:

1. *We explore maths that is new to schools in the UK* — particularly in the chapter on the intricately developed but simply used Vedic mathematical principles.

2. *We set familiar problem-solving maths in an antiracist context* — as when we teach statistical representation and graphs in relation to, say, land exploitation or state-enforced inequality in South Africa.

3. *We examine pedagogy, classroom interactions and school ethos and organisation* as they apply to mathematics teachers seeking to create non-racist and non-sexist learning patterns and environments.

We hope that you enjoy sharing this critical appraisal of our profession as much as we have enjoyed researching this book.

# Terminology

Before we move on, we need to establish what we mean by certain terms. Accordingly, here is a brief glossary of some widely used in the book.

## Racism.

This broad definition of *racism* is from the 1978 Declaration on Race and Racial prejudice and was the first to be adopted by the General conference of UNESCO.

Any theory which involves the claim that racial or ethnic groups are inherently superior or inferior, thus implying that some would be entitled to dominate or eliminate others, presumed to be inferior, or which base value judgments on racial discrimination.

Racism includes racist ideologies, prejudiced attitudes, discriminatory behaviour, structural arrangements and instituitonalized practices resulting in racial inequality as well as the fallacious notion that discriminatory relations between groups are morally and scientifically justifiable.

## Assimilation.

This is the view that immigrants seeking to improve themselves were let in by slack immigration laws. They should counter prejudices in the indigenous community by doing in *Rome as the Romans do.* They should assimilate, integrate and learn to speak English. Children are children and *we treat them all the same.*

## Multiculturalism.

This view concentrates on the 'celebration of difference', and on learning from 'the diversity amongst us'. Ethnic minorities have a right to live here and *their* cultural differences should be respected. The proponents of a multicultural mode of education believe that by promoting better understanding about *their* culture, History, Religion and Languages, we will all learn to be tolerant, as the British are basically very fair and just-minded people.

## Antiracism.

This view seeks to remove structural *racist, sexist and classist* inequalities by creating a new social order and dismantling the established, institutional discriminatory structures which have been in existence for many centuries. Black people came here because their labour was sought for economic development.

19

According to this rationale, *education* must take on board the teaching of race and racial issues. The power structures must look at the positions of black people within their organisations and eradicate discrimination.

An antiracist mode of delivery looks at the education of the black as well as the white child, and seeks to review and change process as well as content.

## Black

In this book the word black has been used for all people who are not white. It is a political rather than a descriptive term as an umbrella word for all those at the sharp end of racial discrimination.

## Curriculum

We have drawn on Denis Lawton's definition, in *Class, Culture and the Curriculum:*

The word 'curriculum' encompasses a whole set of ideas, beliefs and values in addition to the content of the textbooks and the skills that we teach our pupils. The ideas, beliefs and values form the 'hidden curriculum'.

In our view GCSE AIM : 2.4... 'To apply mathematics in everyday situations and develop an understanding of the part that mathematics plays in the world around them' should be a 'desirable' aim to test.

It is not enough to enable pupils to develop their powers of 'Abstraction, Generalisation and Proof'. We should also be enabling pupils to *extract and interpret mathematical data used to hide ugly realities in the name of development, aid, progress, defence, urban renewal etc.* From cradle to adulthood, the young are conditioned by the education system and mass media to believe that their life is in someone else's control and, worse still, control is acceptable. Mathematical facts and figures are used daily to reflect the 'reality' of the social order, confirming and endorsing the *status quo.*

## Culture and Knowledge

One of the fundamental aims of education is to prepare pupils to acquire skills which will assist them to survive financially, socially and emotionally. This preparation entails the transmission of selected culture in the form of curriculum. We have provided evidence that mathematics, far from being culturally free and neutral, provides for promotion of the dominant ideology .

Terminology is important so that everyone has a shared understanding and a starting point. *Treating all pupils the same* is a much used phrase and yet people cannot simply treat each other equally because they wish to do so. The social order and its institutions have to change to provide a framework in which people have equal opportunities to realise their potentialities. Racism is like a slow growing cancer handed down to us by centuries of methodical exploitation and institutionalisation. Racist myths and related stereotypes were created to justify the notions of superiority and inferiority and the most abhorrent treatment of black people. South Africa is today's reality. At the same time, uprisings in inner cities reflect the growth of black consciousness, never to be oppressed again. In each chapter we have given important considerations to the ' reality' as it is perceived — differently — by blacks and whites.

CLASSROOM MATHEMATICS FOR EQUALITY AND JUSTICE

*Chapter 2*

# Culture of School Mathematics — The Process of Effective Teaching.

> *All in educational pedagogy even if scarcely coherent rests on pedagogy of mathematics.* — ICME 1972

This chapter looks at the influence of social and cultural relations on the process of delivery in the classroom, while chapter 3 explores their influence on the content of lessons.

While collecting materials on the kind of mathematics practised in different societies, we were inspired by the close connection of mathematics with the daily lives of people everywhere. We are talking not about abstract mathematics manipulated by learned scholars to prove points but mathematics used by ordinary people. All have ways of counting: numbers can have symbols, be knots in a string, notches cut into wood, hieroglyphs or beads on a bar. Everywhere, people have wanted to measure lengths, weights, and volumes. Many ancient cities show highly advanced ways of measuring for the purposes of building (for example, the cites of Mohenjo Daro and Harappa, described in *The Wonder That was India*. Basham, 1985).

Mathematical games are a part of leisure activities in all cultures. Many traditional games from cultures as diverse as Africa, India and China seem to have similar, sometimes identical rules (see Tic Tac Toe: Three in a row games. Zaslavsky,1982). All cultures have developed their own calendars, time clocks, ways of using geometric shapes in architecture, navigation by stars, calculations in astronomy and, of course, precision measuring in cooking and in medicine. Before formal schooling and examinations, these traditions were passed on to the next generation by word of mouth. Children learnt mathematics in active interaction with the adults of the family, just as they learnt to cook or plough a field or dig a canal. All learning was in a social, cultural context.

Things have changed: most mathematics learning has now become formal, instrumental, an organised classroom activity, designed to teach techniques which are predetermined by an examination syllabus or a scheme of work. It is sad to realise that what was once done naturally, as part of the whole value system of so many cultures, has become a subject for debate. Educational theories continually dispute whether or not mathematics should be put in a cultural context. In our industrial society, one value takes precedence above all else and is reflected sharply in the school curriculum: the value of earning money.

Social and cultural relationships in the classroom, we argue here, are dynamic motivating factors. Young black British students have to abstract from at least two cultures those values with which they feel comfortable and can use to make sense of the world around them. The white dominant culture may be the one they feel most at home in and yet their parent culture is immensely important in helping them formulate self-perceptions and a proud recognisable identity. Their culture, essentially multi-culture, and the teacher's, primarily mono-culture, both have a tremendous contribution to make to the teaching process and learning outcomes. This learning is considered at two levels:

- The learning that takes place in the presence of the teacher — both content and process.
- Definitions and reflections in classroom images. These images are the fertiliser which enriches the soil in which students' cognitive and conceptual development flourish.

Consideration of both these aspects of mathematics should add quality and be largely decided by the cultures and personalities of the pupils. It is argued sometimes that this interaction is passive. Experiences show that we directly influence our pupils towards liking or disliking mathematics. We can all recall personal incidents which led to the switch-off linked to our 'attainment' level in the classroom, or the switch-on that came from seeing, hearing or reading something specific or watching some show that sparked interest. By getting to know our pupils well, we can use their experiences as a factor for motivating their learning.

Culture is not used here in the narrow sense that differentiates areas of knowledge, as for example: classical music/folk music, pure mathematics/applied mathematics, commercial art/popular art, high culture/popular culture: one value that is commercial and another that is functional. For us, *culture* denotes something of value, unique to one individual but not destructive to another, a dynamic process in which past and present values blend with hopes for the future. The practice we advocate here takes into account the multitude of cultures amongst our students — class and gender cultures, a variety of national backgrounds and the generation culture. We are interested in the process which we as teachers influence in facilitating the contributions from our students so that no culture in our classroom should be a deficit model. Each should be open to debate but not to exclusion. As one of the key speakers at the Fifth International Congress on Mathematical Education, 1984, Ubiratan d'Ambrosio wrote:

> Cultural diversity is so complex, it is a mesh of attitudes and behaviour which has not been sufficiently understood in education, and especially in mathematics education. I would dare to say they have practically never been recognised as important factors in mathematics education. Attitudes such as modes of thought, jargon, codes, interests, motivation, myths, build up to generate very definitive cultural roots, modes of production, modes of poverty, class conflicts, sense of social security, human rights and so on. These are the factors which comprise society, but are usually ignored in mathematics education.
>
> We are faced with a concept of society which grows from individual behaviour, and which is the key issue in our concerns about mathematics behaviour, that is, the relationship between mathematics and society.

Our approach is relevant to all maths classrooms, primary and secondary, since all have pupils who differ in their background, class and gender. When this variety is extended beyond a 'local' set of cultures, and includes, for example, students from Irish, Jewish, Chinese, Pakistani, Indian or Caribbean backgrounds, we should be able to encourage a constant interaction so that all pupils can benefit from the positive aspects of this diversity. The dynamics of a racist society makes this difficult but not impossible. Unless encouraged by us, some students may rarely make a contribution, leaving both themselves and the rest of us the poorer in our experience. Mathematical ideas are worked out through a complicated set of processes. The end product may be similar but the processes are bound to differ according to the cultural context of their origin. For example, some solutions offered by Vedic mathematics can be explained by traditional algebra but the process by which original Vedic mathematics was formulated remains a mystery. Ramanujan, the great Indian mathematician, attributed his genius to a goddess who came in his dreams and told him the complicated theorems. Fifty years after his death, the world's mathematicians continue to struggle over a goddess's utterances!

The process of interaction between teacher and student is as important as the mathematical idea being learnt. The total interaction often determines whether or not students enjoy the mathematics we offer. We have tried to isolate aspects in teacher-pupil interaction which are most influenced by culture, to consider:

1. **Language in the mathematics classroom.**
2. **Teacher perception of 'race' and 'achievement'**
3. **Classroom techniques.**

## 1. Language in the mathematics classroom

The language of mathematics and the kind of English used in classroom delivery have recently been the subject of debate (Cockroft,1982. and *Maths from 5 to 16*, 1988). The debate takes little cognizance of developing bilinguals and does nothing to value their home languages. English is the medium of instruction for mathematics, particularly at secondary school level, for over two thirds of the world. In India, China, and African countries, English is learnt alongside regional languages. In England, however, the acceptance of bilingualism as an advantage has only just begun. Whatever the historical explanation, the English generally seem very disinterested in learning other languages.

Crawford researched (1986a,1986b) how languages operate in teacher-pupil relationships. She reveals 'considerable inconsistency and conflicting social messages.' Using Halliday's (1974) three categories of speech patterns, she showed that the teacher, as the figure of authority, has most control on both the 'field' and the 'mode' part of the discourse, *field* being the topic of discourse and its cultural context (including the current activity), *mode,* the function that language serves in the context, and *tenor,* the role relationship between speakers.

We believe that students are active participants in their learning but cannot deny that in mathematics, students tend to regard the teacher as someone whose knowledge should not be challenged, who knows some special 'truth' about calculations. When teacher and pupil have different cultural backgrounds, other complexities are bound to arise.

In 1974, Strevens asked some key questions:

1. Do the teacher and learner share the same (first) language?
2. Do the teacher and learner share the same culture?

3. Do the teacher and learner share the same logic and reasoning system? (And is this the logic and reasoning system we find reflected in mathematics?)

4. Is there a 'match' between the language, culture and logic/reasoning system of pupil and teacher?

These complexities will create difficulties only if we ignore them. To date, schools have not been good at recognising the variety of language used by the various sections of the 'white' population (see Bullock report, 1974, page 143). We can refer to Welsh and Gaelic of course, but travellers around our country will notice dialects which reflect different words, sounds, inflections and meanings. Children using these dialects bring with them into the classroom, culture and values associated with their language. When we add to this the dimension of class, we are faced with a classroom filled with words

"Right, now we're going to do an investigation, so write this down:

x frogs on the left, x frogs on the right. It takes x(x + 2) jumps for frogs to exchange places.

Substitute the numbers 1 to 10 for x and write down your results . . . quietly!"

STATEMENT 11
If attempts to bring about changes in mathematics teaching rely solely on, for example, adopting new schemes or changing examination syllabuses, then even though the material teachers are using in the classroom may be different, their approach will be essentially the same. Hence, if changes in teachers' behaviour are to be brought about, the teachers themselves must be involved in challenging their beliefs and assumptions.

carrying a variety of meanings and attitudes, expressions and interpretations. It is true that we have to teach our students to be selective, but they should not be devalued in the process.

We noted in Chapter 1 that the views of the Department of Education and Science have not changed a great deal since the early DES circulars on 'immigrant children' in 1965 (see Mathematics 5 to 16. August 88).

Fortunately, the views of classroom practitioners are influenced also by HMI reports such as *Better Mathematics* (1987) and the *Cockroft Report* (1982) and developments nationwide. We have come a long way towards realising that if mathematics is to be an important means of communication then its language must be in tune with the language of our students. Manipulation of numerical symbols and algebraic equations has its own challenge and beauty, but if it is not appreciated by our students it becomes a system for setting up elites and not an enjoyable experience for all.

More research is needed. Many pupils, white and black, will be unable to understand some of what is going on in the classroom because of their different vocabulary — not just the mathematical words or everyday words for measurement, logic and structure, but also words which the teacher may expect to be automatically understood. Some words may have different meanings locally, some may be unknown to the teacher. Cockroft (1982) asks teachers to be aware of:-

• Variation in the level of language skills of students.

• The variety of language used for a particular mathematical expression.

• Some stylised expressions which may make it difficult for students to comprehend the problem and, therefore, choose the correct solution. (Cockroft, 1982. Para 246,306-310)

For teachers of children whose first language is not English, there is an additional factor. Lack of understanding in English must not be mistaken for poor conceptual development. We are less likely to make such assumptions about adults than about young developing bilinguals. The student may have a very clear understanding of certain concepts in his/her first language. Though there is little research into this, this response to bilinguals must affect the achievement of some pupils.

While students develop command of English, whether as their first or second language, they absorb new words without understanding all the word's usages. In the second language it is possible that they may base their interpretation on words they already know. To take an example from science, the difference in meaning between *water* and *liquid* is clear in English. In many languages the same word is used for both, the general understanding being that all liquids are water with differing solutes. A language with few technical words can present problems for students. Strevens has indicated that:

> there is a major difference in mental preparation for mathematics learning between a learner whose language makes use, in some recognisable form, of the international Greek-Roman terminology, its prefixes (pre-, post-, anti-, sub-, co-, mono etc.), suffixes (-ation, -or, -ant, -ize, etc.) and roots (equ, arithm, etc), and a learner whose language contains neither these items... nor any translation equivalents of them.

It is good practice, then, to ensure much talking around a new topic, and to encourage pupils to speak and write in order to enhance their learning of languages as well as the motivation for learning mathematics. Oral exchanges between students and between student and teacher will reduce mistakes. Teacher-talk alone can permit words to be understood incorrectly. In oral mathematics, students who hear the teacher using a word which has one meaning in general English but another technical meaning in mathematics, will form an impression of that technical meaning which might not be correct. Unless students use the word in speech and in writing, they may, undetected, retain the incorrect meaning. Students have trouble, for instance with the words *average, mean* and *mode*. All three have meanings in general usage. What is generally understood by the word *average* is the same as the meaning in mathematics of the *mean*. The word *mean* has a very specific definition unrelated to its other meanings, as has the word *mode*. Words such as *line* have a tighter definition in mathematics than in normal speech. Students who are learning English as a second language will need opportunities to practice both the mathematical and general meanings of such words. The many facets of language: reading, writing, talking, listening, are all useful to mathematicians.

Teachers of pupils of West Indian origin should take care to understand fully the implications of their pupils' language as it relates to mathematics. Earl Beckles (*Multicultural Teaching,* Vol 8 No.2, Spring 1990) argues that West Indians should be recognised as genuine bilinguals who can experience as much difficulty as Asian children in the development of English for deductive purposes. Lloyd Dawe (1983) of the Sydney Institute of Education, argues that more should be done by schools to maintain pupils' first language/s, as a means of developing the cognitive flexibility of bilingual children.

Multilingual and multicultural societies use a multilingual mode for everyday living as well as to disseminate knowledge and information in all areas of study.

The language used in the materials for pupils is important. Textbooks, worksheets, exam papers and other materials should be simplified and scrutinised to check if they favour some students over others. Simpler, clearer English does not mean that concepts have been diluted. Teachers should learn to use the variety of languages and dialects as a valuable resource to enhance both the learning of mathematics and the learning of English by pupils. We are not recommending that work should be translated or even taught in their first language to pupils whose first language is not English. All our students have to learn English if they are to compete successfully in this society. Clearly, however, teachers of mathematics who also speak the first language of the pupils will be in a very strong position to help their pupils to understand mathematical concepts.

Mathematics text books will support language learning if they:-

* use appropriate language and eliminate unnecessary hurdles;

* avoid archaic and obscure terms;

* provide vocabulary support;

* provide pictorial support;

* have uncluttered layout;

* include ideas with which developing bilinguals are familiar;

* actively use languages present in the classroom.

SMILE, developed by the Inner London Education Authority, is an example of such material.

## 2) Teacher perception of 'race' and 'achievement'

Teacher and student perceptions may take several different forms. Before an area like mathematics can actively engage in combating racism and sexism, these perceptions will need to be understood. We will look first at 'race'.

### Perceptions of manifestations of racism and antiracist education.

Much has been written about the manifestations of racial inequality in schools, particularly on bias in curriculum content (Klein, 1985; Arora and Duncan, 1986; Eggleston et al, 1986; Gaine, 1987). There is little published research on the perception of teachers about students who underachieve, and even less on the effect of racism on students, black or white. Our conclusions are based on the experience of years of INSET, classroom practice and staffroom interactions. We found that perceptions surface very sharply in maths lessons and are invariably at the root of the resistance we experience when we first introduce the notion of mathematics for equality and justice. We have looked at these views in the total context of the teacher's general ways of perceiving his/her students which in turn determines whether or not their teaching is equally accessible to all their pupils.

As well as claiming the 'neutrality' of maths, white teachers often express fears of over-multiculturalisation. Some comments heard in the staffroom and during INSET sessions exemplify the immunity to the very real racist experiences of black people:

— Surely it is common sense to assume that people in every country learn from their own perspective. Didn't you do this in India?

— My Asian students have never grumbled about the lack of Asian names in this Maths book and I've used the same book with classes with 90% Asian pupils. They just want to learn Maths.

— If we're not careful the pendulum will swing too far and this could destroy our Britishness.

— I think by going on and on about blacks you spoil your own cause. — If you keep talking about racism, you bring it to their notice.

— Can't you see that this puts the idea of racism into their heads? Before you came they had never even noticed the differences.

— Black, black, black. We are fed up with hearing this word in arts, history, religion. And now maths? What next?

Fortunately, such views are expressed by a minority. Nevertheless they can put pressure on teachers who do not want to engage in 'controversial issues'. Inequality is thus perpetuated by rigid status quo. Often white students are surprised when a white teacher challenges their racist behaviour. For some students, racism is central to their sense of self; their racism is conscious and committed. The majority, however, have absorbed it more in the sense of name-calling and slogans rather than as a rigid set of beliefs. Often colleagues prefer to sit on the fence and take token action or none at all:-

— I feel that I've got to do something for the black kids in my class. There are so many coloured families moving into the area.

— I have no problem as there are no black kids in my class.

Well-meaning though they may be, such views do a great deal to force black students to try to perceive themselves as 'honorary white', beginning to reject their own cultural background in order to be like their peers — a strong urge in all teenagers.

Teachers' resistance to antiracist education is increased by their misconceptions that it is something for blacks. *'I treat all my pupils the same regardless of their colour'* is a predictable reaction. 'Regardless of colour' is far removed from the student-centred education for which we are arguing. Too often, teachers are reluctant to examine their practice because overt expression of these views can cause conflict and pain. Swann (1985), page 326 states :-

> Where there were clear instances of overt racism amongst pupils within their lessons, many teachers were uncertain, reluctant or quite determined that nothing could or should be done by the school to challenge these attitudes. It was often stressed that emphasising 'differences' between various groups could only be counter productive and divisive, and that attempting to tackle 'racial' issues openly could exacerbate the situation.

Black members of staff, in particular, can find themselves in an invidious position. They may find that their own personal commitment to tackling issues of race can alter the 'modus operandi' they have established within a racist institution. Racism that they have sought to transcend comes bearing down on them once again, threatening their working relationships with other colleagues and their students. Though there is as yet no research to substantiate this, black and many white teachers have in fact found that antiracist work can adversely affect their chances of promotion. Media distortion has sent resounding warnings about antiracist teachers labelling them 'race spies' etc.

**Perception of pupil ability and attainment.**
The Swann Report, *Education for all* rejects the idea of racial prejudice and discrimination within the education system and outside it (p.768). Teachers' attitudes to black students and their approach to matters concerning race are clearly identified as potentially damaging.

Mathematics teachers are not exempt from such influences or behaviour. Some will a subscribe to the commonly attributed stereotypes and the students who resent being so labelled may use their alienation to gain status — adding to the anti- school culture common among those who do not succeed at school. A quote from a survey undertaken by a university extramural department, illustrates this point.

> Celtic students said they were called names and fights were picked with them at rates similar to Afro-Caribbean students, but teachers were more

inclined to support their complaints than those from black students (*The Times Educational Supplement* 6.5.88, p.8).

We also have some research evidence of underachievement by girls in mathematics (*Girls into Maths Can Go* Burton, 1986). Attitude to the subject, gender differentiated teacher support, the power of mathematics, the nature of the presentation, were all found by the researchers to affect learning. Underachievement in maths generally is well known to most teachers, who will have encountered pupils who lack commitment, motivation and retention while apparently being capable in everyday aspects of life. Easter leavers often include those students who are 'street-wise' and can think quickly enough when it suits them and even use basic maths for success. And yet they themselves may have been convinced that they could never do mathematics. Amongst those who stay on, there are many in both grammar and comprehensive schools who fail to achieve what teachers feel is their potential. We believe that taking an honest look at our teaching methods and accepting that the performance of pupils is closely bound up with the performance of teachers instead of continuing to blame pupils for being unmotivated and bored by our lessons, would at least enhance our professionalism.

The process and system of setting in maths can cause disaffection and even hatred for the subject. At present, most teachers group or set pupils according to how they perceive ability and not according to the pupil's actual ability. Pupil performance adjusts itself to the set, so that setting becomes a self-fulfilling prophecy. Such decisions are therefore crucial. In *Social Relationships in a Secondary School,* Hargreaves (1967) examined the behaviour of teachers and pupils in a secondary modern school over four years. Because teachers had minimal contact with pupils, their assessment of pupils tended to be based on the pupils' conformity to 'the norm' instead of upon frequent and direct personal contact. The pupil adjusts to the teacher's expectation and the spiral, up or down, is set.

Nash (1973) observed teachers in a primary school and found that in evaluating pupils, teachers used common constructs, the three most common being:

hardworking ——————————————— lazy

mature ——————————————— immature

well-behaved ——————————— poorly behaved

Cecile Wright, in the Eggleston report, provides further evidence of assessment based on behaviour rather than ability. Often a low ability set is taught by a non-mathematician or junior teacher, compounding the problems. Once caught in the spiral of poor performance and low expectation, only an active and systematic intervention can change things. Over the years, countless pupils have had their maths performance savaged by unprofessional decisions about setting. Teachers have been putting hard-working pupils in top sets and pushing perceived troublemakers into lower sets regardless of their mathematical ability. They have not faced their responsibility to do their best for pupils unlike themselves nor to take on the professionally onerous task of placing able non-conforming pupils in the top set and making them work.

In many schools the top sets are filled with hard-working, quiet, academic and passive pupils — the loud, the questioning and the street-wise are placed in lower sets. Racism surfaces when teachers base their assessment of black pupils on stereotyped views. In our INSET sessions, we hear white teachers admitting that they find it easier to detect mathematical ability in a child to whom they can easily talk, relate, and understand. A black child may be quiet, shy, head down... which set? A white child who is lively, joking, has no pen, doesn't look you in the eye... which set? Someone recently arrived in the U.K., poor English, no uniform yet... which set? Someone who seems to get into trouble on the streets and who reacts angrily to name-calling and racist abuse... which set?

If ethnic minority students are found in large numbers in lower ability sets, it is for teachers to find out why and to offer support. The school as a whole should have a strategy for countering such placements, but no pupil can afford to wait for such institutional change. All the cards are in the teachers' hands. It is inexcusable when teachers take their perceptions about a black pupil from the 'informal gossip among staff' (Hargreaves, 1967). Thus do brothers and sisters follow each other through the same low ability classes, often because of irresponsible and unjust categorisation.

Teachers also make judgments about other matters which affect the pupil, from deciding which materials to provide for learning, what topic to teach, how to teach it, how much work to expect from the pupil, how to encourage the pupil and at what level to reward success.

Teachers are evaluating pupils all the time. They correct and mark work and decide on the kind of help given to students who get sums wrong. They decide whether students should move to harder work and which exams they should take. They set exams, test, assess, record and decide on the method of reporting. They are often asked to write references for students who are leaving. This enormous power of teachers puts them in a unique position to influence the final outcome of a pupil's school career. Their actions can leave students with greatly reduced academic performance and correspondingly reduced life chances, and they need regular reminders of this fact.'Treating children all the same' will not do; using written tests alone will not do; setting according to behaviour will not do. A professional judgement is what all parents, whatever their colour, have a right to expect. And this means getting to know each pupil well.

To know pupils well, we need to know their parents well. Within any group of people there would be variations of the inward- looking/outward-looking, competitive/cooperative, family minded/community minded, tolerant/non-tolerant, democratic/authoritarian, etc. — traits and tendencies which will thwart any generality. Not all pupils of Chinese or Asian origin, for example, are hard-working and good at mathematics. Nor are all girls poor at physics just because not many girls take physics. In our classes are students whose culture and religion does not, for instance, encourage competition or foster activities which produce winners and losers. There are children who expect us to know all the answers and to whom a question and answer approach would seem odd and others encouraged by their background to question the teacher and actively seek out answers. Some students will feel that they must learn all that the teacher has prepared for them; others may have been encouraged to reject certain values that the teacher offers and accept only those considered by the home culture to be important. Understanding and accepting these differing abilities and perceptions is essential if we are to construct an appropriate curriculum for all our pupils. The principle of equal access, then, is far more complex than simply valuing each pupil equally. Being equal does not mean being the same.

## 3 Classroom techniques

In the stereotypical 'good' mathematics classroom, the pupils' heads are down, they work in silence and workbooks are full of ticks, not crosses. Teachers and teacher educators have begun to challenge this image. Derek Woodrow sees traditional maths lessons as being very restricting, open only to pupils with certain characteristics. In an article in *Mathematics in schools* he says :-

> As it is currently taught, mathematics in schools demands concentration, self-discipline, accuracy, conforming to rules, quietness, tenacity, precise and sophisticated language. Could not mathematics be taught so as to encourage creativity, group cohesion, intuition, expressiveness, extroversion? We often choose to teach mathematics in a manner which makes these characteristics disadvantageous in the mathematics classroom even though at later stages of mathematical education they may become valuable attributes.

If a teaching technique does not get the best out of our students then it needs close examination. Traditional style maths lessons presented five times a week for eleven years, is for all but a few a sure way to turn pupils off maths for ever. The Cockcroft Report recommends variety (though not in a social and cultural context) because it makes for good maths teaching. This variety should, we argue,reflect the personalities in the class, and include a variety of teaching techniques to motivate pupils to join in.

Such teaching widens the positive acceptance of maths as an interesting and important exploration of life. As part of their professional development, teachers should be required to keep abreast of government reports, HMI documents, LEA statements and teacher association publications. Many of these provide evidence of our society as racist, sexist, classist and ageist, allowing an elite who feel superior and develop an anachronistic view of the world.

Just as society expects doctors to keep up to date with new treatments, builders to be informed about modern techniques and cleaners to be able to use modern equipment, so should teachers show interest in current educational thinking, research and practice. If they take no steps to improve the quality of their work among pupils from a wide range of backgrounds, they are guilty of both professional negligence and of racism.

Classroom techniques which give pupils an equal entitlement and broaden the base and relevance of maths may involve a range of approaches, from

• Teacher-directed lessons, mainly chalk and talk, with activities led from the front of the classroom;

• Group work allowing opportunities for talk and discussion; and promoting cooperation or competition;

• Whole-class activity, giving pupils opportunities to contribute individually;

• Opportunities for investigation and discovery, giving pupils a chance to 'own' a chosen topic and discover;

• Extended pieces of work, allowing detailed study of some aspect or application of a particular maths topic;

• A range of equipment and experiences; practical measuring, use of equipment, outdoor work, drawing, maths related to commerce and industry;

• Project work involving other departments and variety in assessment to recognise a range of worthwhile talents.

One recent development has been in teacher/pupil/parent interactions. These have been slow to develop as a teaching technique in mathematics classrooms. *Sharing Mathematics With Parents,* produced by the Mathematics Association (1987), shows how parents can be involved. The ideas in this book could be enriched by drawing on the everyday experience of parents who use maths to design, draw, plan, investigate — perhaps at work, certainly at home (see 'Using Maths to make things happen' in *Mathematics in school* March 1985. Maths lessons can include movement, drama, feelings, fun, making the usual academic lessons more accessible.

The prime aim for improving teaching is to improve the outcomes for our pupils. We must develop the means for all pupils to gain the highest possible academic standards, the opportunity to go for good careers. Teachers who have empathy with their pupils but who don't get results are not doing a good job. While good results are not the only sign of a successful teacher, they are the only sure route for pupils to gain some power in the system to influence change.

If used skilfully, the ideas in this chapter will enhance teaching, maximise ability and raise the attainment of pupils. We hope that they will also help pupils to recognise and fight inequality and injustice. This can only happen if teachers themselves do so.

*Chapter 3*

# Bias in Mathematics Books

> *It is because of the 'lack' of positive images that the method of 'stereotyping' unfolds, revealing of the 'British' people an inaccurate and lost impression.* Nadeen Ahmed. Age 15.
> *To be knowledgeable of others and still remain ignorant of oneself is functionally idiotic.* Peter.G.Mills. Age 23.
> (Both from ACER'S Black Young Writers Competition 1986)

Black school children often tell us how they feel excluded, unable to feel a part of contemporary British society. In this chapter we look at bias in textbooks: what is excluded, misrepresented and why it is important to redress the balance.

Alongside television and newspapers, school textbooks, reference books, wall charts and displays are powerful media through which children (and adults) receive messages of socialisation in terms of race, class and gender classifications. There has been considerable debate on reading schemes for young children, on history and geography textbooks, and on bias in children's fiction. These include *Catching Them Young* by Bob Dixon (1977), *Reading Into Racism* by Gillian Klein, (1985), work by NAME (National Antiracist Movement in Education), Children's Rights Workshop, and the National Committee on Racism in Children's Books.

A more sinister kind of bias has also begun to be challenged: the 'hidden curriculum' created by obvious or subtle omission. Omissions of famous black people as activists, historians, scientists, mathematicians is common enough. School textbooks rarely show positive role models of black people, nor of women, working classes and other oppressed groups.

With the growth of the civil rights movement in the United States during the 1960s, much energy was directed at analysing racial overtones in school textbooks and about the portrayal of black and native Americans. For instance, McDiarmid and Pratt (1971) found in their Canadian study that in ignoring so many critical social issues:

> So many textbooks mistake a middle of the road position for objectivity, as though immorality inhered in the controversy and not in the subject of discussion. (Hicks 1981)

In looking at different forms of bias in mathematics textbooks our criticism is not of the mathematical content of the textbooks, nor of the authors. We have selected examples to show that mathematics textbooks are as guilty of racist bias as any others. All sources, numbered in brackets, are acknowledged in the bibliography.

Sexist bias in mathematics materials is being recognised. Studies like *Girls into maths can go* show that girls' under- representation in maths courses is directly related to the lack of motivation offered by the learning environment. This includes school textbooks as well as teacher/pupil relationships. There is no conclusive research to show that poor results in mathematics are due directly to bias in books, but no single factor is ever responsible for such an alarming state of affairs. Racism is similarly cumulative and books in schools carry many messages. It was long assumed that mathematics is neutral, a 'pure discipline' and so impervious to bias. But mathematics is not bias-free, as demonstrated by the following 'problem solving approach'.

In a workshop, a group of maths teachers analysed the diagram on page 41 and noted

a) the language used : 'developed' and 'underdeveloped' makes assumptions about cultures. Are 'western' countries developed, or developing? In what ways are the other countries under-developed? The implication is that if they become like us they will have reached perfection. What about the phrase 'third world'? Are we the 'first'? Who is 'second'? Are we labelling countries with the assumption that if they are not like us then they are second or third best?

b) treatment of population growth : the implication is that large growth is bad. But that is simplistic. Some rich countries, capable of providing well for their people have big population growth; some poorer countries have low growth. Does the book suggest that the world will be swamped by 'third world' people? Such simplistic labelling of countries is neither accurate nor educationally sound. Would it not be more interesting and informative for

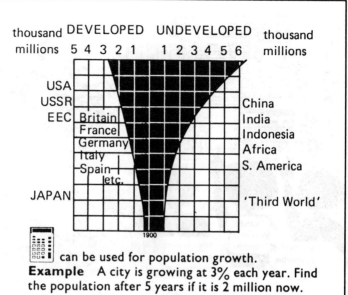

thousand DEVELOPED   UNDEVELOPED thousand
millions  5 4 3 2 1    1 2 3 4 5 6  millions

USA
USSR                                China
EEC  Britain                        India
     France                         Indonesia
     Germany                        Africa
     Italy
     Spain                          S. America
          etc.
JAPAN                               'Third World'

1900

can be used for population growth.
**Example**  A city is growing at 3% each year. Find
the population after 5 years if it is 2 million now.

The population of Mauritania is estimated to increase by 5% each year.
If the population in 1980 was 1,500,000 estimate the population in 1990
giving your answer correct to the nearest hundred thousand.

pupils to look at food produced, imported, exported, daily need, excessive
consumption, wastage and sources of food in a particular country? Such
questions will be closer to students' own experience. The environment issue
is the most crucial of our decade and as the evidence of the damage to our
environment unfolds, subtle racism which lays the blame for global destruc-
tion at the doorstep of the 'developing world' must be exposed. What about
questions like the following:

The population of a country in Africa is 7.8 millions and is growing at
the rate of 10% each year. In how many years will the population reach
10 million or above?

The issue is not whether or not such loaded messages are deliberate, but how
to recognise them and replace them with a more critical and just approach.
Jenny Maxwell, in *Mathematics Teaching*, demonstrates that many such
'hidden messages' flow from lessons, often unnoticed by teachers. In the

same journal, Dawn Gill discusses the settings to questions which teach percentages, observing that:

> as teachers, we need to be aware of the extent to which inequalities are enshrined within the status quo and the fact that many of the students with whom we work are a product of an unequal social system.

Paul Ernest draws attention to the social and political values that are brought to the mathematics curriculum; we do not teach pure abstract mathematics but mathematics related to society. He comments on the authoritarian-democratic ways in which mathematics is taught and observes that:

> the received view of mathematics is that it is neutral with regard to both culture and gender. However, the divorce of Mathematics from its social context which the above neutrality implies, leads to monoethnic, sexist and possibly even racist mathematics.

These examples from textbooks are intended to exemplify 'real-life situations':

On a four horse race, a bookmaker quotes the following odds for each of the four horses to win 3:1 against, 3:1 against, 2:1 against and evens.
(i) Show that these can NOT be true odds.
(ii) Why does a bookmaker not use odds based on probabilities?
(iii) By scaling the 'probabilites' based on the bookmakers odds to make them genuine probabilities, find the true odds for the four horses.

## BEER SALES GO FLAT BUT WINE IS A WINNER

| | Real % change | | | | | | Total Spending 1984 £m |
|---|---|---|---|---|---|---|---|
| BEER | 0.8 | −4.8 | −6.0 | −3.2 | −1.6 | −0.1 | £7,887 |
| WINE | 7.8 | 0.5 | 7.2 | 3.2 | 9.7 | 10.3 | £3,153 |
| SPIRITS | 10.4 | −5.9 | −5.8 | −5.2 | 2.7 | 1.2 | £3,507 |
| | 1979 | 1980 | 1981 | 1982 | 1983 | 1984 | |

Paulo Freire's pedagogical prescription for raising critical consciousness is by problematising reality. Writing up a problem based on some imaginary situation taken out of context, like the two above, does not allow the pupil to become involved in discovering exactly where the simple interest comes from, nor who creates the profit which makes this interest available for the general public.

In Friere's words:

Educators who are problematised by engaging in this kind of action re-enter into the object of the problem through the 'entering into' of the educatees. This way educators continue to learn themselves. The humbler they are, the more they will learn.

In mathematics learning, then, problematisations facilitates an understanding of situations as experienced by our pupils. Ultimately mathematics may be a tool for transforming unjust and unequal positions. It will be part of real life, not separated from it. Problematisation will ensure that skills learnt in mathematics are transferred to a critical interpretation of the real world.

Here is one example of 'problematisation of reality'; there are more in chapter 7.

Use the computer database to find information on various countries. Look up 'land area' and 'population' for at least 20 countries. make sure you choose countries from all parts of the world; some rich, some poor.

Work out the number of people per square kilometer for each country. Write a few words about your results. Do the countries labelled 'poor' always have high density of people? If not, what other reasons might there be for the poverty?

Even if the maths teachers do not notice the hidden messages young children do. Martin Francis uses the a transcription of his tape of a group of third year children to illustrate how children notice many different 'hidden ideas on sexism, missing names of ''coloured kids', and other matters as they look at primary school mathematics books' (*Everyone Counts* by (ILEA)).

There can be no simple consensus on what a textbook should offer student and teacher. Some books provide pages of questions, others worked examples; others a background to each topic, explaining its setting within the world of mathematics and occasionally of society. Some will offer ideas for further study or for the collection of data. A good book will provide instruction, examples, information and should encourage involvement by the student. The Cockroft Report (1982) pointed out that mathematics lessons were often not about anything at all. At least some GCSE examination questions are determinedly set in real-life contexts. A few recent textbooks have avoided the immediate problems of bias in real-life contexts by deliberately being as abstract as possible. We should rather be emphasising the great variety of uses to which mathematics is put throughout the world and providing students with opportunities to apply their mathematics.

As teachers, we have the opportunity to select the background of our lessons. The way is open to biases of many kinds. It is our professional responsibility to be aware of this and not promote unacceptable bias in the classroom. Bias may take a form of endorsing a concept of different races and other cultures. Books should reflect all cultures in Britain and not an undefined British culture as the norm against which others are judged.

Mathematics books are not exempt from the most common forms of bias:

- white supremacy and 'modernity', set against the deficient models of the 'third world' as in the view of certain 'eminent' historians. Mathematics should explode the myth of the multinationals as the great success story of the white world and western high technology. The graph of 'unlimited economic growth from limited resources' is a dangerous notion for the human race;

- Great Britain as all white, all Christian, monolingual and monocultural;

- omitting any mention of dependence in terms of origin of raw materials, and interdependence in terms of import and export (which includes labour, too). The 'success' of white countries is shown as having been achieved by their own efforts and the problems of non-white countries as a result of their inhabitants' laziness, religions, weather or lack of knowledge of high technology;

- undervaluing and grossly misrepresented people of Asian and particularly African descent;

- showing few or no black people as achievers or positive role models.

A book, then, can be said to be racist:

- if it communicates, overtly or covertly, racist concepts or notions to a reader, black or white, adult or child

- if the knowledge selected gives only a negative image of the child's origins

- if the only positive black role models portrayed are of black athletes and pop-idols (with whom both black and white pupils may identify) but which merely creates further danger of stereotyping

- if it fails to challenge racism.

We have investigated recent mathematics textbooks and public examination papers for racial bias along these lines. Many textbooks make no mention of Asian, Caribbean or other non-white cultures, present or past, thus ignoring 84% of the world's population i.e, living outside Western Europe and North America. Reference to any non-English speaking culture is inevitably to white Europeans, not to any of the ethnic minority groups living in Europe. We found that the historical accounts of mathematics gave little recognition to mathematical knowledge anywhere other than Greece. Very little is written about the contexts in which mathematics was born and about how it is used around the world. Many books portray an exclusively white, male, middle class Britain. Not that this group should be denied, but showing only them devalues all other people and gives a limited and misleading view.

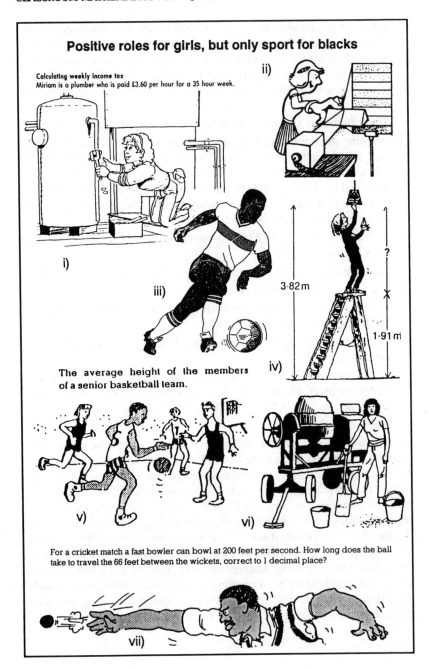

## Positive roles for girls, but only sport for blacks

Calculating weekly income tax
Miriam is a plumber who is paid £3.60 per hour for a 35 hour week.

i)

ii)

iii)

3·82 m

1·91 m

?

iv)

The average height of the members of a senior basketball team.

v)

vi)

For a cricket match a fast bowler can bowl at 200 feet per second. How long does the ball take to travel the 66 feet between the wickets, correct to 1 decimal place?

vii)

Maps feature only the UK and Europe; there are churches but no mosques or temples. Foods are all western, shopping all 'European'. Yet in 1987, The *Good Food Guide* voted Indian food the most popular for eating out. Chinese food shops and pizza parlours could provide further variety of contexts for exercises such as these.

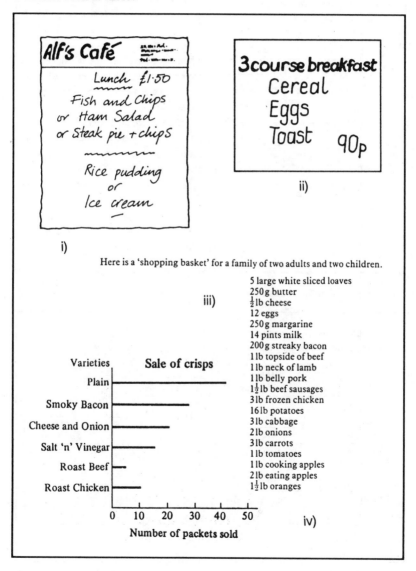

47

The next examples make much of blonde hair and blue eyes. With Europe's history of racism, the superiority of a fair 'race' is a not unfamiliar notion and should not be endorsed.

1. The Venn diagram shows

   & = { girls in class 2A }
   A = { girls with blonde hair }
   B = { girls with blue eyes }

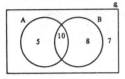

(a) How many girls have blonde hair?
(b) How many girls have blue eyes?
(c) How many girls have blue eyes and blonde hair?
(d) How many girls are in class 2A?
(e) How many girls have neither blue eyes nor blonde hair?

i)

5 children are fair-haired, blue-eyed and left-handed. These come from a group of 300, of whom 18 are left-handed. If the same number x of the left-handed children are fair-haired as are blue-eyed, and there are 7 left-handers who are neither blue-eyed nor fair-haired, find x.

80 children are fair-haired, of whom 60 are niether left-handed nor blue-eyed. Find the number of fair-haired blue-eyed children. If there are 90 blue-eyed children, find how many children have none of the three properties.

If a child is picked at random, what is the probability that he or she has exactly one of the three properties?

ii)

'Travellers' in these examples from maths books, visit only white regimes.

The table below shows ordinary summer and winter temperatures for 8 cities.

| City | Winter temperature | Summer temperature |
|------|------|------|
| London | 4 °C | 18 °C |
| Rome | 7 °C | 25 °C |
| Moscow | ⁻9 °C | 18 °C |
| Johannesburg | 10 °C | 20 °C |
| New York | ⁻1 °C | 24 °C |
| San Francisco | 10 °C | 17 °C |
| Sydney | 11 °C | 21 °C |
| Wellington (NZ) | 8 °C | 17 °C |

BUREAU DE CHANGE

| | |
|------|------|
| FRANCE | 11·86 |
| ITALY | 2350 |
| SPAIN | 225 |
| GREECE | 151 |
| GERMANY | 3·89 |
| HOLLAND | 4·36 |
| AUSTRIA | 27·25 |
| USA | 1·45 |
| CANADA | 1·80 |

iii)               iv)

Alan's family go to a seaside town
near Barcelona, in Spain.

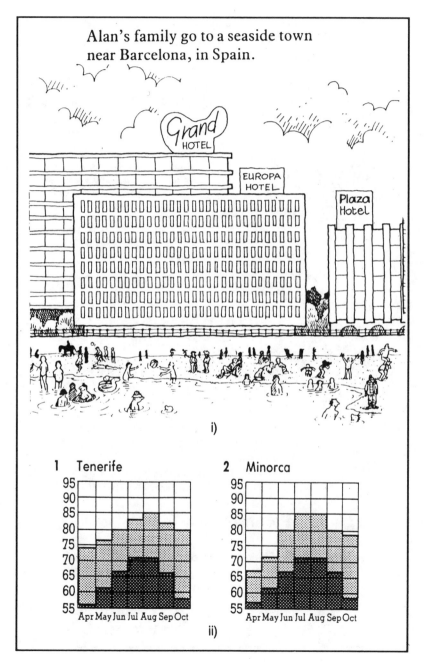

i)

1  Tenerife          2  Minorca

ii)

On the other hand some examples from real life can be too personal. Body measurements can be embarrasing. For example, girls and women are shown as concerned about their weight. Very thin or plump girls and boys in the class may feel bad that attention is drawn to their bodies in this way; it provides an opportunity for comments from classmates. The three different views of Tina, below, may encourage already existing sexist attitudes in the classroom.

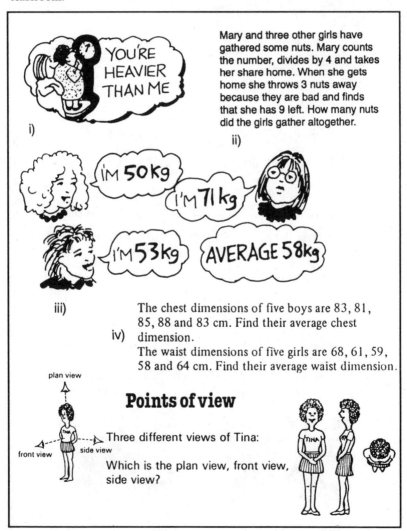

i)

YOU'RE HEAVIER THAN ME

ii) Mary and three other girls have gathered some nuts. Mary counts the number, divides by 4 and takes her share home. When she gets home she throws 3 nuts away because they are bad and finds that she has 9 left. How many nuts did the girls gather altogether.

I'M 50 kg

I'M 71 kg

I'M 53 kg

AVERAGE 58 kg

iii)

iv) The chest dimensions of five boys are 83, 81, 85, 88 and 83 cm. Find their average chest dimension.
The waist dimensions of five girls are 68, 61, 59, 58 and 64 cm. Find their average waist dimension.

plan view
front view
side view

## Points of view

Three different views of Tina:

Which is the plan view, front view, side view?

TINA

These examples for teaching statistics are not racist in themselves, but they do trivialize the subject by basing all the data on simplistic and boring notions, such as the colour of cars passing the school gate. Secondary students would be more interested seeing maths used in more weighty contexts. Why not consider the statistical surveys on racial discrimination in Britain, on students' understanding of South Africa, on what it is about society that most worries young people today? Examination of situations of this kind widens children's perspectives, introduces debate and extends interest in other subjects.

i)

**CLASS INVESTIGATION**                    **VITAL STATISTICS III**

1 Make a frequency table of the heights, weights, or ages of the pupils in your class. Choose suitable class intervals; for example, 150–152 cm gives a class interval of 3 cm with a mid-value of 151 cm, and 150–154 cm gives a class interval of 5 cm with a mid-value of 152 cm.

2 Draw a histogram of the data.

3 Calculate the mean height, weight or age.

---

Collect other data suitable for finding averages.
Some suggestions are:
The shoe sizes of boys or girls in your class.
The number of pets kept by a sample of children.
The number of children in a sample of families.
The number of goals scored in football matches by home teams, compared with the number of goals scored by away teams.
The number of passengers in cars.
The number of customers entering a shop in 1-minute intervals, compared at different times of the day.
The heights of students in your year-group.
The times students spend on their homework.
The ages of cars in a car park. (Estimates based on the registration letter.)
The weekly amounts spent by students on snacks, sweets, drinks, etc.
The distances people travel to work.
The length of time of phone calls.
Guesses from people of the length of a line, the weight of an object or the number of sweets in a jar.

ii)

Several new books have taken the initiative to correct some of the imbalance (for example see Chapter 17 of *Mathematics: Using the Basic Skills* by Farrow and Llewellyn). Many books and examination questions now include some Asian names but it is usually 'Ali', 'Patel', 'Ahmed' or 'Singh' so simultaneously stereotyping and denying the rich variety of backgrounds. Welsh or Celtic names are also rare in English maths books.

People with Asian names can be seen participating in white culture but never in Asian.

i)  Mr Ahmed leaves home at 19.45 and it takes him 20 minutes to walk to Wembley Park station. What is the earliest time at which he can arrive at Croxley?

ii)  Calculator in hand, Mrs Singh went round the Cash and Carry. She calculated the VAT on items, using the flowchart.
Would she get better value at the Cash and Carry or at the Locost Store.

iii)  Hassan has challenged Moira to a round of mini-golf at the seaside course. They count their scores over and under 3 per hole like this:

Hassan

| Hole | 1 | 2 | 3 | 4 | 5 | 6 | |
|---|---|---|---|---|---|---|---|
| Number of strokes | 4 | 6 | 2 | 3 | 1 | 3 | |
| Score | +1 | +3 | −1 | 0 | −2 | 0 | = +1 |

iv)  Make a table for Moira. She took 3, 6, 2, 3, 2, 5 strokes.
Make tables for the next 12 holes.
Hassan: 2, 6, 5, 3, 4, 4, 5, 3, 2, 4, 7, 4
Moira: 2, 5, 6, 1, 5, 3, 7, 4, 3, 2, 5, 3

Nine people, Andrew, Bilkish, Craig, Dhiren, Edith, Faruk, Graham, Helen and Iqbal share a prize of £450 amongst themselves.
Bilkish gets £1 more than Andrew, Craig gets £1 more than Bilkish, Dhiren gets £1 more than Craig, and so on. How much does Iqbal get?

Many modern textbooks do include illustrations of black people. But, as following illustrations from recent publications show, they may be insensitively drawn, even derogatory; or the faces be of white people shaded black. The cost of providing good drawings which depict black young people and adults as they really are, showing variety of feature, hairstyle and dress, can't be any greater than the ultimate cost of denying equal value to our pupils. Insensitive, negative and derogatory images may well be a true reflection of our society's values, but school textbooks should not be reinforcing these values.

Stereotypical or caricatured illustrations will inevitably mean that black figures will be racial stereotypes.

**Does the quality of illustrations matter?**

i)

ii)

iii)

iv)

v)

**Should publishers pay more for good artwork?**

vi)

vii)

# Do some illustrations encourage while others demean?

Illustrations like those below are typical of how Egypt is depicted: the pyramids, a camel, but no modern Egyptians. Russia only gets a mention for Russian dolls to illustrate enlargement or for low temperatures in directed numbers. If Africa or any 'third world' countries are mentioned, it is usually to do with population figures, seldom with trade and modern city life. In one illustration all European countries are shown as 'developed' and the rest of the world 'underdeveloped'! In the example below, statistics are given for wheat, a major crop in the USA but not in Africa; a misleading comparison, especially as there is no mention of maize.

i)

ii)

Discuss the degree of accuracy implied in the following statements. Write each measurement in standard form to a sensible number of significant figures.

a) The population of France is 53.70 million people, of Italy 57.04 million and of West Germany 61.56 million.

b) Production of wheat:

| | |
|---|---|
| North America | 86.32 million tonnes |
| Africa: | 8.63 million tonnes |
| Europe: | 98.45 million tonnes |

c) Number of TV's in use (per 1000 population):

| | |
|---|---|
| UK: 390 | USA: 623 |
| USSR: 320 | Japan: 272 |

iii)

Good practice in mathematics books would include:

*   pictures and settings depicting diverse positive images of people of many ethnic groups and social classes experiencing a variety of life styles, food, work, hobbies and preferences;

*   mathematics applied to many different areas of life such as science and technology, sport, industry, politics and religion.

55

- acknowledgement of the contribution of a variety of past and present cultures to mathematics and to ways of solving problems;
- using up-to-date statistics to challenge institutional racism;
- acknowledgement of social inequality; rich and poor, young and old, healthy living and poor standards and their causes, starvation and greed. These are facts of life and have a place in the curriculum.

**Here are some positive examples:**

i)

iii)

ii)

EQUATIONS WE'VE SOLVED HAD ONLY ONE SOLUTION. WHAT ABOUT INEQUATIONS?

YOU'LL BE SURPRISED

*Example* Solve $p + 1 \leqslant 3$

iv)

These drawings show token black people, marginalised and not fully part of the activity. Pictures of a group of black people, a black family or a mixed race family are rare; publishers fight shy of showing a scene of black people together in a mainstream context.

Use the flowchart and data to work out how much the girl spends at the sweet shop.

iii)

| 3 | Jocky | Sandy | Keith | Fiona | Dave | Lola |
|---|-------|-------|-------|-------|------|------|
| | 3 | Double 14 | Treble 13 | Double 6 | Treble 9 | Double 19 |
| | Double 20 | 9 | Double 15 | 19 | Double 14 | 13 |
| | 5 | Double 11 | 7 | Double 17 | 18 | Treble 8 |

v)

Surely it would be far more profitable to explore these avenues than to continue to encourage some of the most obvious and gratuitous racist approaches found in some textbooks.

A worksheet that was brought home by Sharan-Jeet's son for his homework (source not known) went like this:

---

### The Cannibals and Missionaries

On one side of a river there are three cannibals and three missionaries. They have a boat on their side that can carry two people at a time across the river. The aim is to transport all six people across to the other side of the river. At no time can the cannibals on either side of the river outnumber the missionaries on that side, or the cannibals would eat them.

The children can come together in teams of seven; one to record the solution. Once again it may be advisable to start the children off with the record.

START       CCC
                MMM

Stages
in                 Transfer across river
between

END                             CCC
                             MMM

These exercises are useful because the children need to use (and record) a logical sequence of moves. These skills are important in mathematics and computing.

---

Not all mathematics topics have a social context: many stand on their own — and so they should. But most school mathematics is set in some social context and this is where the problems arise. Many commonwealth countries have rejected the mathematics of colonial days, preferring to publish new textbooks which show modern life in their own communities. The United States has undertaken a major review of its teaching materials. Across the world, teachers are adjusting their books and examinations to suit modern language, culture and societal needs. In Britain the GCSE instigated big changes in teaching methods. Sadly, the National Curriculum which initially identified multicultural education as one of the five cross-curricular themes (Policy to Practice, 1989), has removed it from subsequent documentation. However, under the new Education Act, school governors will have considerable powers. Just as they might be concerned to reduce smoking, under age drinking or use of drugs, they should be concerned to ensure that racist bias is challenged in school textbooks. They may well seek teaching which is in line with local authority statements on equal opportunities for all.

*Chapter 4.*

# Examples of Multicultural Approaches to the Teaching of Mathematics

> *Our number sequence embodies the law of infinite progression. It is an ordered creation of the mind. We use a finite and an amazingly small quantity of number words and symbols. Nothing but numbers demonstrate the one-ness of human race. Our language is Germanic, our writing is Roman, and our numerals are Indian.*
> — Karl Meninger

Chapters 4, 5 and 6 explore multicultural approaches to mathematics in the classroom. Chapter 4 begins with a brief outline of the differences between a multicultural and an antiracist approach. A range of ideas are developed in chapters 4 and 5. Chapter 6 focuses on Islamic and Vedic mathematics.

Much of 'multicultural mathematics' is stereotyped and limited and far more could be done. Exciting works on number patterns and posters, though mostly European based, can be found in libraries. Teachers' centres may have material on the history of mathematics and there are some good, thought-provoking and practical ideas in publications from The Mathematical Association and the Association of Teachers of Mathematics. If multicultural approaches to teaching maths are limited to Rangoli patterns, simplistic notions of Islamic art and some number work in different languages, then Mr. Baker's criticism of multicultural mathematics as 'condescending' is, indeed, justified (Maths 5 to 16, August 1988, p.87).

A multicultural approach should not be trivial. Students are entitled to courses which are rigorous and allow opportunities for real development of their talents. The cultural aspect of the work must be interwoven into the courses so that they do not appear as optional extras but as important aspects of an integrated whole. Questions of triviality and irrelevance do not arise in maths lessons related to people and the world.

Multicultural approaches differ from antiracist examples in their focus. They emphasise inclusion of material from the varied cultural backgrounds of our school students in the form of historical and practical knowledge rather than challenging racism directly. The approach is cross-curricular and should help to make the school more coherent and shed the 'elitist' image of the mathematics department. An antiracist approach focuses on issues of inequality and injustice and aims to engage students in a critical, analytical and solution-seeking process.

Multicultural mathematics does not set up separatist notions of 'our culture' and 'other cultures'. It allows students to bring their cultural background, parents and community to their learning and for these to be valued by the school. The rigour of mathematical content need not be restricted. We aim to challenge students of all abilities. The pedagogy and basic rationale match those of antiracist approaches. Mathematics as an international language for the world of trade owes a debt to dedicated and brilliant mathematicians from all over the world.

The universal activities of learning the key concepts in mathematics and how these are applied for solving real life problems are the basis of our multicultural approach. These concepts include:-

* counting, using number patterns
* measuring, designing and decision making
* playing, logical reasoning, estimating, predicting, chance
* recording, pictures, graphs, models
* symmetry, angles, transformations

Our examples come from :-

* maths developed by people around the world and absorbed into the subject.
* maths of historic interest.
* maths being used by people in a variety of contexts.

Our multicultural approach aims to :

* enable all students and their teachers to develop an awareness of the universality of mathematics,

- enable female and black students to develop a more positive and participatory image of themselves in the maths curriculum, thereby supporting the concept of equality in mathematics.
- create enthusiasm for mathematics by drawing on and linking it to the everyday experiences of our students.

Some topics in which examples from around the world can relate to classroom practice are developed on page 64 , others in Chapter 7 on Project work.

## Famous Mathematicians:

> *Colonialization is the greatest destroyer of culture that humanity has ever known — long suppressed manifestations have to regain their place —*. Samora Machel, late president of Mozambique.

Mathematics learning can be enhanced by teaching a little about those who created the original ideas. The names and lives of mathematicians are generally missing from school textbooks. The names of some live on in theorem or topic titles such as Pythagoras' Theorem, Euclidian Geometry, Newton's laws, Argand diagram. Even when the knowledge preceded them by centuries students may have heard of Omar Khyyam (1050-1153) because of his philosophical poetry the *Rubaiyat,* but few students will know him as the mathematician who investigated Euclid's parallel postulate and developed geometrical methods for solving cubical equations. Research into non-European mathematicians has proved difficult. Sadly, we could find no single authoritative work on early mathematicians from Africa and South America. Some of the famous new mathematicians, such as D'Ambrasio, Gerdes, Nebres, are attempting to reclaim their lost inheritance. Their writings demonstrate alternative constructions of mathematical ideas from traditional cultures.

Aryabhatiya (4th century), Brahamagupta (7th century), Mahavira (9th century) and Bhaskara (12th century) are little known outside India and the Arab world. Their original Sanskrit texts such as Bhaskara's *Lilavati,* have now been translated by mathematicians in East and West. Initially the works were translated by Fiazi, a counsellor of Emporer Akbar. A book on algebra — *Bijganita,* was translated by Rashidi, the son of Mimar, the architect of the Taj Mahal (Jaggi,1981). Bhaskara's other important work, *Sidhanata Siromani,* covers Astronomy. The title means 'Head jewel of accuracy'.

63

| | | |
|---|---|---|
| Temperature | Number patterns | |
| Length | Number puzzles | |
| Weight | Gambling | Calendars |
| Small/large | Games/card tricks | Muslim |
| Volume/Capacity | Magic squares | Modern |
| Area | Number words | Hindu |
| Volume | and languages | Chinese |
| Metric/nonmetric | Number songs/rhymes | Clocks/watches |
| **MEASURING** | **COUNTING/GAMES** | **MEASURING TIME** |

| | | |
|---|---|---|
| **HISTORY OF MATHEMATICS** | **MULTICULTURAL MATHEMATICS** | **FAMOUS MATHEMATICS** |

| | | |
|---|---|---|
| **SHAPES AND SYMMETRY** | **CALCULATION TOOLS AND TECHNIQUES** | **MEASURING INSTRUMENTS** |
| Location | Vedic maths | Hands/feet |
| In nature | Chinese maths | Conventional |
| Animate/Inanimate | Abacus | Scales |
| Aesthetic/Functional | Plumb lines | Coins — Money |
| Properties of shapes | | Knots in a string |
| Use of shapes | | |
| Designs | | |
| Origami/Kites | | Units/Standards |
| Arts | | Weights/measures |

An interesting story is told of Lilavati, Bhaskara's daughter. Lilavati's astrological charts forbade her to wed. As Bhaskara was a great believer in astronomy, he designed a time cup with a tiny hole at the bottom so that it would sink at a given moment, whereupon Lilavati could wed. Lilavati bent over the cup, watched it fill with water and dropped in a pearl, blocking the hole. To compensate for his daughter's misfortune and believing that this would give her eternal life, Bhaskara named his mathematical works after her. The book considers arithmatic, mensuration and some algebra.

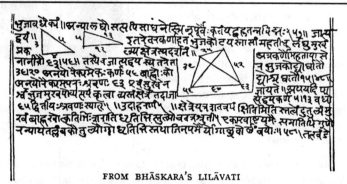

FROM BHĀSKARA'S LILĀVATI

From a manuscript of c. 1600. The original work was written c. 1150. The illustration shows the form of Hindu manuscripts just following the use of palm-leaf sheets. This page has the following statement: "Assuming two right triangles [as shown], multiply the upright and side of one by the hypotenuse of the other: the greatest of the products is taken for the base; the least for the summit; and the other two for the flanks. See" [the trapezoid]. Colebrooke's translation, page 82

Students should look at the nature of mathematics in India, China, Persia etc. and chart the differences. Pi, positive and negative numbers, zero and work on infinity are all developed in *Bijganita*.

Two mathematicians who may spark interest in students are next described.

# S. RAMANUJAN.

Srinivasa Ramanujan was born in Tamil Nadu on 22 Dec.1887. His mathematical genius has only recently been fully acknowledged, fifty years after his death. No one has been able to work out fully where Ramanujan's elegant ideas in pure mathematics came from.

Though he received a scholarship at the age of 11 for his extraordinary abilities in mathematics, he failed all his other examinations so could not go to university.

Ramanujan came to the attention of G.H. Hardy, the English mathematician, when he wrote Hardy a letter with some of his formulae on divergence series. A BBC programme on the life and works of Ramanujan cites Hardy's account of his brief association with Ramanujan in his book *A Mathematician's Apology* in which Hardy wrote:

> I owe more to him than anyone else in the world, with one exception. — My association with him was the one romantic incident of my life.

Describing his own life and works, Hardy wrote:

> I have never done anything useful. No discovery of mine is going to make any difference, large or small to the amenity of the world. When I am forced to listen to tiresome and pompous men around me, when I am depressed, I say to myself, I did something you will never be able to do. I have collaborated with Ramanujan on something like equal terms.

As Ramanujan did not work in a systematic way, Hardy provided the technical skills required to work with Ramanujan's discoveries.

The theory of *Partitioning of numbers.* is one illustration of their work: 7, for example, can be partitioned in 15 different ways. 7: 6+1, 5+2, 4+2+1, 5+1+1, 4+1+1+1, and so on.

Similarly    $P(10) = 42.$
$P(20) = 627.$
$P(30) = 5604.$
$P(50) = 204.226.$
$P(100)= 190,569,262.$

Ramanujan and Hardy wanted to find a formula which would give the partitioning of, say, 200 as accurately as possible. It was considered sufficient to have a formula which would give the answer within a million or so, for the actual answer is close to 4 trillion. Ramanujan, who considered positive numbers as his friends was not satisfied with this.

No one understands how he got his formula, but he developed it and worked out the answer: P(200) = 3,972,999,029,388.004 — the error being .004.

For this answer to be checked by computing by hand took a month. According to Dr. G. Andrews of Pennsylvania University, 99.9% of mathematicians even today, with all the computing facilities at their disposal, would say that such a working out is impossible. Dr.Andrew has done extensive work on Ramanujan's notebooks. In Ramanujan's formula, are, in Dr. Andrew's words:

> transcendental numbers and expressions which at first glance seem unrelated. All his results, new or old, have a mingled argument, intuition and induction of which he could give no coherent description. He reveals unsuspected possibilities and yet the origins of his theorems remain a mystery. The beauty and the singularity of his results is uncanny.'

Inspired by Ramanujan, Hardy wrote :-

> A mathematician is like a painter or a poet, a maker of patterns with ideas, like the colours and words. The ideas, like the colours and the words must speak together in a harmonious way. A mathematician's patterns, like the poet's or the painter's, must be beautiful. There is no permanent place in the world for ugly mathematics.

Ramanujan's theorems are concerned with modular equations and continous fractions to a degree unknown to any mathematician in the world. He said that he got his inspiration from Goddess Namgiri. He could remember the idiosyncrasies of numbers as if they were known to him personally as friends. Hardy once took a taxi to visit Ramanujan when he was ill in a hospital in Putney. The number of the taxi was 1729. Hardy remarked on the odd number of the taxi as possibly an omen. 'Not at all' Ramanujan replied. 'It is quite an interesting number, for it is the smallest possible number expressible as a sum of 2 cubes in 2 different ways.

$$12 \times 12 \times 12 = 1728$$
$$1 \times 1 \times 1 = 1$$
$$1729$$

$$10 \times 10 \times 10 = 1000$$
$$9 \times 9 \times 9 = 729$$
$$1729$$

Ramanujan was the first Indian to receive the Fellowship of the Royal Society and Trinity College. He died in 1920, aged 33, leaving behind many theorems of amazing formulae, identities and relations which mathematicians are puzzling over even today.

## Number patterns and Shakuntala Devi

Shakuntala Devi, a modern mathematical genius from India, is known to many youngsters from TV appearances and her book: *Figuring, the joy of numbers.*

She amazed students at the Southern Methodist University in Dallas when asked to do the 23rd root of a 201 digit number, working it out in fifty seconds while it took a computer sixty seconds to confirm that she was right.

Her book is a source of enjoyment as well as a challenge to the most cynical pupil. She suggests and explores some fascinating ways of making computation fun and easy.

From: *Figuring The Joy of Numbers* by Shakuntala Devi.
Some special numbers with tricks and puzzles:

Example :- 142857 — **The revolving number.**

Draw a table of the products of this number, when multiplied with 1, 2, 3, 4, 5, and 6 . Horizontally and vertically all the digits add up to 27.

$$
\begin{array}{llllllll}
1 & 4 & 2 & 8 & 5 & 7 & = 27 \\
2 & 8 & 5 & 7 & 1 & 4 & = 27 \\
4 & 2 & 8 & 5 & 7 & 1 & = 27 \\
5 & 7 & 1 & 4 & 2 & 8 & = 27 \\
7 & 1 & 4 & 2 & 8 & 5 & = 27 \\
8 & 5 & 7 & 1 & 4 & 2 & = 27 \\
\hline
27 & 27 & 27 & 27 & 27 & 27
\end{array}
$$

This number is known as a cyclical number.

Example of patterns:

Some numbers when multiplied by 3 and its multiples form strange patterns.

| | | | |
|---|---|---|---|
| 12345679 x  3 | = 37037037 | 37 x  3 | = 111 |
| 12345679 x  6 | = 74074074 | 37 x  6 | = 222 |
| 12345679 x 12 | = 111111111 | 37 x  9 | = 333 |
| 12345679 x 15 | = 185185185 | 37 x 15 | = 555 |
| 12345679 x 18 | = 222222222 | 37 x 18 | = 666 |

It is true that all of this work could be done without mentioning the name of the mathematician associated with it, but that is not only dishonest, it is less interesting.

## The Chinese Triangle

This triangular array of numbers is attributed to the French mathematician Blaise Pascal — incorrectly. The great Chinese mathematician, Chu Shih-chieh (1280-1303) in his book, *Precious Mirror,* opens with a diagram of the 'arithmetical triangle', 300 years before Pascal was born. Chu's arrangement shows the coefficients of binomial expansions through the eighth power. In its origin the Chinese discovery of the binomial theorem was associated with root extractions. These facts are rarely acknowledged in the western accounts of 'Pascal's triangle'.

Arithmetical triangle from the *Precious mirror.* Chu calls it the diagram for the 8th and lower powers.

The same from Boyer (1968) page 228

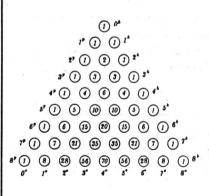
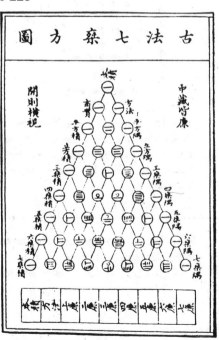

## Magic Squares

Teachers rarely mention the origins of magic squares. China had an advanced knowledge of arithmetical rules 3500 years ago. LO- SHU, the Magic square, is mentioned in the ancient book: *Arithmetic in nine sections,* Figures employed in fortune-telling have been a part of the Chinese tradition since 29 B.C. Legend has it that Emperor Yu was embarked on the calamitous fast flowing yellow river and there appeared before him a divine tortoise with its shell decorated with a figure made up of the numbers 1 - 9, which the great sage recorded and applied. It helped solve Emperor Yu's problems.

Lo-Shu — Magic square as shown in several history books.

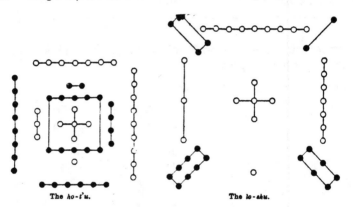

The *ho-t'u.*          The *lo-shu.*

The *lo-shu* is a magic square with the nine figures as its elements as annexed. It comes therefore that the magic squares were called by that name in later China and also by some earlier Japanese mathematicians.[1])

| 4 | 9 | 2 |
|---|---|---|
| 3 | 5 | 7 |
| 8 | 1 | 6 |

In Lo-Shu, every single row, column and diagonal adds up to 15. Two popular names for games derived from the magic square are TIC-TAC-TOE and NEVER-LOSE which is much like noughts and crosses.

# How to Play: NEVER LOSE, a game based on Magic Square

You will need numbers 1-9 written large on a board and some counters.

1 2 3 4 5 6 7 8 9

The challenge is to use the counters to cover any 3 numbers that add up to 15. Take alternate turns to place counters trying to block your opponent. Whoever can get a row, column or diagonal of 15 is the winner. The game can be made more complicated by using a 4th order square.

## Magic Squares: A suggested worksheet

Complete a magic square and invent variations on the answer. There are 8 combinations of the positions of the same digits, and each position can be obtained by rotation or reflection of the original about a suitable axis. This set of motions is known as the dihedral group of order 8 of the square.

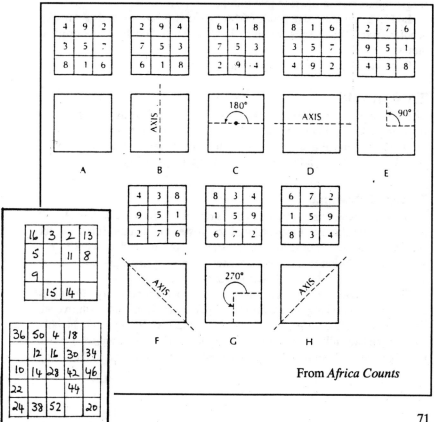

From *Africa Counts*

Now try a 4th order square. It is interesting to note that a 4th order square has 880 variations and yet the sum of rows, columns and diagonals always remains 34. In these magic squares each number can be used once only. Students can attempt to complete a magic square of : 3 2s, 3 3s, 3 4s and so on.

What about a 5th order square? How many variations? What is the sum of rows? Can you invent a formula? An expression which will give the constant for any order magic square is:-

$$\frac{n(n+1)}{2}$$

Next check out for 3, 4, and 5.

Outside of China, the earliest writer to discuss the magic square was an Arab mathematician in the 9th century, Tabit-ibn- Korra. About 500 years later the magic square was introduced into Europe.

In 1732, the extensive work of Mohammed.B.Mohammed, a Muslim scholar from West Africa, came to light in translation from the original Arabic.

Opposite on page 73 is a page of his writing.

# TANGRAMS

The Chinese Tangrams which originated some 4000 years ago, are very popular puzzles in mathematics and story lessons as the following example shows. It is interesting to see the differences for shapes such as a circle or an oval. Does it work equally well? (see pictures on page 74)

## Tower of Brahma

Another interesting puzzle, sometimes referred to as the 'Tower of Hanoi' is a version of the old Indian story of the Tower of Brahma. It is good for developing pattern recognition and spatial visualization, and for working out a recursive solution to a problem. Students working in groups will require support since it is not an easy puzzle to solve.

The story goes that priests at a temple in the ancient holy city of Benaras on the edge of the Ganges were set a task by Brahma, the creator of the world. The puzzle would decide when the world should end. Brahma told the holy men that he had built a tower from 64 large blocks of stone, arranged in order, the largest at the bottom. The problem was that the tower was in the wrong

## Text of Muhammad ibn Muhammad's manuscript

## Tower of Brahma

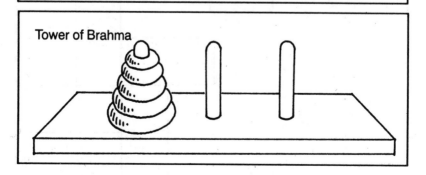

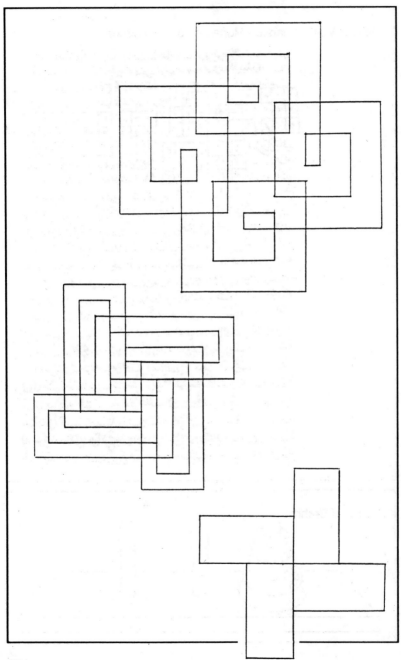

place. The holy men had to move it to the new position, but only according to rules set by Brahma. The rules were:-

* Only one stone could be moved at a time.
* There must never be more than three piles of stones.
* A smaller stone cannot be placed under a large stone as it might break.

The Tower of Hanoi version of this puzzle has three needles and round discs with holes, easily made from dowelling rods and some wood. Students can be asked to start with 2 discs and record the number of moves in a table:

| Number of discs | Estimated moves | Correct number |
|---|---|---|
| 2 | — | 3 |
| 3 | — | 7 |
| 4 | — | — |
| 5 | — | — |

As the number of discs are increased, can the students see a pattern?
Does the solution appear one minute and disappear the next?
Do any other activities have recursive features? — What about a family tree? — rivers? — leaves and branches?
Would it help if students recorded every move in diagrammatical form?
What is a recursive solution anyway?
Can they work out an algebraic function for the moves? or a computer programme? — The function is 2 - 1 where n is the number of blocks. Using the function, work out how long it will take to move the stones.
Could you *ever* do it?
Are there any other functions?

**How does the Chess problem with pennies differ from the Tower of Brahma?**

Start with one penny placed in the corner of the chess board. Double the number of pennies each time you put a cross in a square. Can you generate a formula?

How many pennies will you have when you have crossed all the squares?

## Number games, gestures and cosmology.

Dudeney, Andrews, Gardner have written some excellent books available on mathematical games and puzzles. But sadly, all fail to acknowledge the origin of the discoveries they draw on. Books of mathematical puzzles that make no more than token mention at the end, of some 'other cultures' are misleading to readers.

## Finger counting

Students often get told off for counting on their fingers and yet records from many cultures show that this was one of the first ways in which human beings counted, and it works perfectly. Carrying numbers in one's head is also very good training to learn to perform quick and accurate functions mentally. Consider the number words after 10. The word eleven means 'one left' and twelve literally means 'two left' referring to the additional fingers needed when ten fingers had already been used. There is extensive literature available on finger counting in European cultures.

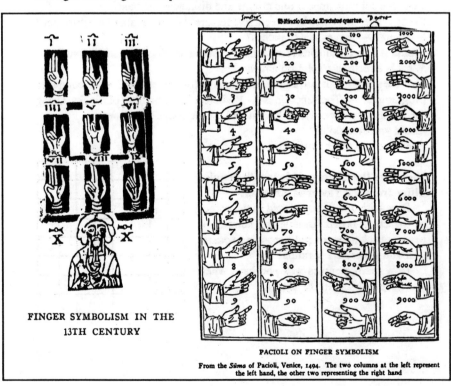

FINGER SYMBOLISM IN THE
13TH CENTURY

PACIOLI ON FINGER SYMBOLISM

From the *Süma* of Pacioli, Venice, 1494. The two columns at the left represent the left hand, the other two representing the right hand

Claudia Zaslavsky's beautifully illustrated and written *Africa Counts* and *Count on your fingers African style,* have proved a valuable source on the history of mathematics in African civilisations.

Here are some examples of finger counting from *Africa Counts.*

| Numbers | Arusha Massai | | Kamba | |
|---------|---------------|---|-------|---|
| 1. | Nabo | | Imye | |
| 2. | Are | | Lli | |
| 3. | Uni | | Itau | |
| 4. | Onguan | | Inya | |
| 5. | Imiet | | Ittano | |

| Numbers | Arusha Massai | Kamba |
|---------|---------------|-------|
| 6. | Lle | Thanthatu |
| 7. | Naapishana | Muonza |
| 8. | Isiet | Nyaanya |
| 9. | Enderuj | Ikenda |
| 10. | Form a circle with thumb and forefinger, then extend forefinger sharply other fingers curled | Ikumi |

# Numbers in sign language.

Great fun to learn for all. Most mathematics teachers would do semaphore as a fun activity, although students are unlikely ever to use it, whereas they would certainly find sign language a useful skill and experience.

# Three in a row games.

Nerenchi is a 3 in a row game from Sri Lanka. Illustrations of this 2000 year old game appear in carvings in the old temples. A special favourite with women and girls, it is played on the 24 points where the lines of the figure meet. Each player tries to get a row of 3 counters along the side of a square, along diagonal lines or along the line joining the mid-points. There are 20 ways of making a Nerenchi.

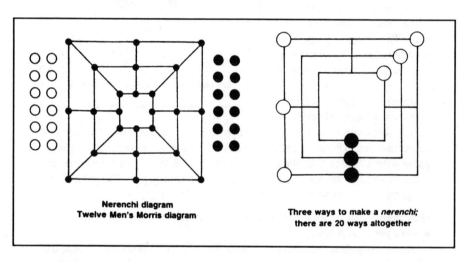

**Nerenchi diagram**
**Twelve Men's Morris diagram**

Three ways to make a *nerenchi*;
there are 20 ways altogether

Nine-Men's Morris is an adaptation of this game and is played with 20 counters, ten of each colour. Students can make their own board by simply drawing a 16 by 16 cm. square and drawing the squares inside as shown.

*Chinese version of the game:-*
Directions for play: You will need 24 counters, 12 in each of two colours. Starting with 5 counters, each player makes one move to points where the lines cross. If the counter falls between two of the opponent's, it is captured and replaced by one of the opponent's counters.

**SHISIMA** (right) for very young players, is a game from Western Kenya, in which each player tries to make a row of 3 of one colour.

**CHESS** has its origin in at least three cultures, Indian, Persian and Arabic. In 1st/2nd century AD writings, there are records of a game called Caturanga — meaning four campaigning armies i.e, the corps of ancient India: elephant, horse, chariot and four footmen. The original game was played by four players controlling the game with a throw of dice. As late as the 12-16th centuries, we find accounts of tales of games played by Indian kings in which real queens, kingdoms and armies were at stake. The game travelled to Persia in the 6th century AD and developed into a two player game with a 'general' at the helm. During the Middle Ages, in Arabia, the game evolved to its modern form, the general becoming the Queen. In India the game continues to be called *Shatranj*.

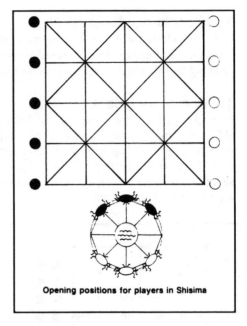

Opening positions for players in Shisima

**How many squares on a chessboard?** (From: ATM activity book *These have worked for us at A-level*)

An investigation complicated enough for A-level students who should use 'the sum of squares' to generate a formula and then generalise.

| Begin by drawing a | | How many squares? | |
|---|---|---|---|
| | 1 x 1 square. | | 1 |
| | 2 x 2 square. | | 5 |
| | 3 x 3 square. | | 14 |
| | 4 x 4 square. | | 30 |
| | 5 x 5 square. | | 55 |
| | | | and so on. |

Students will soon get the desired result :
Are there any links with triangular numbers?
Try similar factorisation and generalisation to find a resolution to : How many rectangles on a chessboard?

# The Chinese game of GO

Mentioned by Confucius (500BC), the game of GO — WEI-CHI — is probably the oldest board game in the world. In the orient, GO is ranked equal to Chess and in Japan it is regarded as a national game.

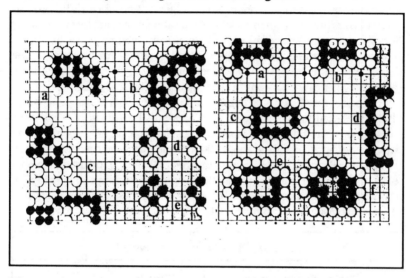

There are international tournaments and GO magazines. In this fighting game, the 19 x 19 board represents the uninhabited world surrounded by sea and to be conquered. Stones are placed in strategic positions to gain territory and capture the opponent. Points are gained for territory but lost for prisoners. The game takes time to learn and becomes extremely complicated as it progresses. Beginners play on a 10 x 10 board.

**The Carem Board** from India is beginning to be known here in England. It has similar rules to Snooker.

**The African board game** is, similarly, a game which has been played by kings, cowherds and presidents alike. There are 2-row and 4-row versions.
Some other names are :-

WARI — played in Ghana on a board with 2 rows of 6 holes.
AYO —  played in Nigeria.
BAO —  the Swahili name of the game as played in Uganda, requiring 64 beans.

Boards may be handsomely carved works of art.

81

In America, the commercial version goes by the name of Pitfall, and requires all the same mathematical skills. It's surprising that colonials ignored such marvellous educational and entertaining facets of African life with its advanced mathematical mental calculations. Perhaps they did not square with the image they wished to promote, of 'savages and primitives'. It is educational to compare the mathematical and educational complexity and value of Wari with, say, snakes and ladders or ludo. By encouraging games like these, students learn naturally of the multicultural nature of mathematics, while developing the important skills of decision making, estimating, predicting (by making logical deductions), counting, computing and grouping.

A good source of games is Johnny Ball's *Games From Around The World* (1989) produced to coincide with the Pop Maths Roadshow of 1989/1990. These games provide ample opportunities for practicing probability and expectation. Some date from about 3000BC and may have been the origin of backgammon games. *Pavolli,* the Aztec word for beans, is still used for pieces today. *Nyout* is a very old game and the boards may be found in the shape of a circle, a cross or a square, painted on a rafia mat for easy carrying. The game of Ludo may well derive from Nyout.

---

### Games from around the world

| Tablan (Southern India) | | Patolle | |
|---|---|---|---|
| 4 coins are used. Score | | 5 coins are used. Score: | |
| 1 tail | 2 | 1 head | 1 |
| 4 tails | 8 | 2 heads | 2 |
| 4 heads | 12 | 3 heads | 3 |
| others | 0 | 4 heads | 4 |
| | | 5 heads | 10 |
| | | all tails | 20 |
| Calculate the expected score for a throw. | | Calculate the expected score for a throw. | |

**Puluc (Central America)**

Use either 4 coins or an ordinary die (but ignore the 6's)

| 1 head | 1 | First, calculate the expected score per |
|---|---|---|
| 2 heads | 2 | throw when using 4 coins. Then calculate |
| 3 heads | 3 | the expecrted score per throw when using |
| 4 heads | 4 | a normal die (ignoring the 6's). |
| all tails | 5 | Which gives the faster game? |

## The Royal Game of Ur (Iraq)

Use either a pyramid die or three coins.

| | | |
|---|---|---|
| 0 heads | 0 | First, calculate the expected score per |
| 1 head | 1 | throw when using a pyramid die. Then |
| 2 heads | 4 | calculate the expected score when using |
| 3 heads | 5 | three coins. |

The rules given in *'Games from around the world'* say the player can throw again if a 5 is scored. How does this effect the expected scores?

## Nyout (Kora)

Use either 4 coins or 4 double-sided dice (flat on one side and curved on the other — like a round pencil sliced along its axis)

| | | |
|---|---|---|
| 1 flat side up | 1 | Finally claculate the expected |
| 2 flat sides up | 2 | score using coins, |
| 3 flat sides up | 3 | How can you calculate the chances |
| 3 flat sides up | 5 | of a flat side up with one double- |
| 4 flat sides up | 4 | sided die? |
| (throws of 4 or 5 win | | Calculate the expected score when |
| another throw) | | playing Nyout with double-sided die. |

## Checking out the perforations

Students can be asked to measure or count the number of perforations per centimetre around the edges of stamps. Do they differ in different stamps or is the number constant?, stamps from different countries?

Find out from the philatelic bureau if the number has any significance and how it is decided.

# Foreign Currencies

Many maths textbooks use holidays as a context for foreign exchange sums. Usually the settings are European and so is the currency. Exchange rates from around the globe can be acquired from any high street bank and used in calculations.

How about a page from the financial section of an Indian newspaper? Looking at the names of multinational companies from another country can increase students' knowledge. Asking why these names are not internationally known, will lead to debating how world trade operates and so to issues of equality and justice.

| Country | Currency Unit | We Se |
|---|---|---|
| Afghanistan | Afghani | REI |
| Albania | Lek | RE |
| Algeria | Dinar | 59 |
| Angola | Kwanza | NC |
| Argentina | Austral | NC |
| Australia | Dollar | 2( |
| Austria | Schilling | 22 |
| Bahamas | Dollar | 0.1 |
| Bahrain | Dinar | 9C |
| Bangladesh | Taka | 3 |
| Barbados | Dollar | 6( |
| Belgium | Franc | 4 |
| Belize | Dollar | 1 |
| Bermuda | Dollar | N |
| Bolivia | Boliviano | 4 |
| Botswana | Pula | |
| Brazil | Cruzado | |
| Brunei | Dollar | |
| Bulgaria | Lev | |
| Burma | Kyat | |
| Burundi | Franc | |
| Canada | Dollar | |
| Cape Verde Is. | Escudo | |
| Cayman Is. | Dollar | |
| C.F.A. | Franc | |
| C.F.P. | Franc | |
| Chile | Peso | |
| Colombia | Peso | |
| Costa Rica | Colon | |
| Cuba | Peso | |
| Curacao | Guilder | |
| Cyprus | Pound | |
| Czechoslovakia | Koruna | |
| Denmark | Krone | |
| Dominican Republic | Peso | |
| Djibouti | Franc | |
| East Caribbean | Dollar | |
| Ecuador | Sucre | |
| Egypt | Pound | |
| El Salvador | Colon | |
| Ethiopia | Birr | |
| Falklands Is | Pound | |
| Faroe Is | Krone | |
| Fiji | Dollar | |
| Finland | Markka | |
| France | Franc | |
| Gambia | Dalasi | |
| Germany (East) | Ostmark | |
| Germany (West) | D. Mark | |
| Ghana | Cedi | |

| Country | Currency Unit | We Sell | We Buy |
|---|---|---|---|
| Paraguay | Guarani | 1800 | REFER |
| Peru | Inti | NO | MARKET |
| Philippines | Peso | 35 | 40 |
| Poland | Zloty | 7300 | 7700 |
| Portugal | Escudos (Large) | 258 | 266 |
| | 1000/500 (Small) | 258 | 266 |
| Port Guinea | Escudo | REFER | REFER |
| Qatar | Riyal | 6.26 | 6.41 |
| Romania | Leu | 155 | 170 |
| Rwanda | Franc | 450 | 850 |
| Sao Tome & Ppe | Dobra | REFER | REFER |
| Saudi Arabia | Riyal | 6.4850 | 6.5850 |
| Seychelles | Rupee | 9.15 | 9.65 |
| Sierra Leone | Leone | 70 | REFER |
| Singapore | Dollar | 3.26 | 3.41 |
| Somali Rep. | Scellini | 60 | REFER |
| South Africa | Rand | 4.45 | REFER |
| S. Arabian Fed. | | 1.15 | REFER |
| Spain | Peseta (Large) | 198.25 | 201.25 |
| | (Small) | 196.75 | 199.75 |
| Sri Lanka | Rupee | 56 | REFER |
| Sudan | Pound | 40 | REFER |
| Surinam | Guilder | REFER | REFER |
| Swaziland | Lilangeni | 5.00 | 5.30 |
| Sweden | Krona | 10.85 | 10.95 |
| Switzerland | Franc | 2.71 | 2.74 |
| Syria | Pound | 75 | REFER |
| Taiwan | Dollar | 47 | 57 |
| Tanzania | Schilling | 250 | REFER |
| Thailand | Baht | 42 | 46 |
| Tonga | Pa'anga | 4.70 | REFER |
| Trinidad | Dollar | 7.60 | REFER |
| Tunisia | Dinar | 1.60 | REFER |
| Turkey | Lira (Large) | 3125 | 3725 |
| | 5000 (Small) | 3125 | 3725 |
| Uganda | Shilling | NO | MARKET |
| Uruguay | Peso | 825 | REFER |
| Un. Arab Emirates | Dirham | 6.32 | 6.47 |
| U.S.A. | Dollar | 1.7225 | 1.7375 |
| U.S.S.R. | Rouble | NO | MARKET |
| Venezuela | Bolivar | 70 | REFER |
| West Samoa | Tala | 10 | REFER |
| Yemen | Dinars | 20 | 21.50 |
| Yugoslavia | Dinar (Large) | 14800 | 15800 |
| | 5000/100 (Small) | 10500 | 11500 |
| Zaire | Zaire | 100 | REFER |
| Zambia | Kwacha | 40 | REFER |
| Zimbabwe | Dollar | 5.00 | REFER |

NO

| Currency Unit | We Sell | We Buy |
|---|---|---|
| Pound | | |
| Drachma (Large) | 1.01 | 1.0350 |
| 1000/5000 (Small) | 265 | 273 |
| Quetzal | 265 | 273 |
| Syli | 4.60 | REFER |
| Dollar | REFER | REFER |
| Gourde | 75 | REFER |
| Guilder | 30 | REFER |
| Lempira | 3.5725 | 3.6125 |
| Dollar | 6.75 | 8.75 |
| Forint | 13.27 | 13.47 |
| Krona | 134 | 144 |
| Rupee | 82 | REFER |
| Rupiah | 29 | 31 |
| Rial | 2750 | 2950 |
| Dinar | NO | MARKET |
| Pound | 3.80 | REFER |
| Shekel | 1.1875 | 1.2050 |
| Lira (Super) | 2.88 | REFER |
| 5000/1000 (Small) | 2330 | 2360 |
| | 2326 | 2356 |
| Dollar | 2332 | 2362 |
| Yen | 11 | REFER |
| Dinar | 221 | 226 |
| Riel | 0.97 | REFER |
| Shilling | NO | MARKET |
| Won | 34 | REFER |
| Dinar | 1125 | 1325 |
| Kip | 0.4975 | 0.5075 |
| Livre | NO | MARKET |
| Dinar | 825 | REFER |
| Franc | 2.00 | REFER |
| Pataca | 66.55 | 67.30 |
| Kwacha | 15 | 17 |
| Ringgit | 11.50 | 13.00 |
| Franc | 4.63 | 4.78 |
| ira | REFER | REFER |
| upee | 0.5750 | 0.6150 |
| eso | 24.30 | 27.30 |
| rham | 3800 | REFER |
| etical | 14.50 | 15.25 |
| pee | REFER | REFER |
| lar | 270 | 300 |
| doba | 2.7325 | 2.9325 |
| a | 4000 | REFER |
| ie | NO | MARKET |
| | 11.53 | 11.64 |
| be | 0.66 | 0.6875 |
| | 34.50 | 38.50 |
| | 1.65 | 1.75 |

## The abacus

The abacus was one of the first calculation aids, originally devised to save counting figures when working with large numbers. The degree of dexterity, skill and concentration that is needed to work the abacus should also be demonstrated. The process required to learn to do calculations on an abacus allows teachers to enhance several concepts at once. The abacus is still used by Japanese businessmen. Soroban, a popular Japanese abacus, is based on five and ten.

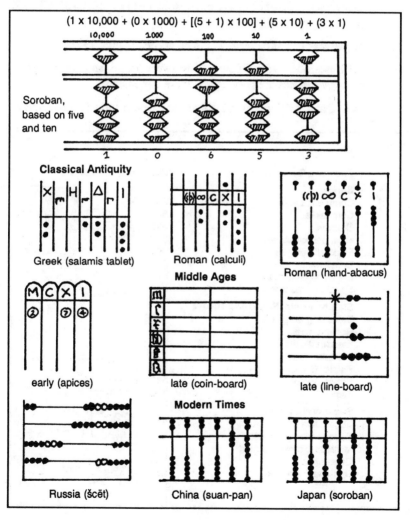

85

**Caribbean foods:** Context for Fractions and Decimal Calculations. Kilojoules have replaced calories in science textbooks yer calories continue to be used as a measure of food value in everyday conversation. Values in these tables, given as per 100 gms are from data complied by the Caribbean Food and Nutrition Institute, 1974. Pictures can show how attractive Carribean food is.

a)  What is the calorific value of 300g of yams?

b)  A recipe uses 250g of blackeye peas. How many calories will this food give?

c)  How many grams of oatmeal would be needed to give 730 calories?

d)  A meal uses 60g sweet peppers, 110g sweet potato, and 70g red peas. How many calories are provided by these ingredients?

Given that 4.2 Kilojoules = 1 Kilocalorie devise sums for conversion

| Food and Description | Calories (Kilocalories) |
|---|---|
| **Cereals** | |
| Cornmeal, degermed, unenriched | 364 |
| Cornflakes | 386 |
| Oatmeal | 390 |
| Rice, parbolied, raw | 369 |
| Flour, all purpose | 364 |
| Bread, white | 269 |
| Bread, whole wheat | 243 |
| Spaghetti, macaroni | 369 |
| **Starchy Fruits, Roots and Tubers** | |
| Banana, green | 110 |
| Banana, ripe | 97 |
| Breadfruit | 81 |
| Plantain, ripe | 122 |
| Potato, English | 82 |
| Potato, sweet | 117 |
| Yam | 105 |
| **Sugar and Syrups** | |
| Sugar, dark brown, crude | 373 |
| Sugar, white, granulated | 385 |
| Molasses, cane, medium | 232 |
| Cane syrup | 263 |
| Jam and Preserves | 272 |

| Food and Description | Calories |
|---|---|
| Whole peas | 340 |
| Peanuts | 564 |
| Peanut butter, salted | 581 |
| Cashew nut | 533 |
| Coconut, mature | 296 |
| Coconut, immature, jelly | 122 |
| Coconut, water | 22 |

**Vegetables**

| | |
|---|---|
| Beans, snap, string | 32 |
| Beet greens | 24 |
| Cabbage | 25 |
| Carrot, fresh, raw | 40 |
| Christophine | 31 |
| Lettuce, green | 18 |
| Mustard greens | 23 |
| Pea, green, immature | 84 |
| Pepper, sweet | 22 |
| Pigeon pea, green | 118 |
| Pumpkin, mature fruit | 30 |
| Spinach, raw | 26 |
| Avocado pear | 162 |
| Beet, common, red | 42 |
| Cauliflower | 25 |
| Celery | 19 |
| Cucumber | 14 |
| Egg plant | 24 |
| Okra | 25 |
| Onion, mature bulb | 40 |
| Marrow | 15 |
| Tomato, ripe | 21 |

**Fruits**

| | |
|---|---|
| Grapefruit | 41 |
| Grapefruit juice, canned, sweetened | 53 |
| Lemon | 29 |
| Limes | 32 |
| Oranges | 49 |
| Orange juice, canned, sweetened | 52 |
| Apple, fresh fruit | 58 |

**Pulses and Nuts**

| | |
|---|---|
| Bonavist, dry | 334 |
| Red peas, kidney bean | 337 |
| Blackeye peas | 341 |
| Lentils | 340 |
| Split peas | 348 |
| Dry peas, (Pigeon peas) | 337 |

**Four colour map problems:** Students can create their own designs in order to break the four colour rule, but they may find it more interesting to use real maps. Ask them to find out the names of countries in the bottom map, and then to colour them in with less than four colours.

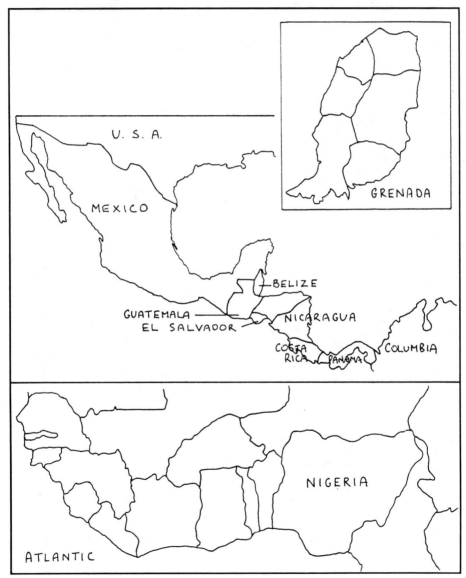

**Maps for Area:** Simple maps of the outlines of different countries can be used to assist with calculating areas of non-standard shapes. The students can draw parallel lines a centimetre apart over the maps, but it is better still to use a see-through square grid.

Some preparatory discussion about scales and area will be needed.

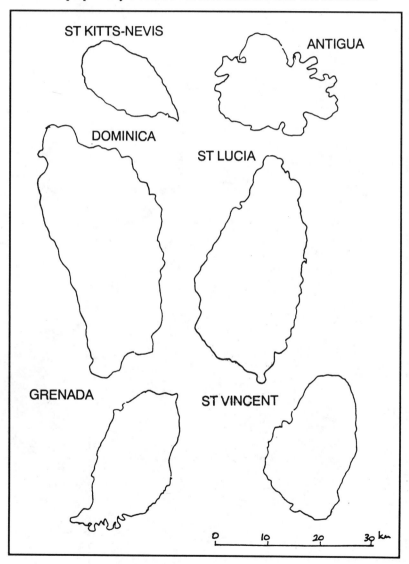

Maps can be used for scales, contour work, bearings, gradient, line of sight problems, shortest routes and so on. They provide a good opportunity for cross-curricular work with Geography. Any school atlas is a good resource. Use maps of Carribean or Asian countries to suit the needs of your pupils. From: *Longman's School Caribbean Atlas.*

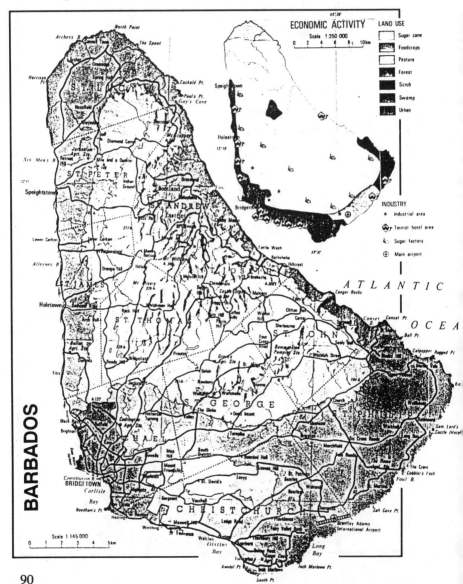

*Chapter 5*

# More Multicultural Approaches

## The History of Mathematics

> *The Arabs called mathematics 'the Indian art' (hindisat). —Most of the great discoveries and inventions of which Europe is so proud would have been impossible without a developed system of mathematics. — The unknown man who devised the decimal system of numerals was from the world's point of view, after the Buddha, the most important son of India. His achievement was the work of an analytical mind of the first order, and he deserves much more honour than he has so far received.* Basham *in* The Wonder That Was India, *(1985)*

Books about the history of mathematics need to be selected with care. Some mistakenly attribute the origin of much mathematics to ancient Greece and Rome and portray Arab mathematicians as no more than messengers passing on Hindu mathematics. Arab traders just happen to pass by, carrying their mathematical knowledge. History is more complex than this simplistic explanation would have us believe. Most concepts in mathematics, including calculus, were known by Indian, Chinese and Arab mathematicians long before Greek times. Records show that most of Algebra (an Arabic word) and Trigonometry owe their origins to Arab scholars. Many original records were taken out of the countries of their origin during colonial times. Some can be found in the Wellcome Institute of London.

In an article in *Race and Class* (XXVIII, 3 1987), G.G. Joseph outlines how science and mathematics from Asia and Africa came to be neglected during colonialization. These disciplines were resurrected later — as a European phenomenon. Questions are now being asked, with the result that existing 'eurocentric paradigmatic norms' are being redefined, even destroyed.

Here are some ideas for worksheets based on the history of mathematics.

**Writing and speaking numbers in different languages:** A good starting point is to consider the different ways in which numbers are written in different languages. Try Urdu, Chinese, Bengali, Hindi, English.

Complete these multiplication squares.

ARABIC

Top row (right to left): ١ ٢ ٣ ٤ ٥ ٦ ٧ ٨ ٩ ١٠
Left column (top to bottom): ٢ ٣ ٤ ٥ ٦ ٧ ٨ ٩ ١٠

PUNJABI

Top row: ੧ ੨ ੩ ੪ ੫ ੬ ੭ ੮ ੯ ੧੦
Left column (top to bottom): ੨ ੩ ੪ ੫ ੬ ੭ ੮ ੧੦

**Counting in Braille:** Draw a 3 x 2 dot rectangle on squared paper and work out all the possible patterns.

What happens to the number of patterns if you use a smaller rectangle?

Can you find any other rectangle or square pattern which will be as useful as 3 x 2?

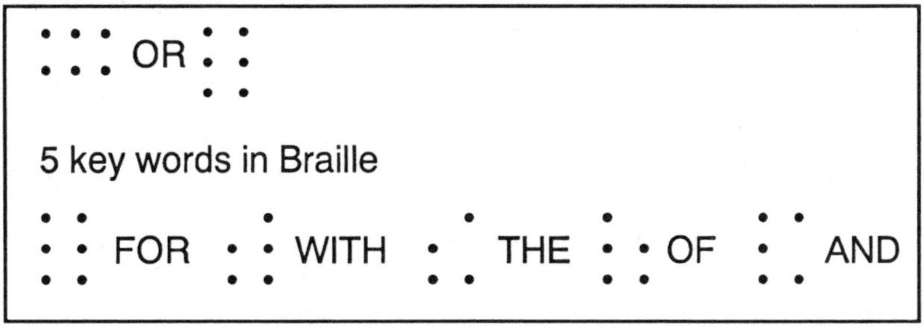

∴ OR ⠆

5 key words in Braille

⠿ FOR ⠒ WITH ⠪ THE ⠯ OF ⠿ AND

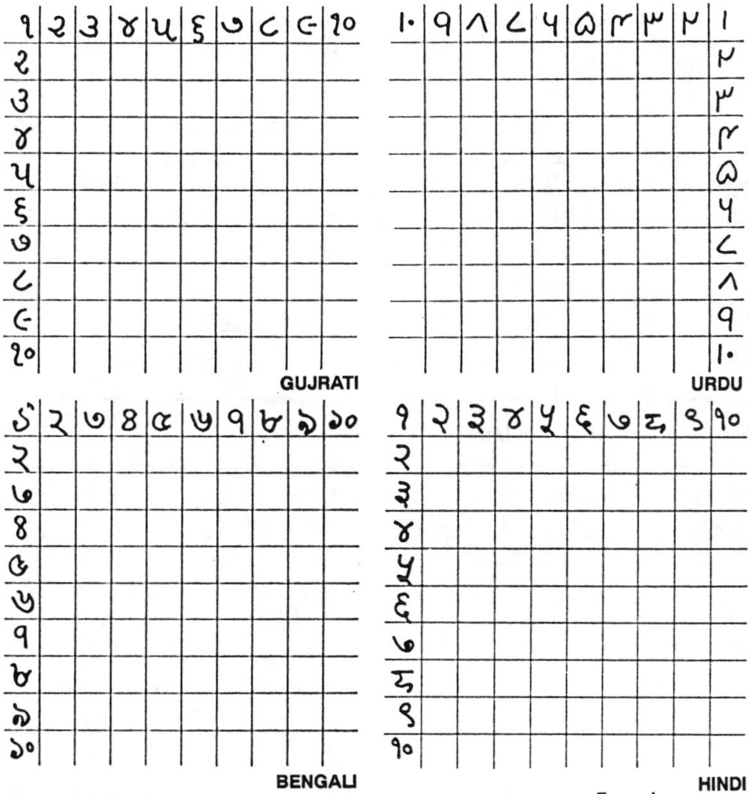

Gujrati, Urdu number grid charts

**GUJRATI**

**URDU**

**BENGALI**

**HINDI**

*Chinese Number Symbols*

| 一 | 1 | 十 | 10 | 五 | 5 | 九 | 9 |
| 二 | 2 | 百 | 100 | 六 | 6 | | |
| 三 | 3 | 千 | 1,000 | 七 | 7 | 萬 | 10,000 |
| 四 | 4 | | | 八 | 8 | | |

*Examples*

| 十三 | 13 | 五十 | 50 |
| 三十 | 30 | 五十三 | 53 |

**Number words** provide a record of the origin of modern languages and invite mathematics teachers to explore language a little. The oneness of the human race is powerfully demonstrated; Indo-European languages have common ancestors: Sanskrit from the East and Celtic from the West. It is thought that the Aryans, the original Indo-Europeans, many thousands of years ago inhabited a long belt extending from the Central Asian Islands across the Caspian Sea into Europe or, alternatively, regions of Central Asia or somewhere between the Baltic and the Black seas. A worksheet around number words demonstrates the linguistic affinity that exists amongst Asian and European languages.

|    | Sanskrit | Italian | French | Dutch | Danish | German | Icelandic | Greek |
|----|----------|---------|--------|-------|--------|--------|-----------|--------|
| 1  | Ekab     | Uno     | Un     | Een   | En     | Eins   | Einn      | Heis   |
| 2  | Dvi      | Due     | Deux   | Twee  | To     | Zwei   | Tvier     | Dyo    |
| 3  | Trayah   | Tre     | Trois  | Drie  | Tre    | Drie   | Prir      | Treis  |
| 4  | Catvarrah| Quattro | Quatre | Vier  | Fire   | Vier   | Fjorir    | Tettares |
| 5  | Oanca    | Cinque  | Cinq   | Vijf  | Fem    | Funf   | Fim       | Pent   |
| 6  | Sas      | Sei     | Six    | Zes   | Seks   | Sechs  | Sex       | Hex    |
| 7  | Septa    | Sette   | Sept   | Zeven | Syv    | Sieben | Sjo       | Hepta  |
| 8  | Asta     | Otto    | Huit   | Acht  | Olte   | Acht   | Atta      | Okto   |
| 9  | Nava     | Nove    | Neuf   | Negon | Ni     | Neun   | Nui       | En-nea |
| 10 | Dasa     | Deici   | Dix    | Tien  | Ti     | Zehn   | Tiu       | Deka   |

Here is a table of Satem languages:

|    | Indian Sanskrit | Slavic Old Church Slavonic | Baltic Lithuanian | Basic Indo-European |
|----|-----------------|----------------------------|-------------------|----------------------|
| 1  | ekab, eka        | jedinu, -a, -o             | vienas            | oi-nos; oi-qos sems, smia, sem |
| 2  | dvi, dve         | dva, dve                   | du, dvi           | duuo; duo            |
| 3  | trayah, tisrah   | trije                      | trys              | trejes, trie         |
| 4  | catvarah, catasrah | cetyre                   | keturi            | quetuor (es)         |
| 5  | panca            | petj                       | penki             | penque               |
| 6  | šaš              | šestj                      | šeš               | sueks; seks          |
| 7  | sapta            | sedmj                      | septyni           | septm                |
| 8  | asša, astau      | osmj                       | asšuoni           | oktou                |
| 9  | nava             | devetj                     | devyni            | neun, eneuen         |
| 10 | dasa             | desetj                     | dešimt            | dekm; dekmt          |

Investigate old counting words used by shepherds in Lincolnshire, England. (Mathematical Pie: No.103, 1984)

**Questions in a variety of languages:** Students could be asked to figure out which particular topics were the subject of investigation in these pages from a) a Hungarian or b) a Japanese mathematics workbook and then to work out the solutions. The purpose would be to facilitate mathematical skill and at the same time highlight the fact that students all over the world learn very similar mathematics although teaching and learning styles and medium may vary.

---

第 2 章　方程式と不等式

◇　二次方程式の因数分解による解き方

[例 題] 1.　方程式 $3x^2+7x-10=0$ を解け.

〔解〕　左辺を因数分解して,

$$(x-1)(3x+10)=0$$

よって,

$$x-1=0 \quad または \quad 3x+10=0$$

ゆえに,

$$x=1, \quad -\frac{10}{3}$$

練習 3.　つぎの方程式を解け.

(1) $2x^2-x-15=0$　　　　(2) $3x^2+12x=0$

(3) $x(2x+3)=6-x$

---

Másold át a tojást átlátszó papírra! Ragaszd rajzlapra, és vágd fel a vonalak mentén! Válassz egyet a képen látható madarak közül, és azt rakd ki!

Mérnök Miki arra kíváncsi, hogy hány tégla hiányzik az építményből. Szerinted mennyi?

Egy almát hány szem cseresznyével lehetne kiegyensúlyozni?

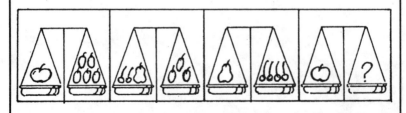

Folytasd! Az adott szabályok közül válaszd ki a megfelelőket!

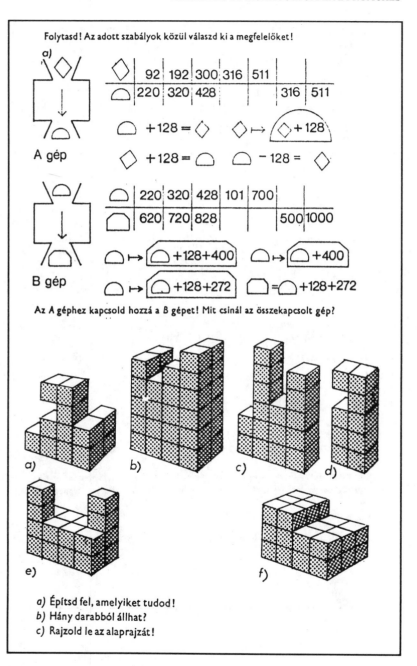

Az A géphez kapcsold hozzá a B gépet! Mit csinál az összekapcsolt gép?

a) Építsd fel, amelyiket tudod!
b) Hány darabból állhat?
c) Rajzold le az alaprajzát!

97

**Numbers and complexity of ancient civilisations:** Many traditional ancient civilisations are at serious risk of extinction, due particularly to the exploitation of the rain forests. One such people are the Maya, an indigenous Central American people. The Mayan system of numbers has existed since about 3000 BC. and uses a base of 20. They also had a very complex and efficient system of measuring large chunks of time . Here is a comparison of the Mayan system of numbering with Egyptian, Babylonian, Arabic, English and early Roman symbols.

Just as our 0 makes a number ten times larger, Maya made it twenty times larger.

Early numbers show traces of notch-recording. Egyptians, Babylonians and Romans used strokes for the first few numbers and different signs for higher numbers.

Ask students to :-
Produce wall displays of addition and subtraction sums; to ask each other to read their dates of birth, their house number etc. in Mayan, Egyptian, Babylonian.

**Numbers and cross-curricular work:** Trace how numbers travelled to different parts of the world and how the symbols changed. This opens up a possibility for cross-curricular work with the History and Geography department. Without such curriculum development, students may never learn about the vast Muslim Empire or the city of Baghdad, the most famous city of learning long before Roman times. It is said that the first Christian ever to study in a Muslim university was a monk who disguised himself as a Muslim. How would computation be possible without the concept of zero? Trace the origins of zero.

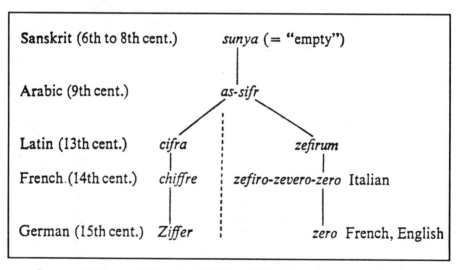

Sanskrit (6th to 8th cent.)   *sunya* (= "empty")

Arabic (9th cent.)   *as-sifr*

Latin (13th cent.)   *cifra*          *zefirum*

French.(14th cent.)   *chiffre*   *zefiro-zevero-zero* Italian

German (15th cent.)   *Ziffer*          *zero* French, English

On page 100 is a multiplication of 123 by 165 in Roman numerals. See if you can work out the answer in Roman numerals.

**Knots as Numerals:** This intriguing form of counting days and objects is found all over the world. The Tibetan prayer strings and Catholic rosary are both forms of number strings, on which the prayer exercises are recorded as knots. On page 100 are some illustrations showing a variety of knots used for the purpose of recording numbers.

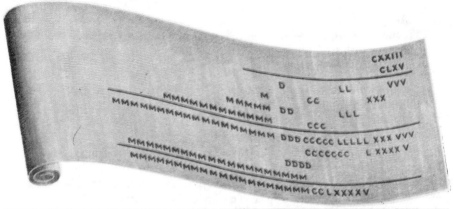

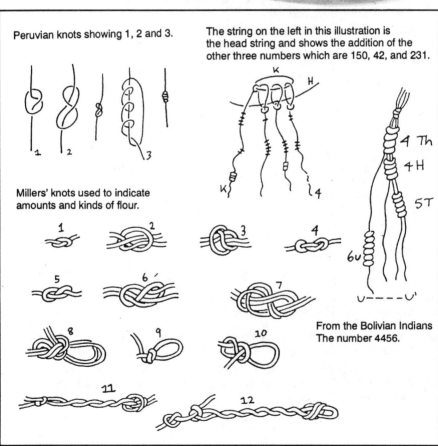

Peruvian knots showing 1, 2 and 3.

The string on the left in this illustration is the head string and shows the addition of the other three numbers which are 150, 42, and 231.

Millers' knots used to indicate amounts and kinds of flour.

From the Bolivian Indians
The number 4456.

**Number symbols and Art:** The art department could be encouraged to do a project on IMAGES as number symbols where students could make plaster casts and tally sticks. The images painted and chiselled on the walls of tombs and temples in Asia and Central America provide us with evidence that, before the existence of number symbols, images of objects were used to represent both numbers and language pictorially. Similarly there is historical evidence that farmers and traders developed their own methods of keeping records of sales, credits etc. by cutting, carving or scratching on sticks and stones.

a) Heads in this Mayan plate are numbered from 1 to 19. The vertical beams represent groups of 5.
b) Hieroglyphic for 6000: This symbol tells a story: 'The Falcon king led 6000 men of the Harpoon Lake'. Halves and quarters.

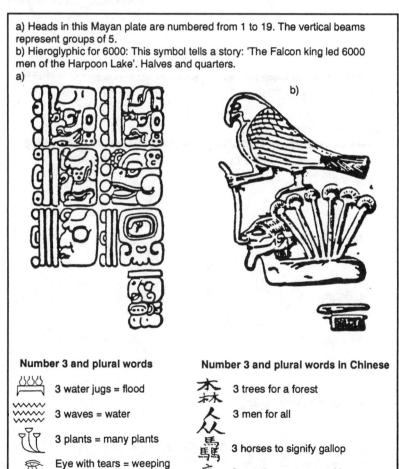

| Number 3 and plural words | Number 3 and plural words in Chinese |
|---|---|
| 3 water jugs = flood | 3 trees for a forest |
| 3 waves = water | 3 men for all |
| 3 plants = many plants | 3 horses to signify gallop |
| Eye with tears = weeping | 3 mouths means speaking |

Egyptian symbol for a million

Egyptian symbol for 100,000

Chinese sign for 10,000 on a 6th century coin.

This sequence is from the CODEX VIGILANS written in 976 AD in Northern Spain.

The number 641 in

|  | 40 | 1 | 600 |
|---|---|---|---|
| a) Persian |  |  |  |
| b) Turkish |  |  |  |

Egyptian symbols for common fractions.

Numbers 1 to 10 in Hindi

## Gambling, Dice and Probability

Many interesting games are based on gambling, such as poker, bridge, dice, betting on horses, predicting football results, lotteries. Experienced players use mathematics to predict and estimate their winning moves, though beginners may play by guess-work. Such pastimes from around the world are a good source of probability investigations.

Sergio Roberto Nobre of Brazil uses a popular lottery to increase the motivation of his students (though it is forbidden by Brazilian law). The 'Animal Lottery' is part of Brazilian folklore and is played all over the country. During their last year in a high school, according to Nobre, it is not easy to sustain the motivation of students. Because the lottery is a familiar, everyday part of their lives, the students themselves supply all the information needed to set the context, while the teacher supplies the sums on probabilities of gain. Students who at first feel that gamblers might be able to calculate certain advantageous moves, soon deduce for themselves that the greatest profit is always in the hands of the owners of the business and that chances of any individual winning are very slim indeed. (*The Animal Lottery and the Mathematics Education* Nobre, 1986)

---

### Animal Lottery and its mathematics

The game is said to have originated in Rio de Janeiro to save a zoological park from closing down in 1888. Drawings of animal were promoted by selling tickets which bore numbers relating to the animals in captivity. According to Nobre, the game today involves some 50,000 employees and a daily circulation of $2,000,000,000.

The 25 animals in the list are related to numbers as follows:-

| | | |
|---|---|---|
| 1. — Ostrich | 2. — Eagle | 3. — Donkey |
| 5. — Dog | 6. — She-goat | 7. — Sheep |
| 8. — Camel | 9. — Snake | 10. — Rabbit |
| 11. — Horse | 12. — Elephant | 13. — Cock |
| 14. — Cat | 15. — Alligator | 16. — Lion |
| 17. — Monkey | 18. — Pig | 19. — Peacock |
| 20. — Turkey | 21. — Bull | 22. — Tiger |
| 23. — Bear | 24. — Deer | 25. — Cow |

Each number belongs to a corresponding *group* of animals:-

---

Group of the Cat = 14, Group of the donkey = 3 and so on.

Each animal is designated to a group of tens from 01, 02 — 34, 35, — 49, 50 — to 99. 00.

01 — 02 — 03 — 04 — Ostrich

05 — 06 — 07 — 08 — Eagle

—

—

—

93 — 94 — 95 — 96 — Deer

97 — 98 — 99 — 00 — Cow

To place a bet on which animal might be the 1st or 2nd or 3rd prize of the day, players enter a bet in numbers and observe the tens of winning numbers. For example:-

1st prize: 4188 — if the player had placed a bet on the tens of the tiger (85, 86, 97, 88) he/she will win the first prize. The game is made highly complicated by adding corresponding hundreds and thousands to the list of animals. This decides the amount of winnings. The gambler may bet on all the prizes in all the categories. In order not to lose every time, he/she has to work out how much was put on each game and what it will bring in winnings, which numbers have been played already, which combination will give him/her a higher prob- ability at winnings. Gamblers work out all the probability of gains in their heads and not on paper.

Probability of gain in a *Group* = $\frac{1}{25}$

Probability of gain in a *Hundred* = $\frac{1}{1000}$

Probability of gain in a *Thousand* = $\frac{1}{10,000}$

Comparisons can be made with *real gains* in games such as Bingo, Football coupons, Coin lotteries.

**Dice:** This simplest source of amusement toppled empires in the not so distant past. They feature largely in the doctrines of Hindu, Greek and Persian philosophy. A variety of dice were used in ancient India. Most of these were four-faced, the throws being known as: *Krta* (four), *treta* (three), *dvapara* (two), and *kali* (one). Such was the importance of these terms that they are said to have been applied to the four great periods of time, the *yugas* (ages) in the Hindu cosmology: *Krtayuga. Tretayuga. Dvaparayuga. Kalayuga.*

The lengths of the yugas are, respectively, 4,800, 3,600, 2,400, and 1,200 years of the gods, each being equal to 360 human years. The doctrines of the four ages existed in ancient Greece and in Persia. We are at present in the Kalayuga, which began in 3102 BC, the year of the *Mahabharata* war.

The great epic *Mahabharata* is built around a great gambling tournament — throwing the dice — in which King Yudhishitra loses his kingdom, his brothers and his wife to his wicked cousin Duryodhana. (Basham, 1985)

There are records of six-sided dice in the excavations of the Indus cities.

## Geomancy and mathematics.

The Collins English Dictionary defines Geomancy as: *prophecy from the pattern made when a handful of earth is cast down or dots are drawn at random and connected with lines.* This definition does not do justice to this ancient science which endeavoured to create harmony in human habitats, on the principle that the universe is a continuum. Fields, places of worship and houses were carefully aligned in harmony with sunlight, magnetic variation, the seasons and water sources so as to be in harmony with the cosmic order, with the visible and invisible forces around us. The evidence for such sacred geometry can be found around the world. Examples range from the very first altars for sacrifice to mediaeval churches; from the yantras and mandlas of the Hindu ascetic designed to raise spiritual awareness to the plans for Renaissance ideal cities; from sand paintings of the indigenous North American Indians to the geometric alignments of southern Britain at Stonehenge; from Inca lines in Peru to the burial places of the Pharaohs in Egypt; from hill figures of the iron age to the radiating lines of the Mecca at Kabba; and there are many more.

Nigel Pennick has written comprehensively on the subject, for instance in *The ancient science of Geomancy.*

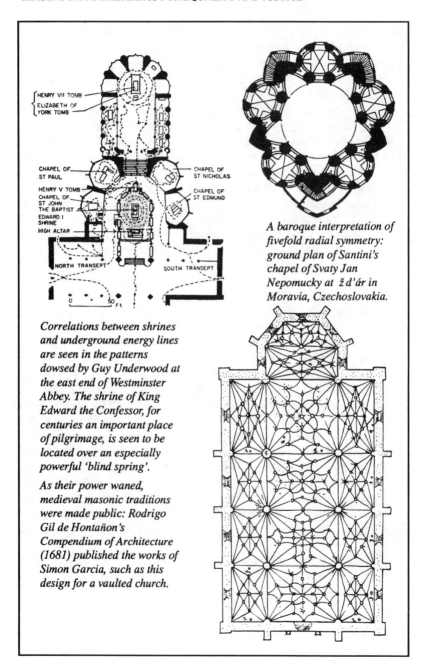

*A baroque interpretation of fivefold radial symmetry: ground plan of Santini's chapel of Svaty Jan Nepomucky at Žd'ár in Moravia, Czechoslovakia.*

*Correlations between shrines and underground energy lines are seen in the patterns dowsed by Guy Underwood at the east end of Westminster Abbey. The shrine of King Edward the Confessor, for centuries an important place of pilgrimage, is seen to be located over an especially powerful 'blind spring'.*

*As their power waned, medieval masonic traditions were made public: Rodrigo Gil de Hontañon's Compendium of Architecture (1681) published the works of Simon Garcia, such as this design for a vaulted church.*

106

## Geometry in the Hindu social setting

Decorating the human habitation for festive occasions is an ancient and still popular tradition in India. Along with song, music and dance, the decorating of floors, walls, doors, steps, gates is an essential artistic tradition that every

Indian, rich or poor, would follow.

The most commonly known to maths teachers are Rangoli floor patterns. Most popular amongst Gujeratis, these are made during Holi, the festival of colours associated with the spring. The patterns are created on a grid made by placing pegboards over the floor and sprinkling coloured chalk through the

holes, leaving a regular pattern which is elaborated upon and filled with coloured powder. Students can make permanent patterns in card or plywood. Join the dots on a grid as shown here and then reflect this in the four axes of

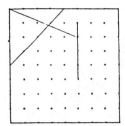  

symmetry. Spread glue over the chosen areas and sprinkle on coloured rice or powder.

## Symmetry

Materials which can be used:
ink blots, folded paper, vegetables sliced vertically to give mirror symmetry, potato prints, leaves, glue and powder, stencils, objects like scissors.
Ideas for symmetrical patterns:
leaves, trees, bridges, houses, famous buildings, mosques, temples, churches, animals, many abstract patterns such as Islamic patterns, Rangoli patterns.

Signs from World Religions

**Compass work using ideas from Botswana baskets**

## Topology

The Bridges of Konigsberg, popularly used as the starting point for a series of lessons in topology, could be varied by using examples from different cultures. In fact, students in some parts of the world find this topic easier than we in the West because their background includes drawings in household and play settings which get them thinking on these lines from an early age. These drawings decorate houses and school buildings. In Vanuatu, an Island of the New Hebrides, the patterns of drawings are accompanied by stories. As the story develops, the pattern changes, the story always ending in the same place as it began.

As Phillip Nelson, from the University of West Indies, has written:

Besides the aesthetic and recreational aspect of these drawings I offer them to teachers as more challenging routes to investigate when studying topology. The pupils from Maekula could never see why the Konigsberg bridges problem should have been posed; to them it is obvious there is no route.

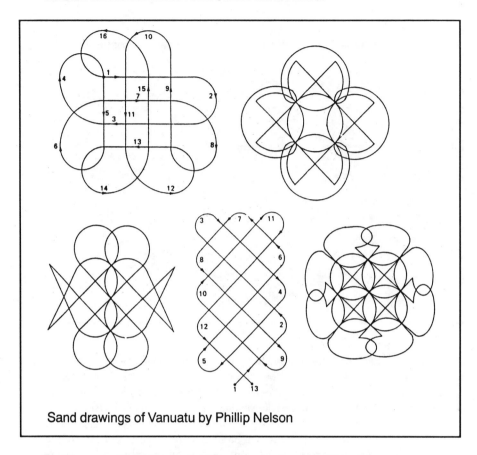

Sand drawings of Vanuatu by Phillip Nelson

## Pythagoras' Theorem and a decorative motif

For a mathematics lesson to make sense, it should be embedded in the cultural environment of the pupils: so argues Paules Gerdes from Mozambique. He has explored a variety of cultural elements from Mozambique and used them as starting points in classroom mathematics. His works are listed in the reference section.

His study of *Decorative motifs for proving Pythagoras' Theorem* became very popular with our colleagues. (*Sharan-Jeet uses her mathematical shawl as the starting point for the study of angles, shapes and transformation geometry —see the section at the end of this chapter*)

In all, there are well over 400 different proofs of the Pythagorean theorem, cited by Loomis (1940, 1972) and by Gerdes (1986c, 1986d). Gerdes takes

110

traditional textile designs as inspiration: two are shown below. Commonly referred to as the 'toothed square' or the 'star pattern', the central design is characteristic of basketry designs of the Salish Indians of British Columbia, mat designs of the Tchokwe of Angola and motif designs for Mexican Indian shawls. The question posed is : Is it possible to transform the toothed square into one or two real squares with the same area? Experimentation by students leads them to discover many possibilities.

The question can then be posed: 'Is there is a relationship between these three squares?' Gerdes states that by drawing the three squares on a grid paper and experimenting with them,

> pupils may be led to conjecture the Pythagorean theorem in general and in this manner toothed squares assume a heuristic value for the discovery of this important proposition. (Gerdes,1988a)

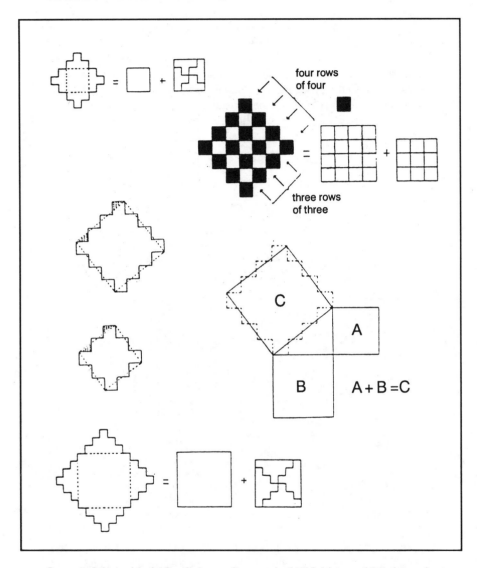

In an article entitled 'On Culture, Geometrical Thinking and Mathematics Education', in *Educational Studies in Mathematics* (19.2.88) Gerdes demonstrates many *alternative constructions of Euclidian geometrical ideas developed from the traditional culture of Mozambique*. One of these shows how a square button woven out of two strips of any material hides Pythagorean considerations which can be used to engage students in finding their own solution to the Theorem of Pythagoras.

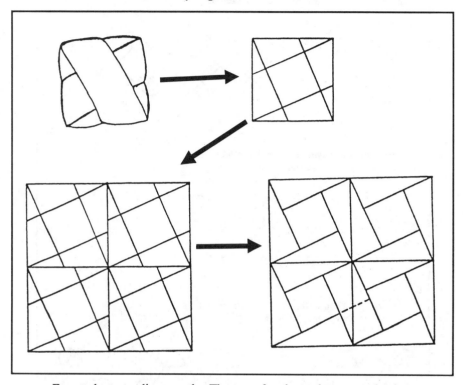

For students to discover the Theorem for themselves must lead to an enhancement of mathematics and an increase in motivation. Other examples include:-

- Fishtraps with their regular hexagonal hole patterns.
- Circular mats and baskets.
- *Angolan and South Indian sand drawings:* Analyse the geometrical algorithm. Find the missing pattern (analogous to finding the missing number).

The third drawing is a **Tchokwe sand representation of a suspension bridge.** Can you draw the missing patterns?

  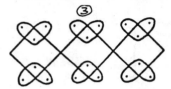

**Traditional Tchokwe and Tamil designs**
Can you draw the missing patterns?

 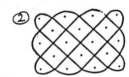  

**Tchokwe representation of a transport bag**
The bag is shown in the third drawing. Can you draw the missing patterns?

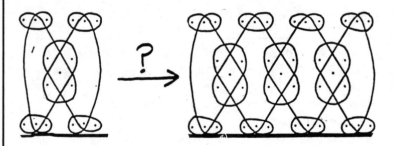

Examples from the Tchokwe of North East Angola and from the Tamil of South India.

Brahma's knot: This symbol of protection is founded as a sand drawing from the Tamils in South India.

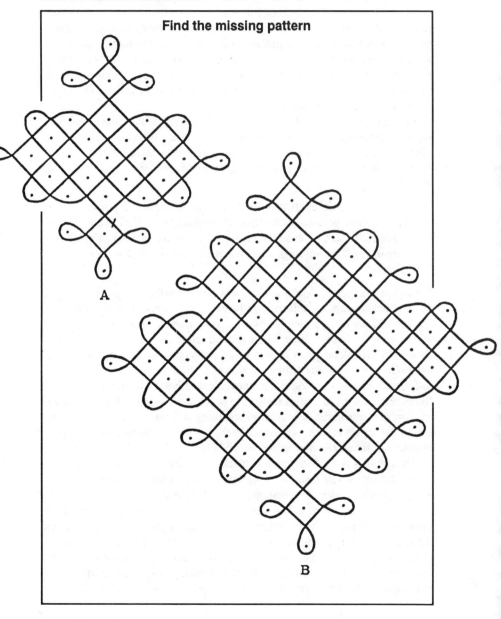

**Find the missing pattern**

A

B

## Mathematics, nature and creative thinking

Many natural creations undeniably demonstrate symmetry and geometrical patterns. Examples of crystalline forms of certain minerals, molecular structures, plankton and algae, butterflies' wings, the isomorphic and zygomorphic symmetry of flowers, corals and starfishes can be the starting points for a study of mathematics in nature. The study can progress to the orderly movement of stars and planets, and the patterns formed by natural phenomena such as volcanic eruptions, the Giants Causeway in Ireland or simply snowflakes and frost crystals.

Mathematical construction and reasoning also forms the basis of creative works of literature, drama and even movies according to Tadasu Kawaguchi, a Japanese mathematician. In *Mathematical thoughts being latent in various artistic activities,* (International Congress of Maths Education, 1988), he asserts:

> Mathematical thoughts themselves are not monopolistic possessions of some limited persons such as mathematicians and scientists but they are universally latent as essential categories of cognitive ways originated in human activities although their possessors may not always *be conscious of them.'*

He argues that novelists and artists use a set of 'mathematical reasonings', i.e, abstract/concept organisation, inductive/deductive reasoning, axiomatic analogical/reasoning, generalisation/specialization etc. The novelists themselves may not describe their 'internal brain activities' as such; nevertheless, their work has elements of operational/functional, analytical/graphical and symbolic activities. According to Kawaguchi, there are only two major differences between artistic and mathematical activities. In mathematics, the 'brain activities' he identifies are used to organise well-defined concepts such as numbers, quantities, algebraic expressions and functions. Secondly, the emotional aspect is more stimulated in the former, while there is a stronger assertion of the intellectual aspect in the latter.

Though it is not too difficult to transfer this form of reasoning to some artistic activities, say music composition, it is not easy to recognise mathematical connections in the creations of novelists and the film world.

To explain his claim to his western audience, Mr. Kawaguchi used the example of the movie *Twelve Angry Men,* in which a jury of twelve examines the case of a 17 year old accused of murdering his father and with strong evidence against him. The mathematical reasoning begins when all but one of the jury have been convinced by the evidence provided in court that the boy is guilty. Only this one jury member, aware that the boy, who is only 17, will have the course of his life decided by the verdict, methodically challenges each item of evidence and the boy is acquitted.

Mr. Kawaguchi sees mathematical reasoning in every aspect of life: the next section of this book has been inspired by his passionately held and objectively demonstrated view.

---

**My mother's mathematics** *by Sharan-Jeet Shan.*

My mother did not go to a formal school, but I realise today how well educated she was and how cleverly she applied mathematical reasoning to her sewing, knitting and embroidery. (A shawl embroidered by Sharon-Jeet Shan's mother is reproduced on pages 118/119) These days patterns are placed on a woven cloth according to computer instructions and cutting is done by machine. My mother must have employed many mathematical processes when she arranged the cloth in the most economical manner and cut it symmetrically: she used no paper patterns or computer instructions. I never realised then how cleverly she was applying the rules of geometry such as rotation, translation and reflection, and how skilled she was in spatial thinking.

Most of the cloth she used was homegrown and homespun, finally woven on a home-loom. I have vivid memories of my mother and her friends weaving durries, light Indian carpets (popular in Britain today and readily available at exorbitant prices in British supermarkets), singing folk songs while the spiral, angular, multicoloured patterns unfolded out of yards and yards of coloured string. I never saw them use pen and paper and have often wondered how they worked out those perfect measurements, even as they sang. Could it be that if we are taught to rely for accuracy on mechanical instruments, we lose a lot of our ability to imagine, deduct and reason?

My mother embroidered many beautiful things for our house. I watched her create many intricate designs simply by counting the number of threads, working out the angles and lines of the design and committing them to memory in order to obtain precise measurements. Many women still develop their own designs, inspired by nature, something they have seen in a movie or done by a friend, drawing their own patterns for cushions, curtains, duvets or the latest fashion in Shalwar-Kameez. On page 120/121 are some examples drawn by a friend who teaches young Asian women to sew.

Design for a Dhoti Shalwar by Tehsin Aslam.

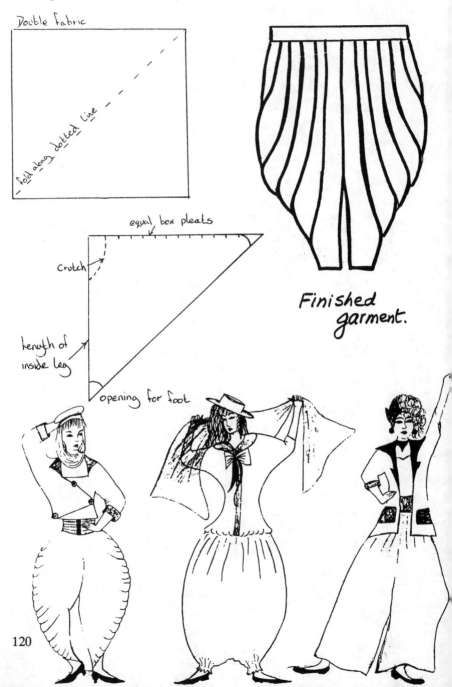

Double fabric

fold along dotted line

equal box pleats

Crotch

length of inside leg

opening for foot

Finished garment.

PLAIN SHALWAR

BASIC KAMEEZ

Salwar trousers

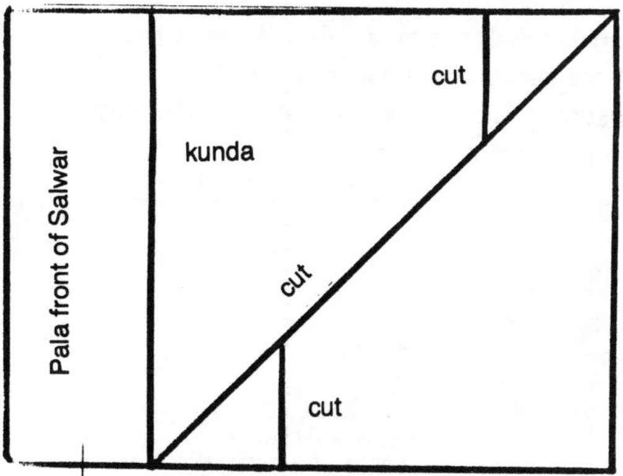

cut

kunda

Pala front of Salwar

cut

cut

Deeper
shaping
for front

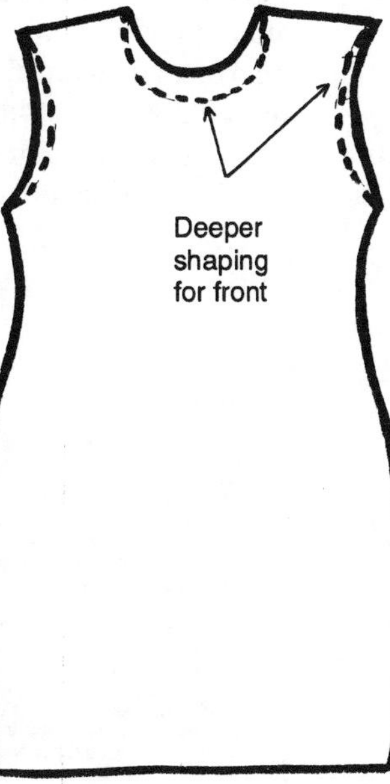

Double fabric — the fold again for
the 'pala' to size of opening for foot.

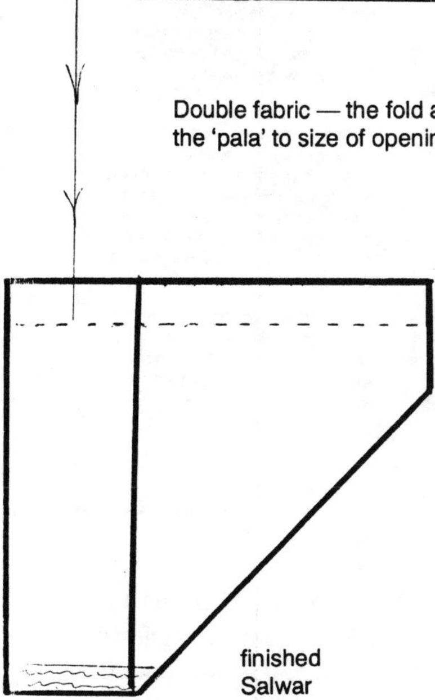

finished
Salwar

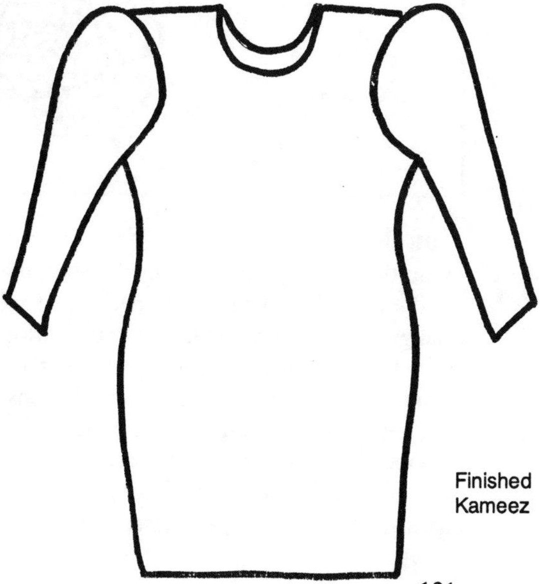

Finished
Kameez

121

**Maths in work** by Mary Harris (Department of Mathematics, University of London, Institute of Education), explores the skills of garment makers from around the world, particularly those who work at home and examines the kind of mathematical skills that I failed to notice in my mother. A whole range of skills are identified, from transformations and rotational symmetry to analysis, scale, optimisation and costing, in activities which may be deemed simple by those interested only in abstract mathematics.

## Naksha

Nakshi Kantha means "embroidered, patched cloth." Bangladeshi women make them by sewing together old saris and other cloths, then embroidering them with the coloured threads pulled from the saris.

They use many designs but they always put a circular design in the centre. The circular design represents the lotus flower with its very many petals. The women sew the outline of their designs, then fill them in by using different stitches, threads and colours.

Choose a number of petals and design a lotus for nakshi kantha. When you have made some lotus designs you may like to try SMILE 1731, (Rose) on the micro.

**MiW Cabbage**
Drawing by Mary Harris
© Maths in Work

## নকশা

নকশী কাঁথার মানে হলো "এমব্রয়ডারী করা জোড়াতালি দেওয়া কাপড়"। বাংলাদেশী মহিলারা পুরনো শাড়ির সাথে অন্যান্য কাপড়-চোপড় জোড়া লাগিয়ে এই কাঁথা তৈরী করেন। পুরনো শাড়ি থেকে বিভিন্ন রংয়ের সূতা খুলে নিয়ে তার ওপর তাঁরা ওই এমব্রয়ডারী করেন।

এমব্রয়ডারীতে তাঁরা বহু ধরনের নকশা করেন কিন্তু তাঁরা সব সময়েই ঠিক মাঝখানটায় একটা গোলাকার নকশা বানান। ওই গোলাকার নকশাটি পদ্মফুল ও তার বহুসংখ্যক পাপড়ির প্রতীক। প্রথমে মহিলারা তাঁদের নকশার একটা রূপরেখা সেলাই করে নেন। তারপর নানা রকমের সূঁচ, সূতা এবং রং ব্যবহার করে তাঁরা ওই রূপরেখাটি ভরাট করেন।

কয়েকটি পাপড়ি বেছে নিন এবং নকশী কাঁথার জন্য একটা পদ্মের নকশা বানান। কয়েকটি পদ্ম নকশার পর আপনি হয়তো SMILE 1731 (গোলাপ) মাইক্রোতে বানানোর চেষ্টা করতে পারেন।

## Conclusion

A multicultural approach to mathematics, then, is not a matter of giving a pat on the back for 'ancient cultures' nor of merely adding some designs and changing some names in the textbooks. Most importantly, it is not about the need to acknowledge different cultures present amongst us. Developing cognitive processes should, we have demonstrated, not be separated from the real needs of the pupils. Mathematics will continue to be dull, boring and unpopular if it is learnt only in order to pass examinations. There is nothing to stop us from bringing some of the more enchanting and satisfying mathematical activities into our classrooms — except our prejudices.

*Chapter 6.*

# Islamic Arts & Vedic Maths: Mathematics Or Magic?

प्रातः प्रभति सायातम्
सायादि प्रातन्तरतः
यत् करोमि जगन्नाथ
तदस्तु तव पूजनम्

सुबह से शाम तक, शाम से सुबह तक,
मैं जो कुछ भी करता हूँ, हे जगन्नाथ
सब तेरी ही पूजा, तेरी ही उपासना हो जाए ।

## The mathematics of Islamic arts

Just as Vedic mathematics emerges from the Vedas which are believed to be an embodiment of all the different facets of human life, so were the mathematical activities of ancient Islamic communities steeped in philosophy, religion, science, astronomy and psychology. Islamic art in all its forms expresses the fundamental philosophy of Islam. It is based on a complete cosmology and balanced world view and affirms the three most essential relationships in human existence: *with the Creator, with each other* and *with the earth.* Students in the West can readily appreciate the obvious forms of Islamic art, namely calligraphy, geometric patterns and Islamic architecture.

All religions including Christianity seek expression in arts so Islamic arts are not exceptional. Christianity focuses on church painting and music, Hinduism on stone sculpture.

The 'seventh wonder of the world', the Taj Mahal in India, is a mosque.

## Calligraphy and Geometry

Islamic calligraphy and geometric patterns are great creations of the Muslim mind, and adorn Muslim homes and buildings all over the world, ever since the 7th century when the *Quran* was written down. They can provide students, whether Muslim or non-Muslim, with a means for enhancing their enjoyment of mathematics and a potential career.

Early calligraphers were confined solely to copying *Quran,* solving problems of design and composition, mastering the different forms of script, learning their history, the relationships of lines and word forms. These complex designs were also exquisitely sculpted in stone and steel for the mosques.

A mid 16th-century Persian steel plaque set with a poetic text.

Geometry is used in the construction of the letters, as the drawings on the opposite page, taken from the thesis of an Egyptian artist, Ahmed Moustafa: *The Scientific Construction of Arabic Alphabets* (1979), show.

The canon of proportions of the alphabet in the system of ibn Muqla' (272–328/886–939–40), reconstructed by Ahmed Moustafa in thesis *The Scientific Construction of Arabic Alphabets*, 1979.

a. *Alif*: it consists of one vertical stroke, which must be straight, leaning neither forward nor backward. [It does not correspond to any other letter in length or shortness (i.e. it is the basic module for the alphabet). If three or four *alifs* are written next to one another the space in between should be equal.]

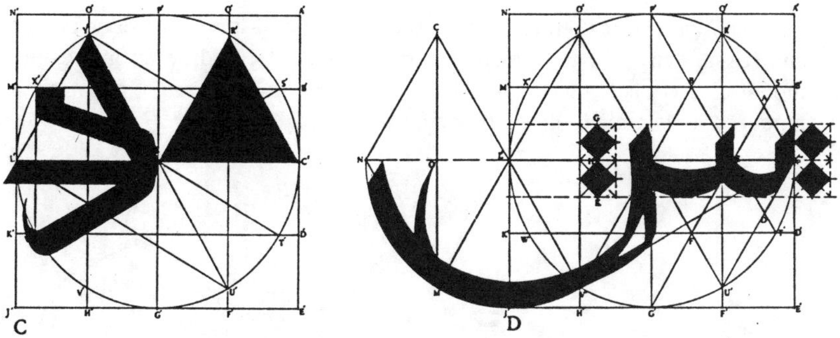

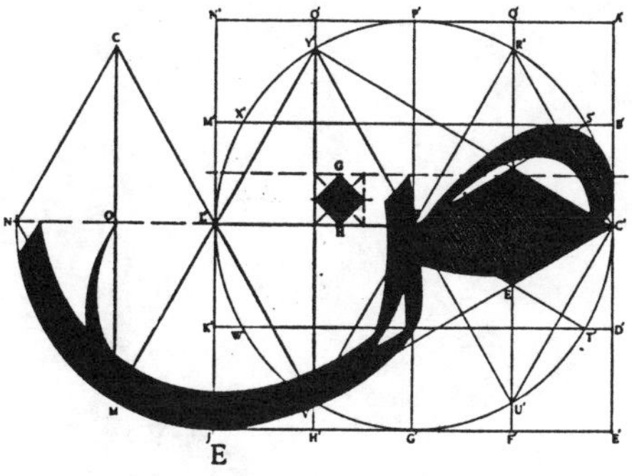

b. *Ba*: the letter is made up of two strokes, one vertical and one horizontal. Its length should be equal to that of *alif*. [A test of its correct execution is that if one of its two barbs is extended by the length of *alif*, it becomes the letter *lam*.]

c. *Dal*: its form consists of two strokes, one ascending, the other horizontal, the total length of which is equal to *alif*. [A test of its correct execution is that an equilateral triangle is formed when the two ends of the letter are joined up.]

d. *Sin*: its form is made up of five strokes: vertical, curved, vertical, curved and curved. [A test of its correct execution is that two parallel lines drawn above and below will not cut it.]

e. *Saè*: it is made up of three curved strokes. [The criterion of its correctness is that you make a quadrilateral whose angles are equal.]

125

## Islamic Architecture

J.R.Gibson in *Arts and the Islamic world* (1983) writes:

In addition to the devout sense of the greatness of the Creator, an equal importance is given to the mystical quality of grace arising from the craftsman's 'dhikr' or benedictions uttered during his creative endeavours. In contrast, Western Architecture is the antithesis of all this...

...The majority of us are unaware how completely buildings around us frame our very existence. Most of human kind has the built environment imposed upon them by the triumvirate of architect, government planner and the speculative developer; a tripartite alliance whose world views and values have little in common with those of the intended occupants in that their priorities and objectives are those of the accountants' amortisation sheets rather than a respect for the social and cultural values of society. The proofs of this are littered across the inner cities of Europe and America in the form of high rise blocks. People are doomed to dehumanisation and disintegration in these concrete jungles, as they are dislocated from their cultural roots.

Islamic architecture could be the starting point for classroom work on circles and trignometry. As a subject for special study it could be an interesting module for course work in the Arts for GCSE. Students might construct a model of an Islamic building based on their study.

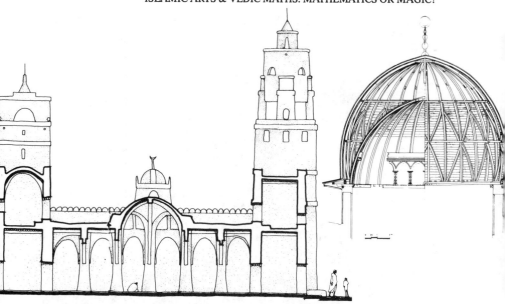

Techniques and materials used in Islamic architecture were, and often are, traditional. The building material is often earth, demonstrating a perfect adaptation which seeks to enhance rather than destroy the environment. Scientific principles and complex mathematics are employed to create an extraordinary harmony with nature, a vast satisfying feeling of space and a practical, cool working environment in countries where the daytime temperatures can soar to 120 Fahrenheit. Before the advent of air cooling systems, artistic yet functional pillars were often erected in the centre of buildings to allow maximum circulation of air. The beautiful filigree effect windows are not merely decorative but cut out harsh sunlight without hindering air flow. Examples of such images can easily be found in Islamic bookshops and displayed in the classroom.

In modern times, special Awards such as the Aga Khan Award have been set up to encourage buildings throughout the Islamic world which are excellent in design and also place great value on social, cultural and environmental ambiance. We can not do justice to this enormous subject in this book but have to be content with one example of a building that won the coveted Aga Khan award.

The building on page 128, the Hajj Terminal at King Abdul Aziz International Airport in Jeddah, Saudi Arabia, has pushed building technology beyond established limits and demonstrates how a massive structure can be

127

aesthetic as well as light and airy; a 20th century echo of the traditional tent structures that worked so well in desert climates.

It is described in *Arts and the Islamic world*:

> Covering 40.5 hectares, this unique building with its tent structure of over 100 teflon-coated, fibreglass tent forms, suspended from pylons and held by steel radial cables, almost certainly can never be replicated.

It was cited by the jury 'For the brilliant and imaginative design of the roofing system which met the awesome challenge of covering this vast space with incomparable elegance and beauty'.

## The spiritual dimension of mathematics in Islamic art.

Before engaging our students in experimentation with popular Islamic art patterns, they require a brief introduction to their spiritual dimension. The foundations of the Islamic art form in mathematics are sacred to Muslims all over the world. Essentially of a geometric nature, Islamic art is, in K.Critchlow's words:

> A means of relating multiplicity to unity by means of mathematical forms which are seen, not as mental abstractions, but as reflections of the celestial archetypes within both the cosmos and the minds and souls of men.

He explains the mathematical foundation of the art like this:-

> Islamic art is a balance between pure geometrical form and biomorphic form: a polarization that has associative values with the four philosophical and experiential qualities of cold and dry — representing the crystallization in geometric form — and hot and moist — representing the formative forces behind vegetative and vascular form. The one aspect reflects the facets of a jewel, the purity of the snowflake, and the frozen flowers of radial symmetry: the other the glistening flank of a perspiring horse, the silent motion of a fish winding its way through the water, the unfolding of the leaves of the vine and rose. In human beings this polarization is characterised by the rigidity and geometry of the skeleton on the one hand and the flowing, ductile, fibrous muscular system which activates it.
>
> (*Islamic patterns — an analytical and a cosmological approach*)

The point, a focus, represents a point of origin. The circle is a whole unity, a perfect expression of equality and justice. Within its finite space are contained the origins of all polygons, the triangle being the simplest, keeping the three circles from which it emerges in close touch (Figure 1). Further expansions give rise to bigger polygons. (Figure 2).

Hexagons and triangles have joined to give a basis for an intricate pattern. Selective shading and colouring will produce stunning effects. Repeated grids, based on any one of the many simple 3-fold or 5-fold symmetry or more complex combinations, have been used to produce breathtaking effects inside and outside mosques and moghul palaces, as well as patterns in cloth.

129

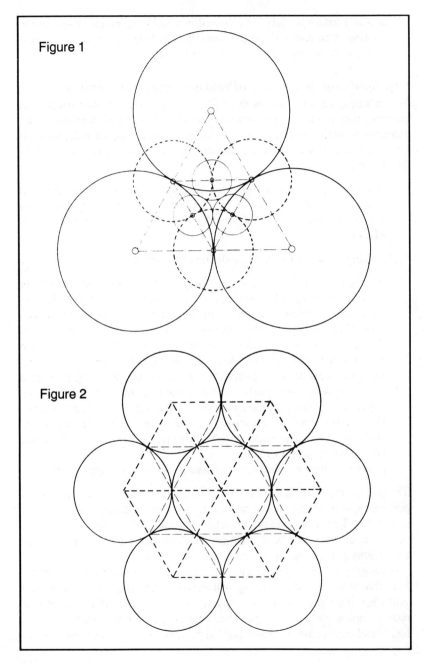

Figure 1

Figure 2

Turning symmetry, space filling and curvilinear arrangements show many other aspects of the differentiation to which the basic patterns can be subjected, to aesthetic effect.

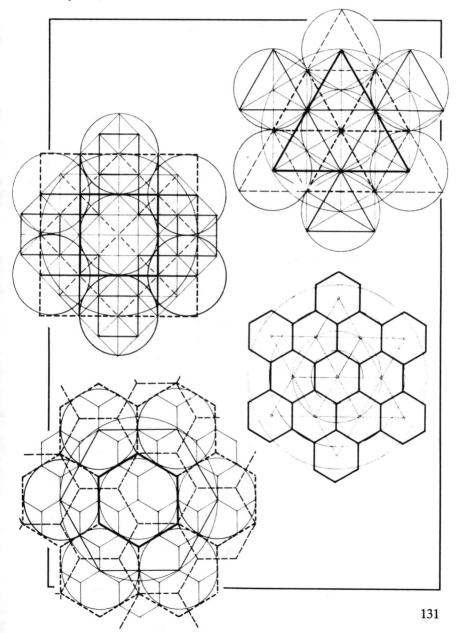

Creating patterns involving all aspects of geometry

## Decorative patterns involving mathematics.

*Visual Elements — World Traditional Folk Patterns* (1988) gives examples of decorative patterns from all over the world. Here is a glimpse:

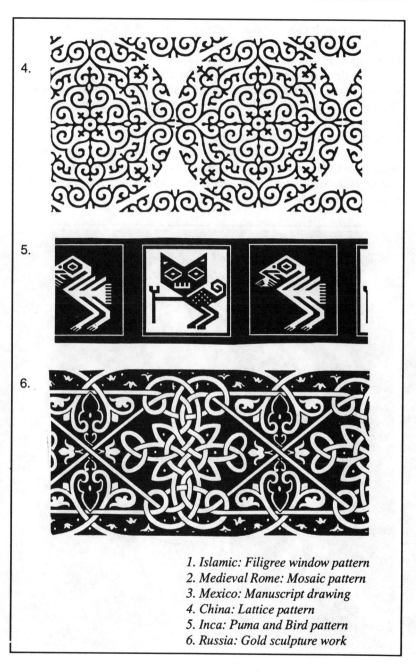

4.

5.

6.

1. Islamic: Filigree window pattern
2. Medieval Rome: Mosaic pattern
3. Mexico: Manuscript drawing
4. China: Lattice pattern
5. Inca: Puma and Bird pattern
6. Russia: Gold sculpture work

These examples show mathematics to be integral to Muslim life. It is not only buildings which are adorned with exquisite mathematical designs. Tent makers of Cairo are famous throughout the Muslim world. They copy the geometric designs found in the walls of Cairo's mediaeval mosques on their huge, colourful and prestigious tents and marquees for special celebrations. The exquisite geometric patterns are in brilliant reds, greens, blues and yellows and all are sewn entirely by hand. *Suradeq*, the art of tent making, is one of the oldest arts of ancient Egypt.

In Cairo today, thousands of traditional examinations are taken in midsummer under the enormous spread of *suradeq* awnings. Though, for a time, modern high- tech hotels had begun to overshadow these delightful splendours, they do not have the magic of the *suradeq*.

# VEDIC MATHS:
## Magic from the ancient Hindu holy books.

---

युक्तियुक्तं वचो ग्राह्यं बालादपि शुकादपि ।
युक्तिहीनं वचस्त्याज्यं वृद्धादपि शुकादपि ॥

*Whatever is consistent with right reasoning should be accepted,
even though it comes from a boy or even from a parrot; and whatever
is inconsistent therewith ought to be rejected although emanating
from an old man or even from the great sage Shree Suka himself.* —
Sri Bharati Krsna Tirathji.

---

Examples in this section are adapted from the book *Vedic mathematics or
Sixteen simple mathematical formulae from the Vedas* by His Holiness
Jagadguru Sankaracarya, Sri Bharati Krsna Tirathji Maharaj of Puri, India
(1884-1960). Vedic mathematics offers an interesting system for mathematical calculations such as multiplication and division, factorization, equations,
calculus, analytical conics. Once learnt, it is very efficient and magically easy
and quick. A.P. Nicholas and K.R. Williams of North London Polytechnic,
who have studied the monumental work of Bharati have written several
booklets giving detailed examples of applications of Vedic mathematics.

The Vedas are the most ancient Indian scriptures and the holy books of the
Hindu religion. Written before 500BC, they are the oldest written religious
works in the world. In the words of Bharati:

> All the Vedas, put together, contain within themselves all the knowledge
> needed by human kind relating not only to the spiritual matters, but also
> to those usually described as purely 'secular' 'temporal', or 'worldly' and
> also to the means required by humanity as such for the achievement of
> all round, complete and perfect success in all conceivable directions...

The Vedas are written in Sanskrit and are said to contain complete instructions
and guidance on all mathematics since the whole universe is believed to have
a basic mathematical structure obeying the rules of mathematical relations
and measures.

There are four Vedas and four Upavedas. Together they are said to 'form
an indivisible corpus of divine knowledge as it once was and as it may be
revealed'. Each of the Vedas and Upavedas deals with a specific set of ideas
in a body of knowledge.

137

| VEDAS | UPAVEDAS |
|-------|----------|
| Rgveda | Ayurveda |
| Samaveda | Gandharvaveda |
| Yajurveda | Dhanurveda |
| Atharvaveda | Sthapathyaveda. |

Ayurveda, for example, deals with anatomy, physiology, hygiene, medical science and surgery; Dhanurveda with archery and other military sciences, developed not to foster combat but in order to quell and subdue all invaders from abroad and all insurgents from within; Gandharvaveda deals with the science and art of music; and Sathapathyaveda deals with engineering, architecture and all branches of general. Vedangas deal with subjects such as grammar, prosody, astronomy, lexicography which, according to the Indian cultural concepts, are inherent parts of spiritual studies.

In the Vedic language the simple mathematical formulae are known as sutras. They are condensed statements of a very precise nature and deal with different concepts in mathematics. Even seemingly complicated problems which involve many operations are reduced to a few simple steps, requiring only a fraction of the time normally taken using traditional western methods. Children open to learning these methods very quickly.

The sutras provide solutions for general cases, but occasionally special cases arise. Sub-sutras are provided to solve these difficult problems. The student has to learn to recognise the particular type of problem and select the appropriate sutra. For more complicated problems, sutras can be combined to find easy solutions. Even so, the longest of the methods of the Vedic system is far quicker than corresponding process in western methods. Some of the sutras and sub-sutras are listed on the opposite page. For a complete Sanskrit name for each sutra, refer to Sri Bharati Krsna Tirthaji (1965). This single chapter can only skim the surface of a subject like Vedic maths.

It is said that Bharati took 8 years to decode the sutras from the Vedas. His work was to be published in 16 volumes but he died, sadly, after completing only the first volume. Eminent mathematicians from around the world are trying to unravel this ascetic's discoveries although some historians oppose them because the work is sc incomplete.

Even though much remains to be rediscovered, there is enough knowledge of these methods of calculation to provide great fun in mathematics lessons. And they are especially valuable at a time when calculators and computers discourage the development of computational skills in teachers and students. The tricks of these unfamiliar methods intrigue students and motivate them to learn more.

## Some Sutras and Sub-Sutras

*   **Nikhilam** — all from nine and the last from ten. Often used for subtraction and multiplication.

*   **Urdhva-tiryagbhyam** — vertically and crosswise. Very popular for multiplication and division, particularly of larger numbers.

*   **Anurupyena** — proportionately. Applied in connection with the use of multiples and sub-multiples, in multiplication and division.

*   **Sankalana-vyavakalanabhyam** — by addition and by subtraction. Used for working out the special type of simultaneous equation where x and y co-efficients are interchangeable.

*   **Lopana-sthapna** — by alternate elimination and retention. Used for solving harder quadratic equations.

*   **Vyastisamastih** — using the average for harder quadratics.

*   **Ekadhikena Purvena** — by one more than the previous one. Gives one line answers to big recurring decimals.

*   **Pravartya** — transpose and apply. Used in many algebraic and arithmetic operations.

*   **Sunyam anyat** — if one is in ratio then the other one is in zero. Used for solving harder simultaneous equations.

*   **Sunyam Samyasmuccaye** — when the Samuccaya is the same, that Samuccaya is zero, i.e, it should be equated to zero. Used for solving simple equations of many different types.

*   **Adyamadyena** — the first by the first and the last by the last. Used for solving quadratic equations at a glance.

*   **Gunitasamuccayah Samuccayagunitah** — the product of the sum of the coefficients in the factors is equal to the sum of the coefficients in the products. Used to establish the correctness of answers in factorisations and many other computations.

# Examples using Nikhilam sutra

This sutra provides a quick, easy, efficient method of working out tables up to any number you wish. The only table that has to be committed to memory is the 5 times table up to 5 x 5.

This fascinates children and encourages them to have fun with tables thus improving understanding and motivation.

Learning how to identify the key operators will take a little time, but, once mastered, it takes only a few seconds to write down any table.

Let us take the table of 19 . In terms of the relationship of this number with the tenth and the unit place, we have:

19 = 20 - 1 = 2 x (10) - 1 x (1)

Numbers must be read using the appropriate sign, so that the above statement reads: 10 multiplied by +2 and 1 multiplied by -1.

Two operators have been identified, +2 for the tens and -1 for the units. Now, see how it works.

| | | | |
|---|---|---|---|
| 1 | 9. | x 1 | |
| +2 | -1 | | |
| 3 | 8. | x 2 | |
| +2 | -1 | | |
| 5 | 7. | x 3 | |
| +2 | -1 | | |
| 7 | 6. | x 4 | And so on until: |
| 1　9 | 0. | x 10 | |
| +2 | -1 | | |

Taking 1 in the unit column can only be done if we borrow from the tenth column. Therefore borrowing 1 would reduce the number in the tenth column to 0, when 2 is added. So the next number is:

| | | | |
|---|---|---|---|
| 2 | 0 | 9. | x 11 |
| +2 | | -1 | |
| 2 | 2 | 8. | x 12 |
| +2 | | -1 | |
| 2 | 4 | 7. | x 13 |
| +2 | | -1 | |
| 2 | 6 | 6. | x 14 |
| +2 | | -1 | |
| 2 | 8 | 5. | x 15 |
| +2 | | -1 | |

140

| 3 | 0 | 4. | x 16 |
|---|---|---|---|
| +2 | -1 | | |
| 3 | 2 | 3. | x 17 |
| +2 | -1 | | |
| 3 | 4 | 2. | x 18 |
| +2 | -1 | | |
| 3 | 6 | 1. | x 19 |
| +2 | -1 | | |
| 3 | 8 | 0. | x 20 |
| +2 | -1 | | |
| 3 | 9 | 9. | x 21 | And so on. |

Take a more complicated example: the table for 47. With calculators, no one needs to learn this table! But it is fun to learn how to do it nearly as fast as by pressing the calculator keys.

$$47 = 40 + 7 = 4 \times (10) + 7 \times (1)$$

The operators are +4 for the tens column and +7 for the units.

| | 4 | 7. | x 1 | |
|---|---|---|---|---|
| | +4 | +7 | | |
| | 9 | 4. | x 2 | Note: There is a carry |
| | +4 | +7 | | over of 1 to the tens |
| 1 | 4 | 1. | x 3 | tens column. |
| +4 | +7 | | | |
| 1 | 8 | 8. | x 4 | |
| +4 | +7 | | | |
| 2 | 3 | 5. | x 5 | |
| +4 | +7 | | | |
| 2 | 8 | 2. | x 6 | |
| +4 | +7 | | | |
| 3 | 2 | 9. | x 7 | |
| +4 | +7 | | | |
| 3 | 7 | 6. | x 8 | Note the pattern in the hundreds column. |

And so on.

Taking an even higher number, say 87, an operator can be found for the three columns and the multiplication is done in seconds.

$$87 = \quad 100 - 10 - 3.$$
$$= \quad 1 \times (100) - 1 \times (10) - 3(1).$$

1, -1, and -3 are the operators. It is important to note that 0 can also be used as an operator.

|     | 8  | 7.  | x 1  |
|-----|----|-----|------|
| +1  | -1 | -3  |      |
| 1   | 7  | 4.  | x 2  |
| +1  | -1 | -3  |      |
| 2   | 6  | 1.  | x 3  |
| +1  | -1 | -3  |      |
| 3   | 4  | 8.  | x 4  |
| +1  | -1 | -3  |      |
| 4   | 3  | 5.  | x 5  |
| +1  | -1 | -3  |      |
| 5   | 2  | 2.  | x 6  |
| +1  | -1 | -3  |      |
| 6   | 0  | 9.  | x 7  |
| +1  | -1 | -3  |      |
| 6   | 9  | 6.  | x 8  |
| +1  | -1 | -3  |      |
| 7   | 8  | 3.  | x 9  |
| +1  | -1 | -3  |      |
| 8   | 7  | 0.  | x 10 |
| +1  | -1 | -3  |      |
| 9   | 5  | 7.  | x 11 |

As long as the borrowing and the carrying is remembered, the table can be calculated up to any chosen number.

## Examples of multiplication

Vedic sutras can be used to make large multiplications even easier than this. One would not wish to write a long table every time a calculation of say 87 x 87 was required. Vedic mathematics has a method for this. Two sutras will be used in this section. They are *Nikhilam* (all from nine and last from ten) and *Urdhvatiryagbhyam* (vertically and crosswise).

The usual school method
with minor variation is this:

$$456 \times$$
$$76$$
$$\overline{\phantom{0}}$$
$$31920$$
$$2736$$
$$\overline{\phantom{0}}$$
$$34656$$
$$\overline{\phantom{0}}$$

Notice that this requires two separate operations of multiplication and one of addition. There are also carry numbers to remember. We will come back to this example after we have explained the vedic method for multiplication. In Vedic maths, there are many variations of the *Nikhilam* sutra used for different types of multiplications. With practice, the quickest one to solve the problem can be chosen.

The sutra translates 'all from 9 and the last from 10'. Consider the example 9 X 6. Both the numbers are near base 10. Therefore:

| | |
|---|---|
| 9 - 1 | -1 and -4 are known as the |
| 6 - 4 | deficiencies of 9 and 6, in |
| -------- | other words the difference |
| 5 / 4 | from base 10. |

The right hand part of the answer is obtained by multiplying the deficiencies. The left hand side of the answer can be obtained in 4 different ways:

| | | |
|---|---|---|
| cross subtraction | 9 - 4 = 5. | |
| cross subtraction | 6 - 1 = 5. | |
| ( 9 + 6 ) - base 10 | = 5. | |
| base 10 - 1 - 4 | = 5. | |

This idea can be applied to a large number, for example 87 x 97. The nearest base is 100, so:

| | |
|---|---|
| 87 - 13 | 87 is 13 less than 100. |
| 97 - 3 | - 13 and - 3 signify |
| --------- | the deficiencies from the base. |
| 84 / 39 | LHS 97 - 13 = 84 |
| ------- | or 87 - 3 = 84. |
| | RHS 13 x 3 = 39. |

So the answer is 8439.

Here is a harder example: 865 x 993. The nearest base is 1000.

```
865 - 135
993 -   7
-----------          RHS: multiply. LHS: cross-subtraction.
858 / 945 = 858945.  The sutra 'all from 9 and the last from
-----------          10' supplies the deficiency.
```

The number of digits on the right hand side must equal the number of zeros in the base. Sometimes a number must be carried over to the left and added. An example of this is 112 x 111. The nearest base is 100.

```
112  + 12
111  + 11
----------
123  / 132    RHS has 3 digits. Carry one over to the LHS.
=124 /  32.   = 12432.
```

An example with a plus and a minus deficiency :  109 X 95.

```
109    +9
95     -5
----------
104 /  -45    RHS number is negative,
=103 /  55    therefore a subtraction must take place.
```

The answer is therefore 10355.

When the numbers to be multiplied are such that the deficiency from the base is too large to be multiplied, a convenient multiple or a submultiple of a suitable base can be taken as a working base. At the end, we multiply or divide the result as necessary.

This is the *Anurupyena* sutra (proportionately).

Example: 43 x 43.          The nearest base 10 or 100 will give too large a
                           deficiency. We take 50 as the working base.

```
43  - 7
43  - 7
---------
36 / 49.
---------
```

Divide the LHS by 2 as 50 = 100 ÷ 2.  The answer is 1849.

What if the left hand side is an odd number ?
Example:48 x 49.  Take 50 as working base.

    48 - 2
    49 - 1
    ---------
    47 / 02.   ( remember : the RHS must have the same number of
                            digits as in the real base. )
Now 47 + 2 = 23.5    Answer is 2352.
If we now return to our very first example, we will find that we can choose
the best method to solve it from a variety at our disposal.

**Examples with the 'vertically and crosswise' sutra**
The examples shown in the previous section were of numbers near the base
chosen and of one base only. The sutra 'vertically and crosswise' can be used
to find the product in other kinds of multiplication. Two digit multiplication
looks like this:

Step 1.  Take the vertical product on the right. (4)          4   1
Step 2.  Take the two cross products in any order.
         Add them (16+3=19). Put down the unit and           3   4
         carry the ten as usual.                          ------------
Step 3.  Take the vertical product on the left,              12 / 19 / 4
         and add the carry number. (13)                   ------------
                    The sutra gives 41 x 34       = 1 3 9 4


Steps increase : In three-digit multiplication, for example 405 x 516.

Step 1.  5x6 = 30. Put down the 0 and carry 3.          4   0   5
Step 2.  0x6 + 5x1 = 5. 5+3 = 8. Put down 8.            5   1   6
Step 3.  0x1 + 4x6 + 5x5 = 49.  Put down the          --------------
         9 and carry 4.                                2 0 8 9 8 0
Step 4.  0x5 + 4x1 = 4. Add the 4 from before         ---------------
         and put down 8.                                  4   3
Step 5.  4x5 = 20. Put down 20.


An example of a four-digit multiplication:

Step 1.  5x1 = 5.                                         4  6  3  1
Step 2.  3x5 + 8x1 = 23. Put down the                    3  7  8  5
         3 and carry 2.                                -------------------
Step3.   6x5 + 3x8 + 7x1 = 61                          17 5 2 8 3 3 5
         61 + 2 = 63. Put down the 3 and carry 6.      -------------------

Step 4.  4x5 + 6x8 + 3x1 + 3x7 = 92          5 9 9 6 2
         92 + 6 = 98. Put down 8 and carry 9.
Step 5.  4x8 + 3x3 + 6x7 = 83.  83 + 9 = 92.
         Put down 2 and carry 9.
Step 6.  7x4 + 6x3 = 46.    46 + 9 = 55
         Put down 5 and carry 5.
Step 7.  4x3 = 12.  12 + 5 = 17.
The answer to 4631 x 3785 = 17528335.

Sums of the type 567 x 34 can also be calculated using this method, simply by placing zeros in the empty space. for example, 567 x 34.

5 6 7    7x4 = 28. Put down the 8 and carry 2.                              8
0 3 4    7x3 + 6X4 = 45. Add the carry 2. = 47. Put down 7, carry4.        7
------   7x0 + 5X4 + 6X3 = 38. 38+4=42. Put down 2 and carry 4.            2
         5x3 + 6X0 = 15, 15+4=19. Put down 9 and carry 1.                  9
         5x0 = 0. Add the carry 1 from before. Put down 1.                 1
So  567 x 34 = 19278.

### Examples of squaring of numbers

For the squaring of numbers a corollary of the *Nikhilam* sutra can be used, or for more difficult ones, the *Urdhav Tiryak* sutra or the *Ekadhikena*. Most students will be able to calculate the squares of 1 to 10 mentally. By the method below, they can also square numbers bigger than 10.

Method for squaring  12    11+ 1          Nearest base 10.
                           11+ 1          Number more than 10.
                           ---------      Increase not reduce.
                           12/ 1  = 121.
                           ----------

The step can be simplified further by using only the one line i.e, 11 + 1. So that :-

$12^2 = ( 12 + 2 ) = 14 / 2x2 = 144.$
$13^2 = ( 13 + 3 ) = 16 / 3x3 = 169.$
$14^2 = ( 14 + 4 ) = 18 / 4x4 = 18/16 = 196$

The digits on the RHS must equal the zeros in the base. Extending the same rule to higher numbers:

$92^2 = ( 92 - 8 ) = 84 / 8x8 = 8464.$
$93^2 = ( 93 - 7 ) = 86 / 7x7 = 8649.$
$97^2 = ( 97 - 3 ) = 94 / 3x3 = 9409.$

146

So long as the deficiencies are not very large, we can use this method for squaring very large numbers and it will still only take one line. When the deficiencies are large, use *Nikhilam* sutra as shown in multiplication of two different numbers.

$$989^2 = ( 989 - 11 ) = 978 / 121 = 978121.$$

Nearest base is 1000, there are 3 zeros, therefore 3 digits on the RHS.

$$993^2 = ( 993 - 7 ) = 986 / 049 = 986049$$
$$9989^2 = ( 9989 - 11 ) = 9978 / 0121 = 99780121.$$

The algebraic explanation of this is as follows:

$$97^2 = ( 100 - 3)^2 = 10000 - 600 + 9 = 9409.$$
$$108^2 = ( 100 + 8)^2 = 10000 + 1600 + 64 = 11664.$$

Though easier than conventional multiplication, this takes longer to work out for someone with no knowledge of algebra.

For certain special squares, where the deficiency is going to be large and the numbers end with 5, *Ekadhiken* sutra is used (by one more than the previous one).

Example:- The number 25 is not close enough to any base to give a deficiency for working out easily. Follow the Ekadhiken sutra, and no matter how high the number, the pattern will follow.

$$25^2 = 2 \times 3 / 5\times5 = 625.$$
$$35^2 = 3 \times 4 / 5\times5 = 1225.$$
$$45^2 = 4 \times 5 / 5\times5 = 1625.$$
$$55^2 = 5 \times 6 / 5\times5 = 3025.$$
$$85^2 = 8 \times 9 / 5\times5 = 7225.$$
$$95^2 = 9 \times 10 / 5\times5 = 9025.$$
$$105^2 = 10 \times 11 / 5\times5 = 11025.$$
$$125^2 = 12 \times 13 / 5\times5 = 15625.$$
$$165^2 = 16 \times 17 / 5\times5 = 27225.$$

It must be remembered that Vedic mathematics considers long and laborious mental calculations unnecessary. Simply switch to a more appropriate sutra.

## Examples with simple equations

The *Sunyam Samyasamuccaye* sutra, used here, means 'when the samuccaya is the same that samuccaya is zero'. *Samuccaya* is a technical term which refers to the common factor in the equations. In a simple equation such as $8(x+1) = 6(x+1)$ there is no need for any steps. For the two sides to be equal, by mere observation, x has to be zero. This is an axiom. x is the common *samuccaya* on both sides.

Another example: $(x+6)(x+8) = (x+4)(x+12)$

By observation, it is clear that product of the two independent terms is equal, x is therefore zero.

Here is a more complicated example.

$$\frac{2x+9}{2x+7} = \frac{2x+7}{2x+9}$$

The traditional solution is:-

$$(2x+9)(2x+9) = (2x+7)(2x+7)$$
$$4x^2+36x+81 = 4x^2+28x+49$$
$$36x - 28x = 49 - 81$$
$$8x = -32$$
$$x = -4$$

Using the sutra, we observe that
numerator + denominator is equal on both sides:

$$4x + 16 = 0$$
$$x = -4$$

This is true also if the sum total of both numerators is equal to the sum total of both denominators. If a numerical multiple is involved, then that is removed.

For example:

$$\frac{3x+4}{6x+7} = \frac{x+1}{2x+3}$$

The sum of numerators is $4x + 5$. But the sum of denominators is $8x + 10$, which is $2(4x + 5)$

$$4x + 5 = 0$$
$$4x = -5$$
$$x = -5/4$$

148

When the coefficients are such that multiplication produces a quadratic, the sutra is applied to give us the two roots of the equation.
For example:

$$\frac{3x+4}{6x+7} = \frac{5x+6}{2x+3}$$

Using the *samuccaya*, we look for a common factor. The sum of the two numerators is equal to the sum of the two denominators.

$$8x + 10 = 0$$
$$x = -5/4$$

But the product of the coefficients of x gives us two different answers. We write down the difference between the numerator and denominator on both sides and note that the differences are also equal.

$$3x + 3 = 0$$
$$3x = -3$$
$$x = -1$$

In harder quadratics we require our students to cross multiply, equate the denominators, expand them and so on. If they see that there are equal terms of the different types as explained in the preceeding section, they should proceed to solve it by using the *samuccaya* sutra.

Example:

$$\frac{1}{x-7} + \frac{1}{x-9} = \frac{1}{x-6} + \frac{1}{x-10}$$

We can see by observation of the denominators as well as the numerators that their sum is equal on both sides:

$$2x - 16 = 0$$
$$x = 8$$

In some equations it may not be obvious that a *samuccaya* can be found.

Example:

$$\frac{1}{x-8} - \frac{1}{x-5} = \frac{1}{x-12} - \frac{1}{x-9}$$

But if we transpose so that all the minuses are pluses:

$$\frac{1}{x-8} + \frac{1}{x-9} = \frac{1}{x-12} + \frac{1}{x-5}$$

It can be seen that the sum of the denominators is equal on both sides.

$$x - 17 = 0$$
$$x = 8\frac{1}{2}$$

149

The next example does not at first look solvable by this method.

$$\frac{2x-3}{x-2} + \frac{3x-20}{x-7} = \frac{x-3}{x-4} + \frac{4x-19}{x-5}$$

There are, however, two equals to be found here.

- the coefficients of x are 2/1, 3/1, on the LHS and 1/1, 4/1 on the RHS.
- the two denominators are equal i.e, 2x-9 = 0

Using the second equality, x = 4½

## Squares and square roots

In the chapter on multicultural maths, we saw many different examples of patterns that numbers tend to follow. Mathematicians from all over the world have contributed to this fascinating aspect of numbers. In Vedic mathematics we find a process, called the *Dwandayoga* or the Duplex Combination process, an interesting pattern used for calculating squares, square roots, cubes and cube roots.

This is what it means:

For a 1-digit number,    the DUPLEX is its square.
For a 2-digit number,    D is twice their product.
For a 3-digit number,    D is twice the product of the outer pair +
    the square of the middle digit.
For a 4-digit number,    D is twice the product of the outer pair + twice the
    product of the inner pair and so on.

Examples of calculating duplex of 5, 45, 245, 3245 and 13245.
The Dwanda Yoga is denoted by D. This is how the duplexes are calculated

    5.    D = 25
    45.    D = 2 x ( 4x5 ) = 40.
    245.    D = 2 x ( 2x5 ) + 4x4 = 36.
    3245.    D = 2 x ( 3x5 ) + 2 x ( 2x4 ) = 46.
    13245.    D = 2 x ( 1x5 ) + 2 x ( 3x4 ) + 2x2 = 38.

Next, using the duplexes, find $5^2$, $45^2$, $245^2$, $3245^2$ and $13245^2$.

$5^2$.    The duplex of 5 is 25.  $5^2 = 25$
$45^2$.    The duplexes of 4, 45 and 5 are 16, 40 and 25

$45^2 = 16 / \ 40/ \ 25.$     Carry 2 - add to 40
$\quad = 20 / \ 2/ \ 5.$     Carry 4 - add to 16.
$\quad = 2025.$

This whole process, once learnt, need only take up one line.

$245^2$.  Write down the duplexes of 2, 24, 245, 45, 5.
$245^2 = 4 / 16 / 36 / 40 / 25.$     Carrying to the next columns:
$\quad = 60025.$

If the carrying stage is difficult, the duplexes can be written out like this:

```
      2 5
      4 0
      3 6
    1 6
    4
    ---------
    6 0 0 2 5
    ---------
```

$3245^2$.  We need the duplexes of 3, 32, 324, 3245, 245, 45 and 5.

$3245^2 = 9/12/28/46/36/40/25.$     Carry over the figures on the
$\quad = 10530025.$     left.

$13245^2$.  We need the duplexes of 1, 13, 132, 1324, 13245, 3245, 245, 45 and 5

```
        1    D = 1
       13    D = 6
      132    D = 13
     1324    D = 20
    13245    D = 38
     3245    D = 46
      245    D = 36
       45    D = 40
        5    D = 25
```

$13245^2 = 1/6/13/20/38/46/36/40/25$
$\quad = 175430025.$

After a few hours' practice, the square of any number can be done mentally. **Example:** Find the square of 356728

$356728^2$ =D3,D35,D356,D3567,D35672,D356728,D56728,D6728, D728,D28,D8.

= 9 / 30 / 61 / 102 / 118 / 152 / 153 / 124 / 116 / 32 / 64

= 127254865984.

The whole process can take less than a minute. Students with a gift for maths will enjoy this method and gain confidence and motivation.

*Dwandayoga* can also be used to calculate square roots though this takes longer to understand; for example: **Find the square root of 178929.**

Firstly, we group the digits in pairs
starting from the decimal point:    17 : 89 : 29 . 0 : 0 : 0

Then we find the square root of the number closest to the first LHS digit pair. This is 4, being the square root of 16 and is the first digit of the answer. Double 4 and use 8 as the divisor for the rest of the working out.

|   | 17 ₁892 9 . 0 0 |   |
|---|---|---|
| 8 | -------------------- |   |
|   | 4 / 2 | 8 into 18 goes 2, remainder 2. |

|   | 17 18 ₂92 9 . 0 0 | The dividend 29 is divided by the divisor |
|---|---|---|
| 8 | -------------------- | 8, but only after the Dwandayoga of the |
|   | 4 / 23 | previous answer 2 is subtracted from it; 29 - 2x2 = 25. 8 into 25 goes 3. |

|   |   | The remainder 1 is put with the next |
|---|---|---|
|   | 17 ₁8 29 ₁2 9 . 0 0 | digit 2 and we get a dividend of 12. |
| 8 | -------------------- | Calculating the *Dwandayoga* of the two |
|   | 4 / 230 0 | previous quotients gives us the net dividend: 12 - 2 x (2x3) = 0. |

As there is no dividend we move on to the last digit .

9- 2 (2x3x0) = 9. 8 into 9 goes 1 remainder 1. 1 take away the D again will leave 1. 8 into 1 does not go and the division now terminates. The only rule that we need now is to know where to put the decimal point . The rule here is that there are as many digits in the answer as there are pairs in the number to be square rooted.

So that  1 7 8 9 2 9  = 4 2 3.

**Here is another example:** calculate the square root of 18.

The square root of 16 which is the nearest whole number digit is 4. Double 4 and use it as a divisor.

```
        18 . 0  0  0  0
8       ----------------
        4 /
```

```
        18 . 20 40 40  0
8       ----------------     8 into 20 goes 2, remainder 4.
        4 / 2  4  3          40 - D of 2 = new dividend = 36.
                             8 into 36 goes 4, remainder 4 and so on.
```

For average use 4.243 is a sufficient answer. When negative dividend and quotients appear, Vedic maths uses other equally suitable sutras.

Two books by Nicholas, Pickles and Williams *Introductory Lectures on Vedic Mathematics* and *Vertically and Crosswise* will provide many more examples for the enthusiast.

## The Vedic square — more Vedic magic

Like the Chinese magic square, the Vedic square has its own unique mysteries. This multiplication square was the basis of a whole mathematical system within which numbers formed symmetrical shapes. Some have called it a model of the universe. It appears in the Vedic texts and also in the work of Arab mathematicians, illustrating yet again the universality that mathematics brings to our lives.

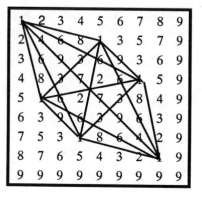

| 1 | 2 | 3 | 4 | 5 | 6 | 7 | 8 | 9 |
|---|---|---|---|---|---|---|---|---|
| 2 |   |   |   |   |   |   |   |   |
| 3 |   |   |   |   |   |   |   |   |
| 4 |   |   |   |   |   |   |   |   |
| 5 |   |   |   |   |   |   |   |   |
| 6 |   |   |   |   |   |   |   |   |
| 7 |   |   |   |   |   |   |   |   |
| 8 |   |   |   |   |   |   |   |   |
| 9 |   |   |   |   |   |   |   |   |

| 1 | 2 | 3 | 4 | 5 | 6 | 7 | 8 | 9 |
|---|---|---|---|---|---|---|---|---|
| 2 | 4 | 6 | 8 | 1 | 3 | 5 | 7 | 9 |
| 3 | 6 | 9 | 3 | 6 | 9 | 3 | 6 | 9 |
| 4 | 8 | 3 | 7 | 2 | 6 | 1 | 5 | 9 |
| 5 | 1 | 6 | 2 | 7 | 3 | 8 | 4 | 9 |
| 6 | 3 | 9 | 6 | 3 | 9 | 6 | 3 | 9 |
| 7 | 5 | 3 | 1 | 8 | 6 | 4 | 2 | 9 |
| 8 | 7 | 6 | 5 | 4 | 3 | 2 | 1 | 9 |
| 9 | 9 | 9 | 9 | 9 | 9 | 9 | 9 | 9 |

153

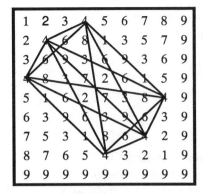 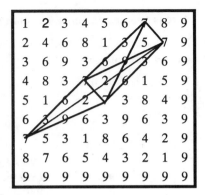

Exercises for pupils can be based on the square. The matrix is completed by multiplying the horizontal row with the vertical column. If the product of the two digits is more than 9, add the two digits together — keep going until you get a single digit.

Try joining up all the 1's in every way that you can.

What do you notice? Repeat with other numbers.

What happens when the 9's are joined up? There are many palindromic patterns. How many can you spot? What is the sum of each row, each column? Fill in the border around the 2 x 2 square. What do you notice? Add the numbers along the borders? Add the digits. What do you notice?

The Vedic square contains many algorithms of number sentences, in triples. Spot any such 3 triples that make a mathematical statement using the four basic operations; for example:

3, 6, 9, ⇒3 + 6 = 9. 7, 5, 3, can be 7 + 5= 12 ⇒ 1 + 2 = 3.

## Spirolaterals in the Vedic Square.

These have recently become popular. The process is very simple and the result intriguing. Choose a set of numbers. Join them in an order and repeat. Always turn right, up, left, down, through 90 degrees until you return to your starting point. Why does this happen? Here are some examples.

A. 3,6,9.
B. 4,8,3,7,2,6,1,5,9.
C. 1,2,3,4,5,6,7,8,9.
(see drawings opposite)

Derek Bunyard and Alan Brine have used the Vedic square and the spirolateral patterns to produce a LOGO programme, available on Micromath Disk 3.

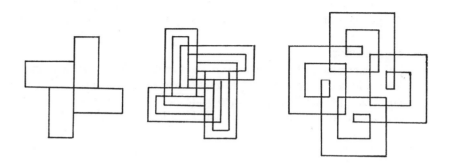

155

The programme enables students to produce Islamic patterns quickly and easily. This is an interesting link between Vedic maths and Islamic geometry, but students must be reminded that the original calligraphy and geometric designs were and still are created using only a ruler, compass and protractor.

## Conclusion

This chapter has just touched the surface of an exquisite, precise and appealing tradition of Islamic art and the mysterious Vedic mathematics. We must not miss opportunities to pass on to our students the unification in diversity, the great ideas being rediscovered, unfolding into the wider world.

*CHAPTER 7*

# Challenging racism through classroom mathematics

---

*The purpose of education is liberation... not the development of objects... whether they be pyramids, or irrigation ditches, railways and palaces.*
President Nyerere's speech on education in Dar es Salaam 20.5.74.

*You learn by doing. You grow by experience.*

*There is a need for a new relationship between the industrialised and the so-called developing countries, a partnership which goes beyond Charity and Aid to what many are no calling Solidarity.*
Tools for Self-Reliance

---

The Home Office study (1981) found that 69.7 Asians out of every 100,000 and 51.2 black people out of every 100,000 could expect to be the victim of racially motivated incident during a two month period in the area studied.

A survey in Leeds (1985-86) suggested that the level of racial harassment runs at about 10 times higher than indicated in the Home Office (1981) figures. Research in Glasgow (1986) found that 49% of Pakistanis and 55% of Indians have experienced damage to their property, over 80% of both groups racial abuse, and 18% of Pakistanis and 22% of Indians physical attack. Nor is the number of reported incidents decreasing. Metropolitan Police figures show a 25.7% rise from 1986 to 1987 (Home Office, 1989).

157

The Runnymede Trust reports that job prospects for people of ethnic minority groups remain as bad as when the Race Relations Act was passed in 1976. Nor is this all. The Health Education Council report, *The Health Divide (1987)* notes that:

> Other indirect measures of affluence and poverty, like housing tenure and employment status also highlight inequalities in health... the unemployed have much poorer health than those with jobs. It is now also beyond question that unemployment *caused* a deterioration in mental health and there is increasing evidence that the same is true of physical health. There is strikingly high mortality from hypertension and strokes among people of Caribbean and African origin and markedly higher mortality rates for babies of mothers born in Pakistan and to a certain extent for babies of mothers from the Caribbean.

The Commission for Racial Equality report *Learning in terror* (1988) exposes some of the racism to which schoolchildren have been subjected and there is little sign that matters will improve. Many of the 650 student teachers who took part in a survey in the West Midlands (reported T.E.S. 21.7.89), revealed hostility to an examination of racial stereotyping, embellishing questionnaires with swastikas, references to the Ku-Klux-Klan etc. The lecturers were reluctant to tackle the issues, arguing that they were being paid to teach their subject and not sociology.

According to research carried out by Janet Graham and Susan Lynn (1989) at South Bank Polytechnic, primary pupils displayed stereotyped ideas about people from 'Third World' countries as all living in 'primitive' conditions, even though they had been shown pictures illustrating quite the contrary.

Some examination groups such as the LEAG, MEG and SEG and the NEA have provided guidelines on issues of race but there is no way of knowing whether the mathematics examiners follow them.

The teacher unions have also proffered guidelines and expressed their concern. In the words of the National Union of Teachers:

> Racism is a feature of British Society which affects us all. If white children are not given a positive antiracist education they will grow up unconsciously absorbing racist attitudes.

The report by the Home Affairs Sub-committee on Race Relations and Immigration *Racial Attacks and Harassment* (1986) includes a summary from the DES:

Some LEAs monitor racial incidents, and an increasing number have issued guidelines to schools on the identification of incidents of racial hostility and procedures to deal with them...

Kenneth Baker, Secretary of State for Education and Science — 1988, said on the Burnage Report:

I want to make it absolutely clear there is no place for racial prejudice or discrimination in our schools.

The rhetoric is there, but there is little evidence of commitment by the DES, or most LEAs, rather a mismatch between what is said and what is done. Yet schools and LEAs that have responded with, for instance, anti-racist policies have been grossly misrepresented and attacked in the media.

● 'At times it seems that what is being discussed is the youth worker sliding off a production line fitted with right words, but with the foresight of a brick wall.'

The Mathematical Association has published booklets in support of anti-racist policies and runs workshops on anti-racist approaches to mathematics. The London-based SMILE maths project has a published policy, which readers of this book may wish to adopt or adapt.

## SMILE ANTI-RACIST POLICY

As teachers we aim to encourage an active multicultural teaching approach. Against what background do we do this? We live in a racist society. One result of colonialism and imperialism has been the suppression of the culture and science of the Third World peoples and the creation of the myth of 'European Science' as a seamless body of truth. In this way it promotes the inferiority of black people and encourages white chauvinism. Too much of the way we teach mathematics shares in this. We do little to show that mathematics is the product of the thinking and achievements of all the people in the world. We must not allow the universality of mathematics to be lost.

Anti-racist mathematics teaching, therefore, must mean at a minimum:

1.  Teaching mathematics with a strong emphasis on its historical development, showing how at each stage mathematical developments have arisen as the response of different peoples to the problems they had to solve — be they Indian astronomers, Egyptian farmers, Spanish navigators or whoever.

2.  Deliberately seeking out knowledge of the mathematics of the Third World peoples and making it easily accessible to all children learning mathematics.

3.  Making deliberate use of the different mathematical methods brought by children to the classroom — e.g. different counting systems.

4.  Critically assessing the content of present mathematics from the point of view of its relevance to living in a multicultural society.

Such an approach may involve a number of different methods — case-study materials (e.g., development of number systems), or study of particular civilisations — or it may require the deliberate inclusion of more historical background material with existing activities. So far as possible, such work should be linked to other progressive cross-curricular material.

The recruitment of a more culturally representative teaching staff will contribute immeasurably to such work.

Whatever the method, the aim is to promote the dignity of all peoples and to understand that mathematics has a vital role to play in this.

When one form of oppression is overtly challenged, other connections are often made, as with gender, class and power structures, and with discrimination against people with disabilities and the aged. Schools which take up the challenge of racism tend to be the same schools as have recognised other forms of injustice.

Moving from policies to action, we turn to ways in which the issue of racism can be raised in the mathematics classroom. Teachers should allow children to discuss sensitive and important matters, otherwise children may conclude:

- that teachers are afraid of certain issues;
- that teachers cannot contribute to the discussion;
- that teachers are not capable of understanding;
- that these problems do not exist;
- that these issues are not important;
- that discussion might provoke trouble;
- that maths is not about people.

Antiracist maths can be taught:

- by raising matters of discrimination directly
- by using statistics from which racism can be inferred
- by generating confidence and an awareness of injustice through mathematics.

Teaching anti-racist mathematics requires care and considerable preparation. Certain strategies have been found helpful:

> Begin with a multicultural approach and only address racism more directly when you feel confident. It helps to have the support of other teachers and to share ideas. It also helps to know your class well.

> If the issues should arise naturally as a part of the lesson, allow 5-10 minutes for discussion but don't use up the whole lesson — it is a maths lesson! Explain your ideas only when asked to and without imposing your views. Be clear, however, that discriminating on grounds of race or gender is unlawful and that this is not negotiable.

> Don't be horrified or discouraged by some pupils' opinions — they are shaped by the adult world. The changing of opinions, feelings and attitudes is influenced by many agencies, and students must be given choices. It seems wiser to keep trying new ideas rather than sticking to a formula. But do take care that you are not in danger of reinforcing stereotypes when you are striving to challenge and dispel them.

## Short questions

One of the most effective ways to promote discussion on issues of racism and other forms of bias in mathematics is to build a few short questions into some (but not all) worksheets and exercises. These will be questions dealing with abstract maths, so that maths is used in a wide range of situations. But maths questions based on everyday situations should face reality squarely and should not reflect the values of only one section of society.

---

**FOOD FOR THOUGHT**

Iron, steel, copper and aluminium are the most easily recycled metals. Refuse of ferrous scrap can give 70% saving in energy, 90% saving in the use of virgin materials, 40% reduction in water use and an 86% reduction in air pollution.

Bottle banks were introduced in 1977. Returnable bottles are not so easy to find now because most supermarkets use plastic bottles. Plastics in everyday use are difficult to recycle and also cause very heavy air pollution on burning.

Oil is an easily recycled product, yet most people are unaware of this. Each year over 10 million gallons of oil are simply poured down the drain, causing pollution. A refining company could recover 70% of this.

---

Not all the examples that follow relate specifically to racial injustice. It is not always easy (nor desirable) to separate out forms of injustice. We have been criticised for raising issues of capitalism and socialism but we believe that if the effects of some aspects of capitalism promote an injustice towards one group of people, it is right to make connections. So we include ideas such as unfair trade, IMF terms, consumerism, Aid, the Cold War etc, and their effects on financially poorer countries.

The examples are grouped under mathematical topics.

# Number
The following are taken from the Friends of the Earth booklet on

# Rainforest and Recycling

Q. Every year 140,000 square kilometres of tropical forest are cleared. Approximately the same amount is seriously damaged each year. How many acres is this every week? How many acres every minute?

Q. In Britain over 6 billion glass bottles and jars are used each year. These could be recycled. Write down this huge number using a 6 and noughts.

Q. In 1984 over 11 billion food and drink cans were produced in the U.K. All can be recycled. How many is this per week?

Q. UNICEF estimate that about 14 million children die each year from hunger and disease.
How many will die each week?
How many each minute?
How many will die during our maths lesson?

A question such as this needs to allow some time for discussion.

## Causes of death

2.6 million children die each year from diseases which immunisation could prevent. Far more are affected by malnourishment. A typical pattern of hospital deaths is that 20% are caused by malnutrition and in 50% more, malnutrition is a contributory factor.

Taking the figures available for 1977, it has been calculated that the world's military expenditure for just 17½ days would have made it possible to:

|  | $ million |
|---|---|
| — Vaccinate all infants against infectious diseases (95 per cent are not vaccinated) | 600 |
| — Increase adult literacy programmes (700 million cannot read) | 1,200 |
| — Train health auxiliaries (successful programmes have shown that auxiliaries with 6 months training can handle 85% of a village's health needs | 250 |
| — Help poor countries grow their own food (500 million people get less than the required minimum of calories) | 3,000 |
| — Build decent houses in cities (at least 300 million live in slums) | 750 |
| — Give supplementary nutrition to 200 million undernourished pre- school children | 4,000 |
| — Give supplementary nutrition to 60 million malnourished pregnant and lactating women (cut infant mortality rates which are 5 times higher in developing countries than in developed countries) | 1,500 |
| — Add 100 million new places in schools (in developing countries, only half the children are now in school). To maintain *this* ratio, over 250 million *new* places will be needed by 1984. | 3,200 |
| — Help clean up water supply systems (over 1,200 million people do not have safe water supplies) | 3,000 |
| — 17½ days' expenditure on armaments | 17,500 |

Q. If a BBC orchestra with 24 musicians can play 'Buffalo Soldier' in 6 minutes, how long will it take Bob Marley's 8 musicians to play it?

## Estimation

Q. Using the figures below giving average water usage, estimate the amount of water a household uses in a week? In a year?

| Bath | 90 litres | Shower | 27 litres |
|---|---|---|---|
| Toilet | 9 litres | Wash face, hands | 9 litres |
| Drink | 1 litre | Wash teeth | 1 litre |
| Wash clothes | 118 litres per load | Sprinkler | 9 litres per minute |

(The average U.K. household amount is 1301 litres per day.)

Q. It is much harder to calculate how much water is used on your behalf by the people who provide some of the basic services.

Estimate

a. How much water is used in making the newspapers that you have in your house, if 1,200 litres are needed for one Sunday newspaper?

b. How much water is used to provide for your weekly transport if each gallon of petrol uses about 60 litres of water in the refining process. Note that buses and trains require less fuel per passenger — roughly one quarter.

Q. Now think about countries where water is scarce and consider these agricultural figures (from the USA):

| food produced | Average amount of water required |
|---|---|
| one egg | 175 litres |
| one ear of corn | 360 litres |
| one loaf of bread | 150 litres |
| five pounds of flour | 375 litres |
| one pound of beef | 2500 litres |

Present this information graphically for a class display.

## Volume and Surface Area

Q. Women in some countries have to carry water for miles. Sometimes they use water containers made out of cylinders. If a cylinder has diameter of 80cms height 1m, what is the volume of water? Use the lengths first in centimetres and then in metres.
Calculate your water requirement for a day at home.

Q. A well in Ethiopia is 50ft deep and has a radius of 5ft. The depth of water is 20ft. What is the volume of water? Calculate the area of the walls of the well? If the sides of bricks measure 12" by 5", how many bricks will be needed to build the walls?

## Population Explosion

Q. Use an atlas or Whittaker's Almanac to find information:
Look up 'land area' and 'population' for a number of countries.
Calculate the ratio of people per square mile.
Example : France : land area    —130,165 sq. miles
population  — 54 million.
density of people per sq. mile = 415.

Q. Choose 20 countries from all parts of the world. Work out the number of people per sq. mile for each country. Write a few comments about your results. Do countries usually labelled 'POOR' always have high density of people? If this is not the case, what other reason might there be for their poverty?

## Percentages/calculator sums

Q. In South Africa, the population is divided into four separate and officially separately classified groups:

| | |
|---|---|
| African: | 24,103,458 |
| Coloured: | 2,830,301 |
| Indian: | 890,292 |
| White: | 4,818,679 |

Make sure you can say these numbers in millions and thousands etc. Then calculate the total percentage of various populations.
Present this information on a pie chart.

167

Q.  In Liverpool, the black population, 40,000 in number, makes up about 9% of the city.

In 1983, there were 12 black staff out of a sample of 1000 city centre workers.

In 1983, there were 75 black workers out of every 10,000 in the retail industry.

There were 3 black trainee nurses to of a total of 306. A total of 110 black workers were employed out of 16,000 counter staff.

A.  Work out the percentage of black workers in each of the above.

B.  How many black workers should have been employed in each group to bring the total up to 9%?

Q.  In Brent, 60% of the population is black. But there are only 280 black teachers out of a total of 2,800. How many black teachers should there be to keep the same ratio as the population?

Q.  Use these figures (from *Teaching Development Issues)* to calculate an index for the amount of food eaten by people from different parts of the world (1 : world average):

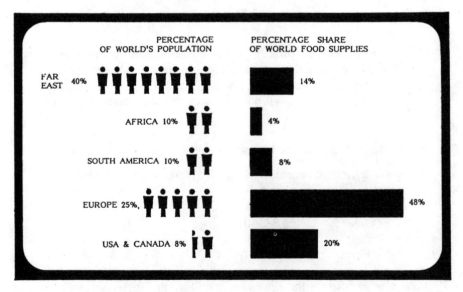

Q.  Which area has most food for its population? Which areas have too much, which have too little?

Q.   In the U.K. the infant mortality rate is 11. (The IMR is defined as the annual number of deaths of children under one year for every 1,000 live births.) For some other countries the figure is :

| | |
|---|---|
| Barbados | 23. |
| Norway | 8. |
| Japan | 7. |
| Ghana | 102 |
| Sri Lanka | 38. |
| Pakistan | 124. |
| Kampuchea | 201.   (1984 figures from UNICEF) |

Work out the expected number of deaths for children born in the following places:
a)   200 children born in Birmingham
b)   1,500 children born in SriLanka
c)   3,526 children born in Accra, Ghana
d)   738 children born in Kampuchea
e)   7,548 children born in Tokyo, Japan
f)   924 children born in Karachi, Pakistan
g)   279 children born in Bridgetown, Barbados
h)   385 children born in Oslo, Norway

# Infant mortality

| Region | Death rates | |
|---|---|---|
| | 0-1 year (per 1000 live births) | 1-4 years (per 1000) |
| West Africa | 161 | 30 |
| Middle Africa | 173 | 30 |
| East Africa | 145 | 35 |
| Mid-South Asia | 136 | 14 |
| Southern Africa | 118 | 30 |
| South-East Asia | 116 | 8 |
| Northern Africa | 131 | 28 |
| South-West Asia | 115 | 10 |
| Tropical South America | 99 | 7 |
| Middle America | 70 | 6 |
| Caribbean | 65 | 3 |
| East Asia | 58 | 2 |
| Temperate South America | 72 | 3 |
| Oceania | 28 | 1 |
| Europe, USSR, N. America | 20 | 1 |

Source: WHO/FHE estimates based on a variety of sources

UNICEF News 1981

## Pie charts, percentages

Q.  Using a protractor, draw pie charts for the following:

SOUTH AFRICA: Population in thousands (in 1980):

| AFRICAN | COLOURED | ASIAN | WHITE |
|---------|----------|-------|-------|
| 20,863 | 2,600 | 821 | 4,500 |
| or 72% | 9% | 3% | 16% |

Percentage of the nation's income:

| | | | |
|---|---|---|---|
| 26 | 7 | 3 | 64 |

Money allocated to education (Million Rand)

| | | | |
|---|---|---|---|
| 254 | 197 | 9 | 1,010 |

Percentage allocation of land

| | | | |
|---|---|---|---|
| 13.7 | 0.68 | 0.1 | 84.2 |

---

*This idea is not sensible to split whites and blacks in different places because there is less place for blacks and more place for white, more schools for whites and more farms.*
(Nadeem Ghalib)

*The way sir has divided the classroom was stupid because we did not need all that room (whites) when the blacks did.*
(Zaida)

*I think that it is unfair to separate blacks and whites. They should stay together.*
(Shahnaz Begum).

*I think it is not fair for the blacks in South Africa. The whites should give back some of the land.*
(Zafran)

*I think it is not fair being squashed in one little place all together and the whites having all the room.*
(Gita Vara)

**Students' comments after the maths lesson on South Africa**

---

## SOUTH AFRICA — THE BANTUSTANS

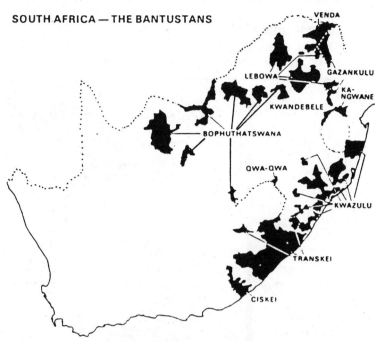

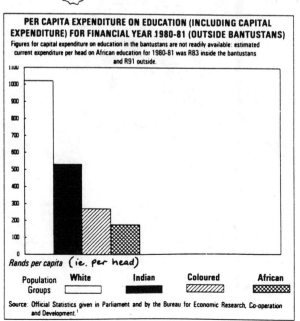

**PER CAPITA EXPENDITURE ON EDUCATION (INCLUDING CAPITAL EXPENDITURE) FOR FINANCIAL YEAR 1980-81 (OUTSIDE BANTUSTANS)**

Figures for capital expenditure on education in the bantustans are not readily available; estimated current expenditure per head on African education for 1980-81 was R83 inside the bantustans and R91 outside.

*Rands per capita* ( ie. per head)

| Population Groups | White | Indian | Coloured | African |

Source: Official Statistics given in Parliament and by the Bureau for Economic Research, Co-operation and Development.[1]

171

## Logarithmic Scales

Q. Here are some figures which show approximately how many kilojoules of energy are needed to produce 1 kilojoule of food.

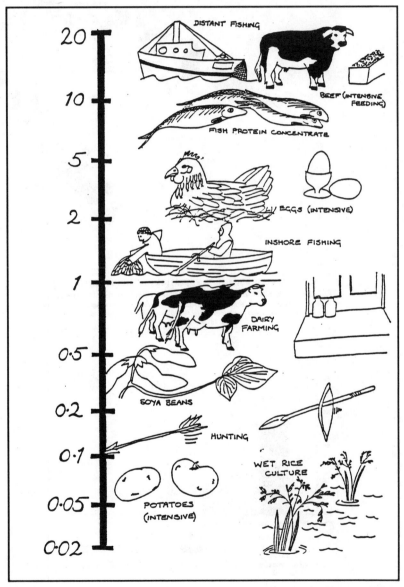

*Drawn by Frances Khan*

| Type of food production | Energy needed to produce 1 kilojoule-worth of food |
|---|---|
| Distant fishing | 20kJ |
| Beef (intensive feeding) | 20kJ |
| Fish protein concentrate | 10kJ |
| Eggs (intensive) | 5kJ |
| Inshore fishing | 2kJ |
| Dairy farming products | 0.5kJ |
| Soya beans | 0.2kJ |
| Potatoes (intensive) | 0.05kJ |
| Wet rice culture | 0.02kJ |

Draw a bar chart with a linear vertical axis to show this data. Now use a log scale on the vertical axis to show the data. Discuss the difference between the graphs.

## Feeding the world

Countries like Ethiopia and India grow their own grain. Countries like Britain take that food from where it is needed most to feed livestock over here. Did you know that we imported cereal *from* Ethiopia during the famine just so that we could have our meat?

A third of the world's population is starving, 15 MILLION children die every year because of malnutrition, die slowly and horribly. And yet, this planet could supply ample food for everyone.

The problem is mismanagement — a huge waste of resources — take a look at these figures:

10 acres of land (that's about 5 football pitches) will support:

2 people on a diet of cattle meat
10 people on a diet of maize
24 people on a diet of wheat
61 people on a diet of soya beans

a) Draw a bar graph of these figures

b) How many students are there in your school? Use this figure to calculate how many acres of land would be needed for these different eating styles. Show these on a graph too.

173

c) You might think that eating a vegetarian diet would be bad for your health! Not so. Find out about vegetarian diets (and while you're doing that, why not investigate the costs of going vegetarian too?).

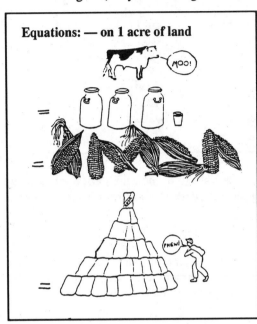

**Equations: — on 1 acre of land**

Q. The UN estimate the world's population to be 4,432 million. It also estimates that:
2,000 million live on annual incomes below £417.
600 million have no jobs or are less than fully employed.
450 million suffer from hunger or malnutrition.
42 million are blind or nearly blind.
2,000 million do not have a regular supply of safe drinking water.
250 million live in urban slums or shanty towns.

In each case calculate the % of the total.

In Britain there were 2.2 million people of 'New Commonwealth' origin in 1982. This amount to 4% of Britain's population. Of this group 80% are black.

a) How many people of the 'New Commonwealth' are black?

b) What is Britain's total population?

Q. In a US city in 1984, 12.4% of black babies and 5.6% of white babies were born underweight. (This is a contributory factor to infant mortality rate) If 5,600 babies are born to black parents and 8,400 to white, calculate the total number of children born underweight in that US city. Why do you think there are different percentages for black children and white?

# Maths error adds up to desegregation trouble

There is a small problem of arithmetic in Kansas City, Missouri, and it threatens to wreck one of the most thorough school desegregation schemes in America.

It was in 1984, after a seven-year court battle, that a federal judge ruled Kansas City schools to be illegally segregated and forced local authorities to take the drastic action.

Dozens of dilapidated buildings were demolished and replaced, and more than half the district's 75 schools were turned into 'magnet' institutions, specialising in mathematics, computers or language. Each magnet school, said the judge, had to enrol 60 per cent minority students, and 40 per cent whites.

And therein lay the problem, for 75 per cent of the district's 35,000 students are black or Hispanic, not 60 per cent.

The result has been that schools have vacancies for white pupils, and are having to turn away blacks who want to fill the empty seats. Black parents, claiming that their children are being victimised and denied the education benefits of the new schools, are up in arms. They are demanding vouchers, covering the cost of tuition at a private school of their choice.

There are 50 such schools in the Kansas City area, and they love the idea. They have 4,000 vacant places that they would be delighted to fill at the state's expense.

The authorities, however, are resisting and accusing the private schools of greed. The parents, in turn, are suing. And so, thanks to a judge's arithmetic, the desegregation issue in Kansas City is right back where it was in 1977: in court.

# Tractors create profits but cut down on jobs
*by Andy Crump*

Wheeling and dealing has gathered pace within the tractor industry over the past few months. When the dust settles, millions of agricultural workers in the Third World are likely to find themselves out of a job. Several major tractor-producing corporations have changed hands and it is rumoured that further mergers and take-overs are imminent.

The immediate aftermath of these activities has been a reduction in tractor-producing capacity as demand for tractors is markedly lower now than it was a decade ago. The future prospects within the industrialised world are bleak, but the Third World is recognised by most manufacturers as having vast potential. According to UNEP's State of the Environment Report (1985), machinery accounted for only 8 per cent of power input in Third World agriculture during 1980. Current trends forecast an increase to 19 per cent by the end of the century.

The Chairman of Deere & Co stated that profits last year were the highest since 1981. He also commented: 'retail sales of farm equipment outside the US and Canada have recovered somewhat, and our profitable overseas division has scheduled production well above last year's level'.

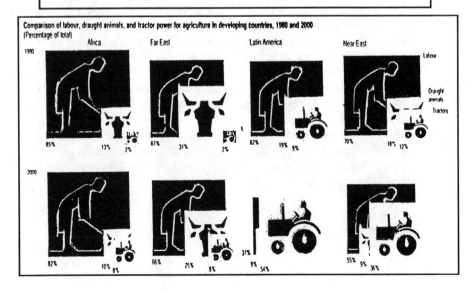

Comparison of labour, draught animals, and tractor power for agriculture in developing countries, 1980 and 2000
(Percentage of total)

Q.  Almost 1 in 8 people in the world are badly undernourished. There are about 4.5 billion people in the world. How many are badly undernourished?

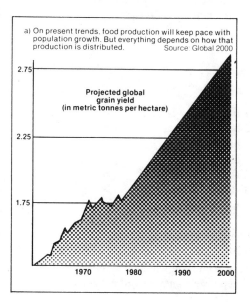

a) On present trends, food production will keep pace with population growth. But everything depends on how that production is distributed. Source: Global 2000

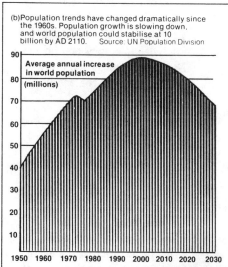

(b)Population trends have changed dramatically since the 1960s. Population growth is slowing down, and world population could stabilise at 10 billion by AD 2110. Source: UN Population Division

**'WHEN I give food to the poor they call me a saint. When I ask why the poor have no food they call me a communist'**

DOM HELDER CAMARA
Archbishop of Recife
North East Brazil

*Photo: Catholic Pictorial*

## Using number for planning : fibre in your diet

Traditional diets of Asians, Afro-Caribbean and Chinese contain a high quantity of pulses, vegetables, fruit and cereals. These contain large quantities of fibre. Modern food processing often removes fibre from the raw materials and adds less beneficial ingredients such as fat and sugar.

## FIBRE IN YOUR DIET

Study the kilojoules and fibre chart.
Now answer these questions:
What is the fibre content of:-

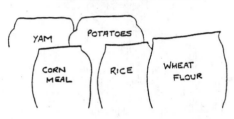

| | |
|---|---|
| 2 oz. of kidney beans | = |
| 2 baked potatoes | = |
| 1 banana | = |
| 1 chapati | = |
| 1 slice of white bread | = |
| 1 slice of brown bread | ⇒ |
| 2 beefburgers | = |

What is the energy value of 2 ozs. of luncheon meat?
What is the energy value of 2 chapatis?
What is the difference in energy value of white and wholemeal bread?
Find the energy value of a meal of 2 beefburgers and a baked potatoes?

Which extra food will you add to this meal to give you extra fibre, but not change the energy value too much?

Find the total fibre content of the following two meals. Use your chart

| | |
|---|---|
| ½ an Avocado | = |
| 3 z. chilli con carni | = |
| 2 z. brown rice | = |
| 1 oz. sweet corn | = |
| TOTAL | = |

| | |
|---|---|
| 2 chapatis | = |
| 2 oz. sabji of green beans | = |
| 2 oz. curry of soya beans | = |
| 1 large mango — 4 ozs. | = |
| TOTAL | = |

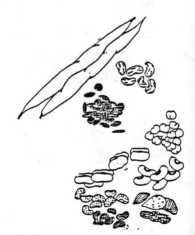

| KILOJOULES AND FIBRE CHART | | | |
|---|---|---|---|
| FOOD | PORTION | KJ | FIBRE in gm |
| Aubergines raw | 7oz (200gm) | 120 | 5.0 |
| Avocado | 3oz | 860 | 2.0 |
| Bacon | 100gm 1 back rasher | | |
| | raw | 600 | 0 |
| | grilled | 340 | 0 |
| | fried | 380 | 0 |
| | 1 steak grilled | 420 | 0 |
| Banana | 6oz (100g) | 320 | 3.5 |
| Mango Raw | 201gm | 152 | 6.0 |
| Honeydew Melon | 149gm | 49 | 5.0 |
| Papaya Raw | 304gm | 119 | 4.8 |
| Raisins Seedless | 145gm | 419 | 1.0 |
| Strawberries | 149gm | 55 | 4.2 |
| Barcelona nuts | 1oz | 720 | 3.0 |
| Beans: | | | |
| Baked | 8oz | 580 | 16.5 |
| Black-eyed | 1oz | 380 | 7.0 |
| Butter | 4oz | 440 | 5.5 |
| Red kidney | 1oz | 300 | 7.0 |
| Runner | 4oz | 80 | 4.0 |
| Soya | 1oz | 447 | 4.0 |
| Beef: | | | |
| Beefburgers | 2oz | 520 | 0 |
| Corn-canned | 2oz | 482 | 0 |
| Fore-rib roast | 1 | 760 | 0 |
| Stewing steak | 3oz | 740 | 0 |
| Beef sausages | 1 large grilled | 520 | 0 |
| Beef & pork sausage | 1 large grilled | 540 | 0 |
| Mince beef | 3oz | 720 | 0 |
| Brazil nut | 1 | 80 | 0.5 |
| Beetroot | 2oz | 100 | 1.5 |
| Bread: Brown | 2 average slices | 680 | 3.5 |

| KILOJOULES AND FIBRE CHART (continued) | | | |
|---|---|---|---|
| FOOD | PORTION | KJ | FIBRE in gm |
| Bread: White | 2 average slices | 640 | 2.0 |
| Wholemeal | 2 average slices | 610 | 6.0 |
| Chapatis | 2 average slices | 860 | 9.0 |
| Rice: Brown | 2oz | 840 | 2.5 |
| Rice: White | 2oz | 866 | 1.5 |
| Lentils | 2oz | 500 | 5.0 |
| Black-eyed beans | 150gm | 190 | 2.5 |
| Mung beans | 105gm | 355 | 4.6 |
| *From a variety of sources* | | | |

Using the Fibre and KJ chart, plan 2 different meals. Each meal should provide you with a minimum of 6000 kilojoules and a maximum of 8000.

NACNE (National Advisory Committee on Nutritional Education) recommend 25 to 30 gm. of fibre every day.

MEAL A. High fibre, vegetarian

MEAL B. High fibre, non-vegetarian

What were the difficulties in planning each of these meals?

Does either of your imaginary meals resemble your daily diet?

Look up the kilojoules and fibre content of some of the meals you have every day.

# Pictograms and diagrams

Q. Use a horizontal bar chart (with pictures if you wish) to illustrate this data about transport. The information shows how far one person can go on one gallon of fuel.

| Type of transport | Passenger miles/gallon of fuel |
|---|---|
| Commuter train | 100 |
| City bus | 95 |
| Underground train | 75 |
| Car (5 people — between cities) | 34 |
| 747 jet | 22 |
| Car (5 people — in one city) | 20 |
| Concorde | 14 |
| Helicopter | 8 |

Now work out how much fuel is needed for each mile in the different forms of travel. Design a diagram to illustrate this information in an interesting and accurate way. (See *The New State of the World Atlas* published by Pan Books for numerous ideas on information diagrams.)

Q. How do you think the following forms of travel fit into your diagram?

| | | |
|---|---|---|
| Bicycle | Walking | Milk float |
| Horse | Camel | Motor bike |
| Horse and cart | Rickshaw | Hoverboard |
| Donkey | Mule | (as in *Back to the* |
| Horse-drawn canal barge | Solar car | *Future II)* |

Q. **Coffee Costs**
For each £1 spent on coffee in England:

10p pays retailer's profit
6p pays supplier's profit
3p pays bank interest and royalties
12p pays advertising
15p pays office wages
13p pays packing material
5p pays transport costs
36p stays in the country of production
(only about half of this goes to the grower)

Present this information as levels on a coffee jar or in a pie chart.

Q.  **Banana Costs**

For each £1 spent on bananas in England:

26p pays packers, importers
12p pays shipping
19p pays ripener
18p pays supplier's profit
14p pays retailer's profit
11p remains in the growing country.

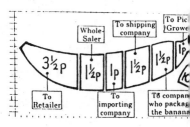

Present this information as slices on a drawing of a banana.

# Cumulative frequency polygons and the trapezium rule

Q.  The diagram, taken from the *'Third World Atlas'* (which includes a short but thoughtful section on social indicators of development), illustrates an example of a cumulative frequency polygon. The grey area gives a measure of the difference between a statistically fair distribution of wealth within a country and the reality.

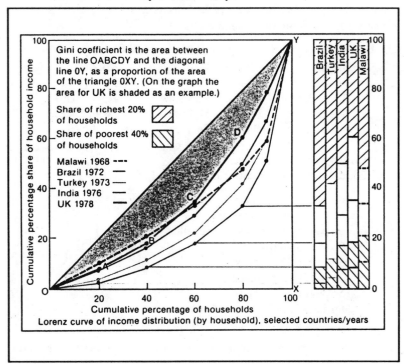

Gini coefficient is the area between the line OABCDY and the diagonal line OY, as a proportion of the area of the triangle OXY. (On the graph the area for UK is shaded as an example.)

Share of richest 20% of households
Share of poorest 40% of households

Malawi 1968 ---
Brazil 1972 —
Turkey 1973 —
India 1976 —
UK 1978 —

Lorenz curve of income distribution (by household), selected countries/years

The Gross National Product gives a measure of how rich a country is but it does not indicate how equitably the resources are distributed within it. The Gini coefficient attempts to measure inequality, with 0 being complete equality, moving to 1 for extreme inequality. A simpler measure of inequality is the percentage of income taken by the lowest forty percent of households. More figures on the Gini coefficient can be found in *Global Problems* (from the Centre for Global Education) for students to gain practice in drawing cumulative frequency polygons and in calculating the area under a polygon using the trapezium rule.

## Sets

*Look at this list of people*
SOJOURNER TRUTH * MAHATMA GANDHI * ISAAĈ NEWTON *
DALEY THOMPSON * WINNIE MANDELA * MARTIN LUTHER
KING * VICTORIA WOOD * BOB MARLEY * MAO TSE TUNG *
MARY QUANT * MARGARET THATCHER * DIANA ROSS *
MOTHER THERESA * GURU NANAK JI * ANGELA DAVIS *
THE PROPHET MOHAMMED * INDIRA GANDHI *

Q.  1. List the following sets of people:

|     |                           |
|-----|---------------------------|
| A   | = (Asian people)          |
| B   | = (people of African origin) |
| Wh  | = (white people           |
| W   | = (Women)                 |
| M   | = (Men)                   |
| P   | = (Politicians)           |
| S   | = (Singer)                |
| R   | = (Religious leaders)     |

183

2. Write down: a) B∩ S   b) A∪ M

3. Complete ∈ A;  ∈ W;  ∉ M ∩ P;  ∈ W∩ S;  ∈ W∪ P;  ∈ R ∩ P ∩ M

4. Fill in the correct names in the Venn Diagram:

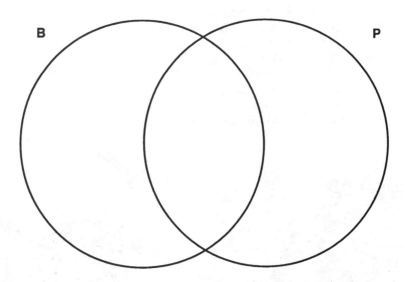

B                                                    P

# Maths and Migration

Q. The diagram below shows details of migrant workers in the UK during the 60s and 70s. You can see that 7.5% of the workforce (1,665,000 people) is made up of migrant personnel. Copy and complete the following table.

| Country of origin | Number of migrant workers | Percentage of total |
|---|---|---|
| Caribbean | | |
| India/Pakistan | | |
| Ireland | | |
| Greece | | |
| Italy | | |
| West Germany | | |
| Other EEC | | |
| Other non-EEC | | |

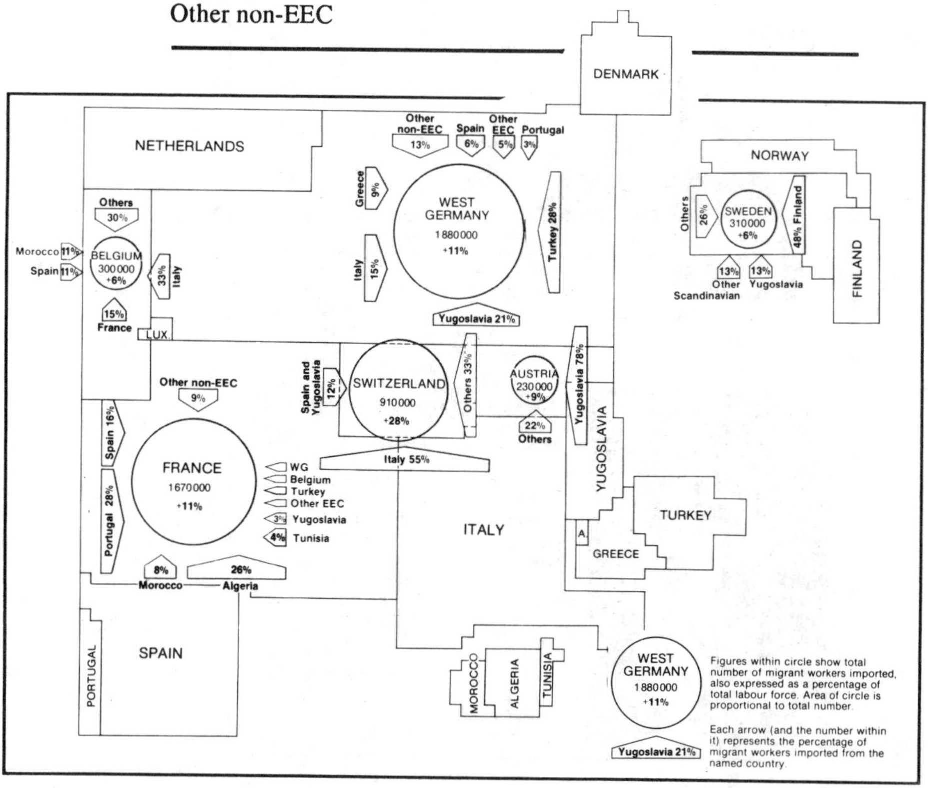

# Measuring the gulf

Racism affects every area of black people's lives. The effects of racism can be seen in the gulf between the black and white experience of work, housing, health and education – among our most basic needs.

## THE FACTS

### WORK

Black people are more likely to be unemployed.

Percentage of each group unemployed:

**AUSTRALIA**
White 7.6%
Aboriginal 24.6%
Vietnamese 26.9%
Lebanese 31.9%

**CANADA**
National average 13.6%
Native peoples 50-75%

**UNITED KINGDOM**

| | Men | Women |
|---|---|---|
| White | 13% | 10% |
| Afro-Caribbean | 25% | 16% |
| Indian sub-continent | 20% | 20% |

White people are more likely to have professional or managerial jobs

Percentage of each group in professional jobs:

**AUSTRALIA**
White 14.2%
Aboriginal 7%
Vietnamese 5.9%
Lebanese 2.4%

**NEW ZEALAND**
Maons 4.6%
Others 17.2%

**UNITED KINGDOM**
White 19%
Indian sub-continent 13%
Afro-Caribbean 5%

### HOUSING

Black people are more likely to face bad housing conditions.

**AUSTRALIA**
Proportion living in improvised shelter:
Aboriginals 9%   National average 0.2%
A Queensland survey of aboriginal housing showed:
Totally unacceptable 63%
Unacceptable but needing repair 34%
On a par with normal white standards 3%

**CANADA**
Proportion with sewerage and running water:
Native 50%   National average 96%
Native population of Montreal (1976):
Resident 250   Transient 6,500

**UNITED KINGDOM**
Percentage of each group allocated council housing by type of accommodation:

| | FLATS | HOUSES | CROWDING |
|---|---|---|---|
| White | 27% | 39% | 5% |
| Afro-Caribbean | 54% | 9% | 20% |
| Indian sub-cont | 54% | 11% | 43% |

Percentage of each group in pre-1919 housing:

| | |
|---|---|
| White | 26.6% |
| Afro-Caribbean | 46.8% |
| Indian sub-cont | 61.7% |

# EDUCATION

Black people are less likely to receive a full education

### AUSTRALIA

Percentage receiving no schooling
Aboriginals 11.7%
Others 0.08%
*(80% of aboriginals have no educational qualifications)*

### CANADA

80% of native indian children do not complete high school

### NEW ZEALAND

Whites are twice as likely as Maoris to complete secondary school and six times more likely to enter university

### UNITED KINGDOM

There are only 800 black teachers nationwide

# INCOME

Black people earn less money.

### AUSTRALIA

Average annual family income:
Aboriginals $ 6.626
Others $12.026

### CANADA

Native indian men earn
60.2% of male average wage
Native indian women earn
71.7% of female average wage
Indo-Chinese people
earn ⅔ of national average

### USA

Average family income $19,661
Puerto Rican family income $9,855
Black people are more than twice as likely to be below the poverty line.

### UNITED KINGDOM

Average weekly earnings:
White £129
Indian sub-continent £111
Afro-Caribbean £109

SOURCES

WORK : AUS.Bureau of Statistics, Dept. of Aboriginal Affairs;CAN.Ministry of Indian & Northern Affairs 1980: NZ. 1981 Census; UK. Policy Studies Institute.

HOUSING : AUS. Bureau of Statistics; CAN.Federal Dept. of Indian Affairs 1980, Council on Social Development 1976; UK. Policy Studies Institute.

HEALTH : AUS.Bureau of Statistics; CAN. Ministry of Indian & Northern Affairs 1980, UNICEF, Statistics Canada: USA. National Center for Health Statistics.

EDUCATION : AUS.Bureau of Statistics; CAN. Statistics Canada 1983;NZ. 1981 Census; UK.Runnymede Trust.

INCOME : AUS. Bureau of Statistics; CAN. Abella Commission; UK. Policy Studies Institute; USA. 1979 Census; Commission on Civil Right.

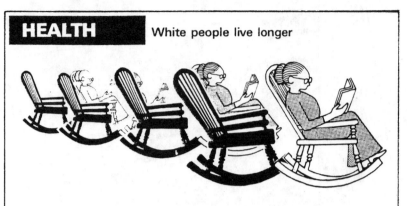

## HEALTH — White people live longer

**Life expectancy at birth**

**AUSTRALIA**
Aboriginals 53 years
National average 73 years

**USA**
Whites live an average of 4.6 years longer than blacks, hispanics and native Americans

**CANADA**
Native Indians 66 years
National average 75 years

**The suicide rate of Canadian native indians is 2½ times the national average**

## Black babies are more likely to die

### Infant mortality per 1000 live births

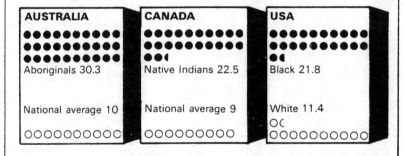

| AUSTRALIA | CANADA | USA |
|---|---|---|
| Aboriginals 30.3 | Native Indians 22.5 | Black 21.8 |
| National average 10 | National average 9 | White 11.4 |

# Trigonometry in 3 dimensions

The pyramids are extraodinary feats of engineering and organization in the ancient civilisation of Egypt.

The largest of the Giza pyramids is 480 feet high and about 740 feet long each side of the square base.

It is made up of about 2 million blocks of stone each tunnelled out of cliff faces, transported by boat and hauled by teams of men, 20 pulling the blocks on rollers, and about 5 pushing along the rollers. During the flooded season, when farming became impossible, an extra 50,000 men were drafted to complete the building.

Q.  For this pyramid, calculate:

   a)   the length of the diagonal across the square base;

   b)   the area of one face of the pyramid;

   c)   the volume of the pyramid;

   d)   the angle each face makes with the horizontal;

   e)   the angle two adjacent slant faces make with each other.

*CHAPTER 8*

# More Challenges in classroom practice

Dr. Joop van Dormolen from the Netherlands has written textbooks for use in Dutch schools. Choosing reality as a primary source for ideas and problems is his guiding principle. He writes:

> The social environment of pupils is a great source for teaching mathematics, not only for practical reasons but also because one can expect the pupils to understand better and be more interested to learn the subject matter involved, but also for ethical and idealistic reasons. It depends on the teacher's and the author's set of values and in what way each of these reasons play a role in their communication with the pupils.
> *Paper for ICME 6, 1988*

Television and newspapers can provide a variety of perspectives and a source for mathematics examples from around the world. A narrow range of examples from the 'real world' have appeared in British textbooks in the form of tables, bus/train timetables, sport scoresheets, building society interest rates and so on. Controversial matters such as South African sanctions or land distribution are avoided.

## Number work based on current events
One of the first examples that we tried in the classroom was built around the Olympic Games in Korea.

Many students were interested in the Games. There was intense media coverage of the preparations, the clearing of beggars from the streets, the building of accommodation, and controversy over boycotts by some countries. Newspapers were a source of many mathematics ideas which we used for revision of past lessons and for practical applications of ideas already learned. The exercise below stimulated discussions about exploitation and wages, importation of goods made by cheap labour abroad, and (briefly) whether such conditions could or do exist here.

## The Olympics Are Coming To Korea

**MEE LEE KIN is 18, Until a month ago she earned £80 a month as an assembler in a computer factory.**

She had to work compulsory overtime, often locked in the factory for 80 hours a week, and she was finally sacked for trying to organise a union which was not company-controlled.

Her home is one of 40 'cells', 5ft by 7ft by 6ft tall, in one of the many beehive blocks in Seoul, the South Korean capital where billions have been spent on creating a stage for the 24th Olympiad.

For her cell, Mee Lee Kim had to pay a year's salary as a deposit and a quarter of every week's wages in rent.

According to the International Labour Organisation, manual workers in Korea suffer the worst conditions in the world.

For a 60-hour week, the average wage is a few pence over £1 an hour. Few rest days are allowed.

'As a Korean, I'm proud we have the Olympics — but like most people I know I won't be able to go and watch the sports, much as I would like to' said Mee lee Kim.

The Olympiad next September is expected to be a carnival and celebration of world sport but for those on the outside looking in, it will bring misery.

To the average citizen, the Olympic Games will have the air of a lavish party on a floor above...to which he is most emphatically not invited.

The South Koreans will welcome 13,600 athletes from 167 countries, 12,000 journalist and many more tourists to the Games.

The Hilton-like hotels for visitors paying 200 dollars a seat for the best events, the showpiece stores and boulevards, are all in place.

Seoul, a city of 11 million, will present a glossy new face to the visitors, but behind this cosmetic facade there is an army of families who have been literally bulldozed into homelessness to make way for Olympic facilities.

# I cried all night

Another 33-year-old worker proudly shows his forearm where thin white scars read, 'Nodong Undong' — Labour Movement. 'I carved this with a razor to remind myself of who I am and what I must live and struggle for.'

Chung was sacked from his job in an electronics factory for demanding the back wages he and his fellow workers were owed.

The company blacklisted him and he has been unable to find a job since.

'I had always been a model worker.' he said, 'turning up 30 minutes early — without pay — to clean my work station. I even opposed the strikes other workers wanted.' But Chung soon became an active union organiser.

'On Christmas Eve, we stayed late because the company promised to pay our October wages — already two months overdue — but a foreman later told us we would not be paid that night. Along with some of the older workers, I cried all night in our dormitory in despair.

When three days later the company made a part payment of arrears Chung was so incensed he stood up and angrily demanded their back wages. The company responded by sacking him.

His job at the Seoul Electronics Factory, which made fluorescent lights for export, was the best Chung had had. He was paid £2.25 for an eight-hour day. Many of his fellow women workers earned less than £1.70 for the eight-hour shift. Overtime was compulsory, and they had to work every day, including Sunday — a 78-hour week.

The 200-strong workforce lived in the company's two segregated dormitories. They ate at the firm's canteen, for which they were charged 60 cents a day.

## THE OLYMPICS ARE COMING TO KOREA

1. How many hours a week did Mee Lee often work?
   How many hours a week do you spend on school work?

2. How big is her room? What is its volume?
   Estimate the volume of your bedroom?

3. Write one billion in numbers.

4. 13600 athletes come from 167 countries. What is the average from each country?

5. How much was Chung paid for an 8 hour day?
   How much is this per hour?

6. How much would the women in Seoul Electronics Factory earn in a week?

7. Mee Lee Kim had to pay a year's salary as deposit for her room, How much was that?

8. When you buy goods made in other parts of the world, do you think about the people who made them?

9. Find out where the clothes and goods in the major department stores in your High Street are made? Highlight these on a map of the world for a wall display.

## The Facts on Paper

1. Every year the students in your school each use three 80-leaf A4 pads of paper. How many trees are used in a year?

2. How many tonnes of paper does the USA consume each year? If no recycled paper is used, approximately how many trees would be required for this amount of paper?

3. How many trees are cut down each year to supply the paper used by your family?

# The Facts on Paper

- Every tonne of recycled paper saves over 17 trees.
- Every tonne of recycled paper saves over 5,000 kilowatt hours of electricity.
- In Britain we use about 130 kilograms of paper per person per year — the equivalent of two trees each.
- One tree will only make about 144 80-leaf A4 pads.
- Worldwide paper consumption is now over 170 million tonnes per annum. The developed Western countries consume 74 per cent of this — almost 126 million tonnes — of which the USA uses half.
- World consumption *per minute* is now equivalent to all the trees being cut down in over 25,000 square metres of 60-year-old forest.
- In temperate climates a forest only grows on average up to one tonne of wood per annum per acre — less than that in colder climates.
- Recycled paper products are available from Green Man, Unit 4, The Labyrinth, Station Street, Eastbourne, East Sussex BN21 4RG.

Malcolm Khanna: 'What do I get out of it? Sore feet and satisfaction'

# Graph work in statistics

'Third world' countries are often portrayed in maths books as if they were stuck in a time warp. Figures on infant mortality rate, diseases, health care, income distribution are presented, without any explanations of the reasons for these conditions. No maths lesson can engage in a full analysis, but we can at least set students thinking. They should also learn something about the progress that has been made despite centuries of exploitation. Here are some examples of exercises that do this.

## Infant mortality

A book produced by OXFAM and called *Recipes from around the World*, contains many figures from countries around the world and explanations of these statistics. Students could be asked to plot graphs of infant mortality per thousand live births and life expectancy for 1960 and 1980. After which they might think what could happen if resources were shared more equitably around the world.

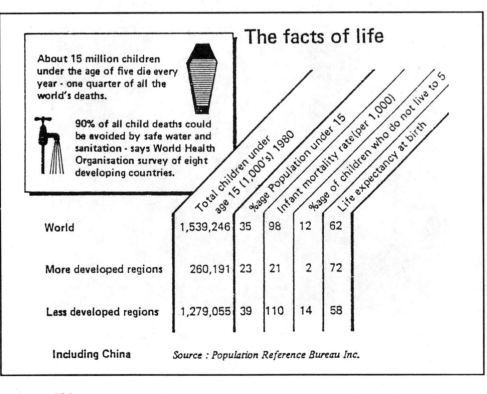

## The facts of life

About 15 million children under the age of five die every year - one quarter of all the world's deaths.

90% of all child deaths could be avoided by safe water and sanitation - says World Health Organisation survey of eight developing countries.

| | Total children under age 15 (1,000's) | %age Population under 15 1980 | Infant mortality rate (per 1,000) | %age of children who do not live to 5 | Life expectancy at birth |
|---|---|---|---|---|---|
| World | 1,539,246 | 35 | 98 | 12 | 62 |
| More developed regions | 260,191 | 23 | 21 | 2 | 72 |
| Less developed regions | 1,279,055 | 39 | 110 | 14 | 58 |
| Including China | | | | | |

*Source : Population Reference Bureau Inc.*

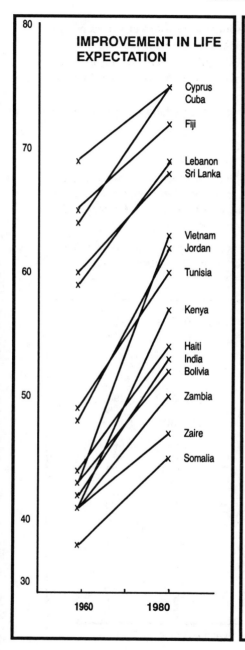

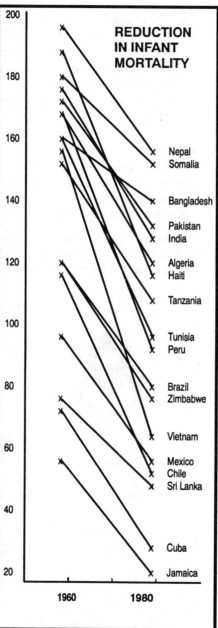

Once the graphs have been drawn, questions can be asked eg:- work out the gradients for some of the lines; what do these gradients mean?

— calculate some percentage changes in life expectancy and in infant mortality. In percentage terms, is it the 'best' or the 'worst' who have the largest percentage change?

— Is it the 'best' country or the 'worst' that has the largest improvement in life expectancy?

## Illiteracy

The table here shows increases in literacy, worldwide, with interesting differences between men and women in some societies. For those who would like to do project work on this topic, the varying amounts of money which different countries spend on education deserves analysis.

The illiteracy rate is generally defined as that proportion of the adult population 15 years or older unable to read or write. The table below is based on the most recent data available.

### The reduction of Illiteracy in the South

| | 1960 % illiterate | 1970 % illiterate | 1980 % illiterate |
|---|---|---|---|
| Africa | 81 | 74 | 62 |
| Male | 73 | 63 | 51 |
| Female | 88 | 84 | 73 |
| Asia* | 55 | 47 | 45 |
| Male | 45 | 37 | 35 |
| Female | 63 | 57 | 55 |
| Latin America | 33 | 24 | 20 |
| Male | 28 | 20 | 17 |
| Female | 37 | 27 | 23 |
| Total | 59 | 50 | 46 |
| Male | 50 | 40 | 36 |
| Female | 69 | 60 | 56 |

*Does not include the Peoples' Republic of China.*

198

# Health Care
Using the figures below, make predictions for the year 2000.

| | 1960 | MORE HEALTH STAFF<br>Population per nursing person<br>1970 | 1980 |
|---|---|---|---|
| Africa | 3364 | 2320 | 2150 |
| Southern Europe | 1285 | 917 | 630 |
| Middle East | 2787 | 2728 | 1350 |
| South Asia | 14655 | 8673 | 3330 |
| East Asia | | 2586 | 2180 |
| Western Hemisphere | 2186 | 1552 | 1220 |
| Industrial Countries | 340 | 316 | 305 |

There are other development success stories in *Teaching Development Issues —Aid and Development,* a section on how development should be measured (p.31).

## More Bar graphs
Some countries are richer than others. If a family wants to go out for a meal, how much could they afford to spend? Pupils could first write down their own ideas about the price of different foods in different countries. Here are figures given by London Weekend TV in 1981.

        American (U.S.)  £20
        British          £11
        Mexican          £ 3
        Bangladeshi       18p

Draw a bar chart to show this information.

## Bar charts
The figures showing the correlation between education and infant mortality can be used to practice bar charts. They are taken from *Women in the World* Pan Books, and show the number of deaths in the first two years of life per 1000 children in some Latin American countries in the early 70s.

After the bar charts have been drawn and displayed, various factors could be discussed: the age (and state of health) of the mothers at time of giving

| Country | Number of years mother spent at school | | | | |
| | 0 | 1-3 | 4-6 | 7-9 | 10+ |
|---|---|---|---|---|---|
| Argentina | 96 | 75 | 59 | 39 | 26 |
| Columbia | 126 | 95 | 63 | 42 | 32 |
| Costa Rica | 125 | 98 | 70 | 51 | 33 |
| El Salvador | 158 | 142 | 111 | 58 | 30 |
| Guatemala | 169 | 135 | 85 | 58 | 44 |
| Honduras | 171 | 129 | 99 | 60 | 35 |
| Peru | 207 | 136 | 102 | 77 | 70 |

birth, health facilities in different parts of the countries, the great differences between the countries (for example Argentina and Peru) and the value of education itself.

## Accuracy in drawing pictograms

The diagrams below are from *Women in the World*. Pictograms can distort the underlying meaning of the figures and it is instructive to test some

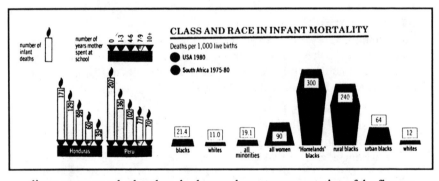

diagrams to see whether they do show an honest representation of the figures. The diagrams in these drawings are hard to check because the coffins are not rectangular. Nevertheless, students can calculate a simple vertical ratio for a first check. For a more accurate check, use a photocopy enlargement and calculate the areas of the coffins. Again, discussion on the background to the statistics is important.

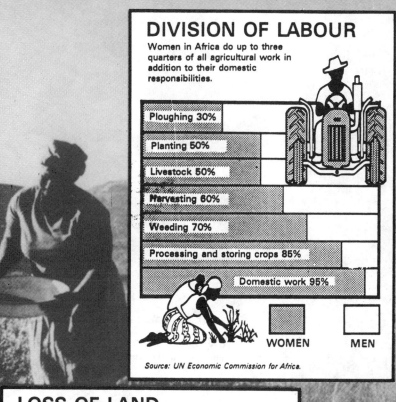

## DIVISION OF LABOUR

Women in Africa do up to three quarters of all agricultural work in addition to their domestic responsibilities.

Ploughing 30%

Planting 50%

Livestock 50%

Harvesting 60%

Weeding 70%

Processing and storing crops 85%

Domestic work 95%

WOMEN          MEN

*Source: UN Economic Commission for Africa.*

## LOSS OF LAND

Many women – especially in Africa – have lost their traditional rights to the land they work because colonial laws and development policies have tended to allocate land only to men.

# FEMALE FARMERS

Women grow half of the world's food. But most agricultural advisors are men – who tend to give advice to men.

Women as % of agricultural advisors

Women as % of agricultural labour force

Source: FAO

| | LATIN AMERICA | AFRICA | | ASIA |
|---|---|---|---|---|
| Women as % of agricultural labour force | 19 | Sub-Saharan Africa 47 | N. Africa and Middle East 25 | 40 |
| Women as % of agricultural advisors | 8.5 | | 2.9 | 0.7 |

# A Closer Look

Local studies show that national surveys invariably underestimate women's agricultural work.

| | National figures | Local figures |
|---|---|---|
| EGYPT | 3.6% | 35 – 50% |
| PERU | 2.6% | 86% |

Source: FAO

# Scattergrams

Scattergrams using world figures of GNP, energy consumption and life expectancy make interesting maths lessons and assist learning about graphs and statistics. Figures can be obtained from development education centres and other sources.
Draw a scattergram for the following:

| Energy consumption per capita and GNP per capita 1986 | | |
|---|---|---|
| Country | Energy per capita kg oil equiv. | GNP per capita US$ |
| USA | 7193 | 17480 |
| Canada | 8945 | 14120 |
| Netherlands | 5201 | 10020 |
| Australia | 4710 | 11920 |
| UK | 3802 | 8870 |
| France | 3640 | 10720 |
| Japan | 3186 | 12840 |
| Saudi Arabia | 3336 | 6950 |
| Argentina | 1427 | 2350 |
| Mexico | 1235 | 1860 |
| Brazil | 830 | 1810 |
| Thailand | 325 | 810 |
| Nigeria | 134 | 640 |
| Egypt | 577 | 760 |
| Philippines | 180 | 560 |
| India | 208 | 290 |
| Kenya | 100 | 300 |
| Ghana | 131 | 390 |
| Indonesia | 213 | 490 |
| Zaire | 73 | 160 |
| Malawi | 43 | 160 |
| Ethiopia | 21 | 120 |

## Gross National Product: Discussion Points

*Gross National Product is the total value of goods and services produced in a country, together with any payments received from other countries, LESS payments made to other countries,*

Find out which services are not included in GNP calculations.

What does GNP tell us about growth and progress? Are there any problems with this?

Here is something to think about. Women all over the world do a large share of the household as well as agricultural work — for which they do not get paid. Why do you think this is and do you think it's right?

Draw a scattergram for the following figures on a separate graph.

| Country | GNP per capita | Life expectation (years) |
|---|---|---|
| China | 310 | 65 |
| Jamaica | 1330 | 71 |
| UK | 9660 | 73 |
| Mexico | 2270 | 66 |
| Pakistan | 380 | 51 |
| Spain | 5430 | 73 |
| USSR | 5940 | 69 |
| Ethiopia | 140 | 40 |
| France | 11680 | 74 |
| India | 260 | 50 |
| Zimbabwe | 850 | 53 |
| USA | 13160 | 74 |
| Nigeria | 860 | 49 |
| Bangladesh | 140 | 47 |

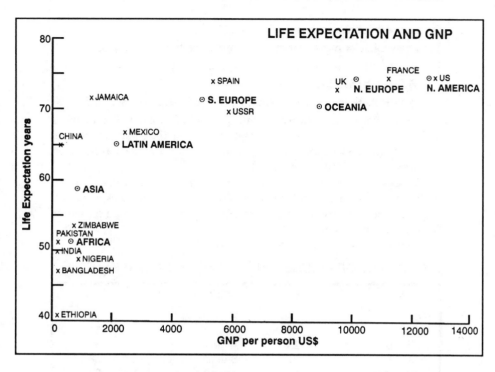

Look at the graph. Do you think that...
... rich nations trade only with each other?
... all nations trade with each other?
... poor nations trade only with each other?

These are the figures for the continents:

| Continent | GNP per capita | Life expectation (years) |
| --- | --- | --- |
| Africa | 810 | 50 |
| Latin America | 2100 | 64 |
| N. Europe | 10380 | 74 |
| S. Europe | 5270 | 72 |
| Oceania | 8700 | 70 |
| N. America | 12980 | 74 |
| Asia | 970 | 58 |

205

Q. For both graphs answer the following:
1. Draw a line or curve that might represent the trend on the graph.
2. For the following GNP, what would be the life expectancy?
   a) $4000 b) $9000 c) $300
3. Why is there such an unequal distribution of energy and wealth?

Dr. E.F. Schumacher, in his book *Small Is Beautiful,* looks at the economics of the world in a revolutionary way, maintaining that the pursuit of progress and profit has led to gross economic inefficiency, environmental pollution and inhumane working conditions.

He talks about *the West engaging in a 'forward stampede' in its aim for 'unlimited economic growth' from 'limited resources'.* Discuss this statement.

It can often be very dangerous to make interpretations based on sets of figures without any context.

Draw a scattergram for the following two tables.

PERCENTAGE OF POPULATION WITH ACCESS TO SAFE WATER

| COUNTRY | % | COUNTRY | % |
|---|---|---|---|
| Haiti | 12 | Philippines | 55 |
| Zaire | 18 | Mexico | 59 |
| Thailand | 23 | Argentina | 60 |
| India | 41 | Bangladesh | 68 |
| Guatemala | 42 | Jamaica | 82 |
| El Salvador | 48 | Trinidad & Tobago | 89 |
| Peru | 49 | Spain | 100 |
| Ghana | 50 | United Kingdom | 100 |
| World Development Report, World Bank 1983 | | | |

DEATHS PER 1,000 OF INFANTS AGED 0-1, SELECTED COUNTRIES

| COUNTRY | 1982 | COUNTRY | 1982 |
|---|---|---|---|
| Zaire | 106 | Argentina | 44 |
| Haiti | 110 | El Salvador | 72 |
| India | 94 | Mexico | 53 |
| Bangladesh | 133 | Trinidad & Tobago | 26 |
| Guatemala | 66 | Thailand | 51 |
| Philippines | 51 | Jamaica | 10 |
| Peru | 83 | United Kingdom | 11 |
| Ghana | 86 | Spain | 10 |

What deductions can you make?

## Presenting Statistics

The two tables below are both concerned with gas emissions. Which table shows the truth more fairly?

| National greenhouse gas emissions World Resources Institute figures for 187 | | | |
| --- | --- | --- | --- |
| Rank | Country | Total (mitonnes) | % of total |
| 1 | United States | 1000 | 17.6 |
| 2 | USSR | 690 | 12.0 |
| 3 | Brazil | 610 | 10.5 |
| 4 | China | 380 | 6.6 |
| 5 | India | 230 | 3.9 |
| 6 | Japan | 220 | 3.9 |
| 7 | West Germany | 160 | 2.8 |
| 8 | United Kingdom | 150 | 2.7 |
| 9 | Indonesia | 140 | 2.4 |
| 10 | France | 120 | 2.1 |
| 11 | Italy | 120 | 2.1 |
| 12 | Canada | 120 | 2.0 |
| 13 | Mexico | 78 | 1.4 |
| 14 | Burma | 77 | 1.3 |
| 15 | Poland | 76 | 1.3 |
| 16 | Spain | 73 | 1.3 |
| 17 | Columbia | 69 | 1.2 |
| 18 | Thailand | 67 | 1.2 |
| 19 | Australia | 63 | 1.1 |
| 20 | East Germany | 62 | 1.1 |
| 21 | Nigeria | 53 | 0.9 |
| 22 | South Africa | 47 | 0.8 |
| 23 | Ivory Coast | 47 | 0.8 |
| 24 | Netherlands | 43 | 0.7 |
| 25 | Saudi Arabia | 42 | 0.7 |

| Per capita greenhouse gas emissions (using WRI 1987 population figures) and per capita GNP (World Bank 1987 figures) | | | |
| --- | --- | --- | --- |
| Rank | Country | National per cap g-gas contribs 1987 (mitonnes) | National per cap GNP 1987 ($) |
| 1 | Canada | 4.52 | 15160 |
| 2 | Ivory Coast | 4.15 | 740 |
| 3 | Brazil | 4.13 | 2020 |
| 4 | United States | 4.06 | 18530 |
| 5 | Australia | 3.81 | 11100 |
| 6 | East Germany | 3.66 | — |
| 7 | Saudi Arabia | 3.11 | 6200 |
| 8 | Netherlands | 2.92 | 11860 |
| 9 | United Kingdom | 2.66 | 10420 |
| 10 | West Germany | 2.65 | 14400 |
| 11 | USSR | 2.38 | — |
| 12 | Columbia | 2.21 | 1240 |
| 13 | France | 2.16 | 12790 |
| 14 | Italy | 2.09 | 10350 |
| 15 | Poland | 1.98 | 1930 |
| 16 | Burma | 1.92 | — |
| 17 | Spain | 1.84 | 6010 |
| 18 | Japan | 1.78 | 15760 |
| 19 | South Africa | 1.31 | 1890 |
| 20 | Thailand | 1.22 | 850 |
| 21 | Mexico | 0.89 | 1830 |
| 22 | Indonesia | 0.78 | 450 |
| 23 | China | 0.34 | 290 |
| 24 | India | 0.28 | 300 |

Provided the figures are correct, both sets of course are 'true'. But they give different messages. Students could examine the tables and consider what they reveal about ways of reducing world gas emissions.

The article which includes these tables favours the second table as fairer, because it shows more clearly the per capita emission. The First world consumer generates on average three tonnes of these omissions per annum, compared with the Third world consumer's 0.7 tonnes, and also links emissions with the ability to pay for the changes needed to reduce the damage to our planet.

## The Egg Machine

## INTRODUCTION

Almost half a billion animals are killed for food each year in Britain. Have you ever thought how these animals are killed, or how they are kept beforehand? It may not make pleasant reading, but if it is painful for you to think about, imagine how painful it is for the animals.

## THE EGG MACHINE

Kept in dismal buildings, in row after row of wire cages, the battery hen will never see daylight and can hardly move. Five hens are crammed in a tiny cage measuring only 18 x 20 inches, so that no hen can spread her wings or even turn round freely.

Her feet are deformed by the sloping wire mesh floor. Even eating causes her pain as she rubs away her feathers and skin in attempts to reach an automated feeder. The cramped and filthy conditions leave her prey to all kinds of disease.

Overcrowding and intense boredom lead to aggression. She could be continually pecked by stronger hens, perhaps to her death. This would never have happened in her natural environment.

The farmers' answer to this is not to allow the hens more room, but to hack off the end of their beaks when still fluffy chicks.

A single worker may mutilate 1000 or more birds in a day. In 1964 a government welfare body stated that this causes 'severe pain', and more recently another recommended that the whole battery system be abolished —yet 9 out of 10 eggs sold today come from hens kept like this.

Let us do some work on the space that 5 hens have to live in.
a)  Draw out the space
b)  Use another piece of paper to draw a 'plan' of a hen. Make 'plans' for 5 hens. How can you best fit them into the space? Draw the best arrangement for the hens.
c)  Calculate the area of the space.
d)  Can you find other rectangles which have the *same area* but less perimeter (costing less for cages)? Now consider feeding — can the chickens take turns at feeding?
e)  Can you find other rectangles which have the *same perimeter* and bigger areas?
f)  If you were a battery hen farmer, would you want to change the shape of the cage?
g)  If you were a chicken, would you want the farmer to do anything about the size and space of the cage?

## Relevant technology
### Watering the desert
Q.  A straight boom 300m long moves with one end fixed beside a borehole and the other travelling in a circle, spraying water onto plants growing in the North Libyan desert. The boom is supported by wheels placed at 100m, 200m and 300m from the end beside the borehole.
a)  If the speed of the end of the boom is $v$ ms$^{-1}$ (velocity in metres per second), what are the speeds of the other wheels?
b)  If good spraying requires equal volumes of water on equal areas of land, write down the relationship between $S$ m$^3$ (the volume of water required from a particular nozzle) and $d$ m (the distance of the nozzle from the end near the borehole).
c)  Use your result to obtain a formula for the total volume of water V m$^3$s$^{-1}$, taken from the borehole.

## Economies of scale
Sometimes bigger means better, sometimes not. There are often 'trade-offs' between large and small scale operations. A sugar plantation gains from having large scale operations because the costs of throughput are proportional to the volume being processed, once fixed costs have been paid. However, the costs of transporting the sugar from the growing areas to the process factory are proportional to the distance transported.

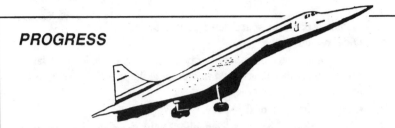

## PROGRESS

**A technological revolution**
This piece of technology knocked 200 minutes off the time it took to transport 100 people from London to New York. It has sonic boom. It costs $40,000,000.

Q.   Consider the total costs of a sugar factory where the processing machinery is at the centre of a circular plantation.

**Another technological revolution**

This piece of technology knocked 14 hours off the time it took to transport a day's supply of clean water for a village from the well. It has no sonic boom. It costs $42.

Write down a formula relating C (total costs of the sugar factory) with r (the radius of the circular growing area). Can you draw conclusions on minimising costs?

## Locust attacks on trees.

Q. Certain trees take 25 years to reach maturity. Locusts can attack and destroy trees. If the probability in any one year that a tree dies as a result of a severe locust attack is 0.01, what is the probability of a tree surviving to maturity?

## Keeping the pumps going

Q. A 1kW pump costs £1400, a 2kW pump cost £2500. Water which supplies a crop requires 4kW power which can be obtained from 2 2kW pumps or 4 1kW pumps. The probability that any one pump will work without failure for any year is 90%. Spares may be bought. The planters require that failure in the pumping system each year should be less than 10%. For minimum cost, would you recommend buying 1kW or 2kW pumps?

## Energy from sun

The sun shines with intensity of 1kWm2 on a horizontal panel at the Equator. The panel, which contains photo-voltaic cells, changes radiated energy into electrical energy at 10% efficiency.

Q.   Write down an expression for the electrical energy produced by the panel at different times during a 12-hour day.

A.   Calculate the total amount of energy produced by the panel during the 12 hours.

Additionally, some light is reflected from the panel depending on the angle of the sun with the panel. If l is the fraction of light getting through the glass, then l = cos q (the angle of the sun with the vertical).

B.   Calculate the total energy produced in a 12-hour day.

C.   If the panel could now be moved so that it always pointed directly at the sun, what would be the total energy obtained?

---

**Our air and ground-water are fouled by the burning of fossil fuel in electricity generating stations, in cars, factories and homes. Sulphur dioxide and nitrogen oxide are released into the atmosphere to be washed back down in rain — with nasty consequences for the environment. And nuclear-powered energy is no alternative as the Chernobyl and Three Mile Island accidents have demonstrated.**

**Ultimately we must use less energy to save nature and ourselves.**

---

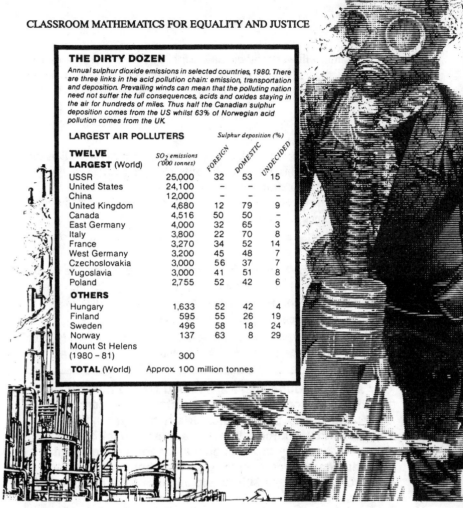

**THE DIRTY DOZEN**

Annual sulphur dioxide emissions in selected countries, 1980. There are three links in the acid pollution chain: emission, transportation and deposition. Prevailing winds can mean that the polluting nation need not suffer the full consequences, acids and oxides staying in the air for hundreds of miles. Thus half the Canadian sulphur deposition comes from the US whilst 63% of Norwegian acid pollution comes from the UK.

LARGEST AIR POLLUTERS — Sulphur deposition (%)

| TWELVE LARGEST (World) | $SO_2$ emissions ('000 tonnes) | FOREIGN | DOMESTIC | UNDECIDED |
|---|---|---|---|---|
| USSR | 25,000 | 32 | 53 | 15 |
| United States | 24,100 | – | – | – |
| China | 12,000 | – | – | – |
| United Kingdom | 4,680 | 12 | 79 | 9 |
| Canada | 4,516 | 50 | 50 | – |
| East Germany | 4,000 | 32 | 65 | 3 |
| Italy | 3,800 | 22 | 70 | 8 |
| France | 3,270 | 34 | 52 | 14 |
| West Germany | 3,200 | 45 | 48 | 7 |
| Czechoslovakia | 3,000 | 56 | 37 | 7 |
| Yugoslavia | 3,000 | 41 | 51 | 8 |
| Poland | 2,755 | 52 | 42 | 6 |
| **OTHERS** | | | | |
| Hungary | 1,633 | 52 | 42 | 4 |
| Finland | 595 | 55 | 26 | 19 |
| Sweden | 496 | 58 | 18 | 24 |
| Norway | 137 | 63 | 8 | 29 |
| Mount St Helens (1980–81) | 300 | | | |

**TOTAL** (World)    Approx. 100 million tonnes

## Wind Power

The power obtainable from a windmill is proportional to the cube of the speed of the wind.

Q. Write down the relationship relating P (kW) with v (ms$^{-1}$)

For wind speeds less than 3 ms$^{-1}$ there is no power; for wind speeds greater than 30 ms$^{-1}$, a stabilizing mechanism operates, and at very high winds (say above 40 ms$^{-1}$) the windmill stops.

Q. Draw a sketch of the graph which illustrates power against wind speed.

The power obtained from one windmill is proportional to the area of the rotating blades (m$^2$) and to the cube of the wind speed (ms$^{-1}$).

212

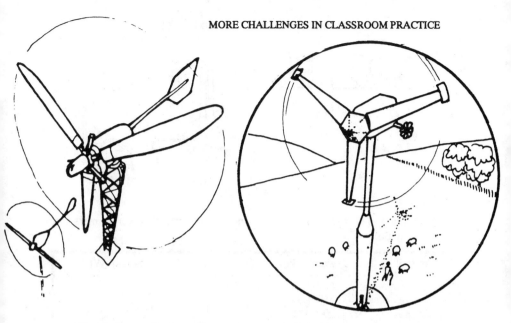

The blades are 5m long. For a windspeed of 10 ms-1 the power obtained is 10.3 kW.

Q. Calculate the power obtained for a wind speed of 17 ms-1.

## Cutting timber

Q. In many countries, timber exports bring in precious foreign exchange. The first figure shows how the cross-section of a log is trimmed to give the 'best' beam. The second figure shows a log trimmed for the 'stiffest' beam.

For each case calculate the percentage wastage of wood.

## Animal power

In many countries animals are used for raising water, grinding grain and many other heavy tasks. A human can work hard for short periods and can, if fit, maintain a power of 60W.

The table below gives typical weights of certain animals. Often animals will walk around a circular track at about 0.7 ms-1. At a rough estimate, an animal can exert a force of about one tenth of its own weight.

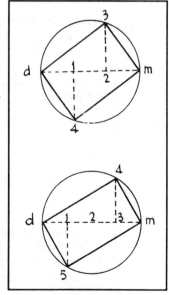

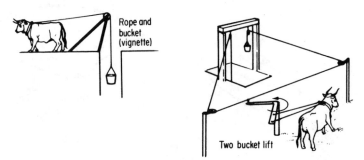

Q. Copy and complete the table to find out how much power animals can provide.

| Animal | weight (kg) | force (kg) | power (W) |
|--------|-------------|------------|-----------|
| Light horse | 400-700 | | |
| Heavy horse | 680-1200 | | |
| Donkey | 200-300 | | |
| Mule | 350-500 | | |
| Cow | 400-600 | | |
| Bullock | 500-900 | | |

Reduction of power in diesel engines (see p. 235 Longland)

Q. Draw a series of graphs on the same axes, plotting percentage reduction in power against temperature, keeping height above sea level constant for each curve.

*Table 7.4 Diesel engine reduction of power with altitude and temperature**

| Metres above sea level | Temperature (°C) | | | | | | |
|--------|------|------|------|------|------|------|------|
| | 15 | 20 | 25 | 30 | 35 | 40 | 45 |
| 500 | 1.9 | 2.8 | 3.7 | 4.6 | 5.5 | 6.4 | 7.3 |
| 1000 | 6.9 | 7.8 | 8.7 | 9.6 | 10.5 | 11.4 | 12.3 |
| 1500 | 11.9 | 12.8 | 13.7 | 14.6 | 15.5 | 16.4 | 17.3 |
| 2000 | 16.9 | 17.8 | 18.7 | 19.6 | 20.5 | 21.4 | 22.3 |
| 2500 | 21.9 | 22.8 | 23.7 | 24.6 | 25.5 | 26.4 | 27.3 |

* Percentage reduction of power for heights above sea level and temperatures above 15°C.

For continuous use, reduce the normal rating by 25%.

Now, on a different set of axes, hold temperature constant for each curve, and plot percentage reduction in power against height above sea level.

## Energy in the News

Q.

1. What is the average electricity bill of people living in Basingstoke?

2. Find an approximation for the total money collected by electricity companies each year from households with remote TV controls?

3. What is the extra cost for leaving a TV switched on a remote control overnight?

4. What do you understand by the 'greenhouse effect'?

5. What can you work out with your calculator from the information given in this newspaper cutting?

---

## Remote TV controls blamed for £12m waste of electricity

James Erlichman, Consumer affairs Correspondent

Enough electricity to light Basingstoke is being wasted every night by people too lazy to switch off their remote control televisions at the main.

A television turned off by remote control continues to use a quarter of normal power because it needs to be electrically awake to receive the next remote signal to switch back on.

There are 14 million remote control televisions in Britain. At least half are believed to be switched off by remote control every night. The total energy consumed overnight is 70 megawatts, the amount needed daily to supply electricity to a town of around 70,000 like Basingstoke, St. Albans or Methyr Tydfil, according to research published yesterday by Friends of the Earth.

The environmental pressure group calculates that the wasted energy costs £12 million a year and generates nearly 200,000 tonnes a year of extra carbon dioxide (the primary greenhouse effect gas) from power stations.

'People who can must start over Christmas by getting out of their seats and using the switch when they turn off the TV,' said FoE energy campaigner, Mr Simon Roberts. 'That way we stop this demanding and unnecessary pollution.'

*Guardian 22 Dec. 1989*

---

## Logarithmic scale — energy in transport

Students could attempt to draw this diagram on linear graph paper, but would soon realise the need for a logarithmic scale on the horizontal axis. But which graph (linear or horizontal) gives a true perspective on the information contained in the diagram? Students will need time to consider what the information tells them. (See Figure opposite)

## Pictorial representation — energy use

The figure in the diagram can be used by students to draw circles whose areas are proportional to energy use.

Diagram from *The Little Green Book* by the editors of *Vole*

---

### ENERGY

Nuclear power has so far made a small (if dramatic) contribution to energy requirements. There is widespread concern about the health hazards it presents to us and to future generations; about the threat of terrorists getting hold of material to make nuclear weapons; and the threats to civil liberties that such a security- sensitive operation will have (and is already having).

The most responsible energy policies are those which either use finite fossil fuels as economically as possible or else use non- finite renewable sources such as sun, wind and tide.

---

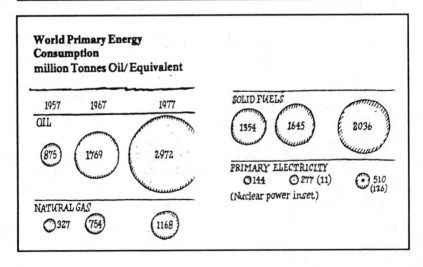

World Primary Energy
Consumption
million Tonnes Oil/Equivalent

| 1957 | 1967 | 1977 |

OIL

875    1769    2972

NATURAL GAS
327    754    1168

SOLID FUELS
1354    1645    2036

PRIMARY ELECTRICITY
144    277 (11)    510 (126)
(Nuclear power inset)

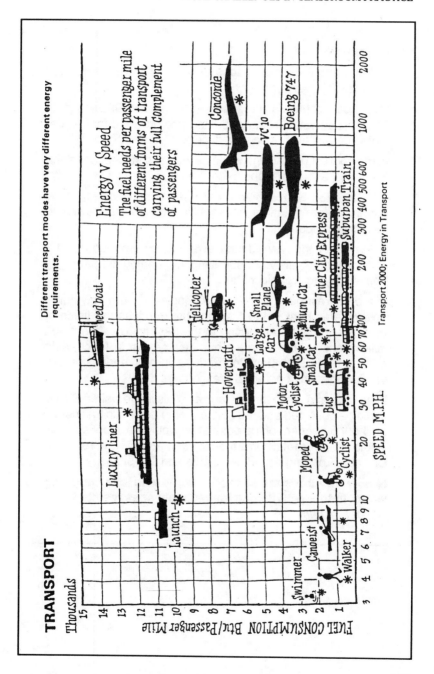

TRANSPORT

Different transport modes have very different energy requirements.

Energy v Speed

The fuel needs per passenger mile of different forms of transport carrying their full complement of passengers

Transport 2000; Energy in Transport

# ENERGY

In India about 68 million tons of cow dung are burnt (very inefficiently) every year.

30 per cent of India's energy comes from wood. 95 per cent of Tanzania's comes from wood. Reliance on wood for fuel depletes forests and can cause deserts.

In the poorest parts of the world as much as 90 per cent of the fuel is in the form of wood or animal dung.

In 1976, 25,000 excrement converters (making biogas by anaerobic fermentation) were sold in India. There are said to be 2 million operating.

In May 1977 the New China News Agency reported that 4.3 million biogas units were operating, generating methane gas from decaying organic matter.

In the poorest parts of the world people will burn cow dung. This creates heat in the fireplace but deprives the fields of valuable nutrients. According to the FAO figures, about 400 million tons of cow dung are burnt every year in Africa, Asia and the Near East. Each ton of dung burned means the loss of 50 kilograms of potential grain output.

If the methane in the farts of farm animals in the United States could be collected and redistributed, the domestic fuel needs of about 8 per cent of the population would be supplied. This would equal the total home fuel requirements of New York City, Chicago, Los Angeles, Philadelphia and Detroit.

**I know why there are so many people who love chopping wood. In this activity one immediately sees result.**
*Albert Einstein*

The chart is not as complicated as it looks. It shows the use and misuse we make of various forms of fuel.

On the left are inputs. On the right and at the bottom are outputs.

If you look at the input of petroleum, for example, you will see how it goes (after refining) into power stations to make electricity, part goes to transport, part for domestic use, and so on.

More than a quarter of the energy potential available in primary fuels wasted, mostly by turning coal into electricity. The chart does not account for the further waste that occurs after the electricity has been delivered to the user.

**Flow of Energy in UK, 1972**

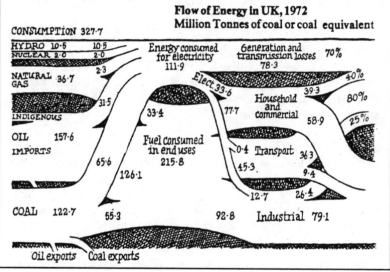

**Simulation**

Maths teachers seldom take time to demonstrate to students that much of what is taught in maths lessons simulates the real world.

Trigonometry, applied algebra, probability and arithmetic problems are all examples of simulation, yet there is usually little discussion on this concept: how precise it is and how it can be extended to other situations. How are computers used for testing possible solutions to real problems? This link to reality can be interesting and motivating for our students and ourselves.

Recently computer programmes which use mathematical simulations have proliferated. The context of the simulation reflects cultural values. Some students are addicted to computer games which are horrifically violent. Some games, however, have immense educational value. The SMP computer simulation *Alarmco,* provide groups of students with opportunities maximise profit in a business situation. Students need programmes which look at aid and trade relations; debts of the superpowers and developing countries; causes of famine; stocks and shares of the commodity market such as tea, beef, cocoa, rice, jute, wheat, sugar and so on.

Susan George's book: *How the other half dies* is a powerful resource for an alternative perspective.

It is important that students are presented with simulation which doesn't only seek to promote competition, greed and injustice. Some simulation can be transferred to computers but those given here are in game form and use dice to simulate the probabilities in society.

## Probability: simulation using dice:-

Before working on this simulation, students should already have been introduced to probability. They will need copies of the duplicated simulation chart, 1-6 dice and 1-20 dice. The aim of the exercise is to show how a dice game can simulate an aspect of life in the UK.

## Teachers' notes:

The 1-20 dice are required because normal 1-6 dice cannot reflect real life probabilities and statistics sensitively. The probabilities for working/unemployment and type of work are based on real life published statistics. However, in order to give everyone a fair 'starting chance', the 1-6 dice are used to provide equal chances for pupils to be cast as Afro-Caribbean, white, Asian, female or male. The chart could be based on real life figures.

> **Method :**Pupils work in pairs. Each pair takes turns in working through the chart, using the dice. Each time they get to a final arrow, they write down a tally mark. They should be given enough time to complete 20 to 30 tally marks. The simulation is halted and frequencies written down. Frequencies may be totalled. The numbers in the frequency column are intended to help obtain form results.

A brief discussion about the results might follow, particularly those concerning unemployment and professional workers, and also whether a simulation using dice can reflect life. For example: Does a simulation like this suggest that life is 'mechanistic' for those who have to face structural discrimination?

220

Does this kind of simulation rule out the possibility of an individual overcoming the injustices of society him/herself?

**Further work:** More complex probabilities come into play if the following figures are included.

Students would be asked to interpret these figures using the 1-20 dice.

| Housing — council allocation to pre 1919 housing stock | | | |
|---|---|---|---|
| | Flats | Houses | % of the total |
| White | 27 | 39 | 26.6 |
| Afro-Caribbean | 54 | 9 | 46.8 |
| Asian | 54 | 11 | 61.7 |

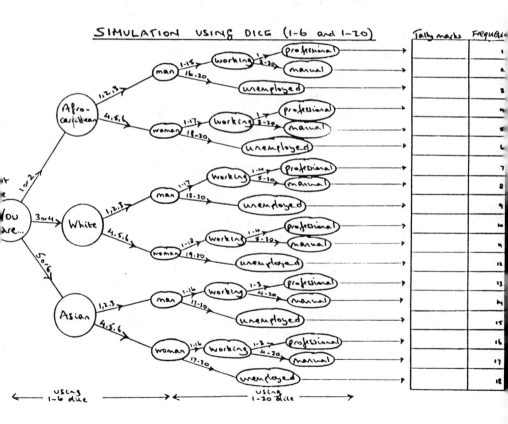

# THIS IS MY LIFE : A game of chance

This is a game of chance we devised to reflect the chances of employment etc. for youngsters living in Birmingham and surrounding area. We have used it successfully with students ranging from third year to GCSE, from predominantly white schools to majority black.

**Teachers' notes:**

The 'Chance' and 'Out and about' cards can be changed either by you or your students after the game has been tried two or three times. If you feel that the game should be amended, please do so and let us know of the amendments.

There should also be a discussion among each group of players at the end of a game. Do make sure to have at least 10 minutes free at the end of the lesson for this purpose. Students could either complete questionnaires or discuss whether or not the game reflects real life.

Here are some questions:

1. Did you enjoy the game?
2. Do you think there are similar problems in real life?
3. Are there more, less or simply different opportunities in rural areas and in inner cities? If so, what sort?
4. Are the situations of black people fairly represented in the game?
5. Can you think of other situations that can be simulated using mathematics? Make a list and see if you can devise some simulations.

# THIS IS MY LIFE

Up to four players can play

# Setting up the game

* Put Chance cards and 'Out and about' cards on board.
* Give paper, pencil and £100 to each player: the £100 can be a piece of paper with £100 written on it. Transactions are by simple techniques of subtraction and addition only.
* Each player chooses a 'YOU ARE' card and places their counter on START.

## PLAY

- Take turns with dice.
- Each time you pass *Pay Day,* add on or take off money.
- Each player keeps score of your money, and what happens to you on each turn.
- If you run out of money, you can give yourself £100, but you must pay £20, each time they pass START, until you've paid back the £100.
- Stop when you want to or when everybody has run out of money.

JAIL
If you land here, loose your job and miss two goes.

DISCO ONLY £2. You don't have to go.

OUT AND ABOUT

CHANCE ???

????? ?????? (CHANCE)

HOUSE FOR SALE. £1000 DEPOSIT. Buy if you wish.

YOU MUST PAY. WHEN YOU PASS. RENT : £30. OR MORTGAGE : £25.

OUT AND ABOUT

GO SHOPPING. YOU CAN BUY. CLOTHES: £40. SOUND SYSTEM: £90.

CHANCE ???

CHANCE

CHANCE

????? ??????

THIS IS MY LIFE

OUT AND ABOUT

OUT AND ABOUT

N.B.C. CONCERT GO IF YOU WANT. EMPLOYED £10. UNEMPLOYED £7.

CHANCE ???

WATER BILLS you must pay £30.00

SUMMER HOLIDAY Package trip to France for £150 if you wish.

CAR FOR SALE £300. BUY IF YOU WANT. £30.

YOU NEED FOOD. YOU MUST PAY. £30.

JUMBLE SALE.
Old Record Player - £3.00
Old Clothes - £2.00
Buy if you need.

NO CAR. PAY £4.00 for bus fares.

CHANCE ???

OUT AND ABOUT

START

PAY DAY. Each time you pass, collect employed-£100 unemployed-£50.

| | | |
|---|---|---|
| **OUT AND ABOUT**<br>MUGGERS ON THE STREET<br>INNER CITY: THROW 1, 2, 3 TO ESCAPE<br>COUNTRY: THROW 1, 2, 3, 4 TO ESCAPE<br>If you are mugged, the thieves take half your money. | **OUT AND ABOUT**<br>WIN RAFFLE<br>FREE DINNER FOR 2 | **OUT AND ABOUT**<br>A WHITE SHOUTS AT YOU, 'GO HOME YOU BLACK BASTARD' |
| **OUT AND ABOUT**<br>POLICE CATCH YOU ON THE STREETS AT NIGHT<br>    1  2  3  4  5  6<br>Black NC F  F  J  J  J<br>White NC NC F  F  J  J<br>NC = no charge.<br>F = £50 disturbance.<br>J = jail, resisting arrest. | **OUT AND ABOUT**<br>DO YOU OWN A HOUSE?<br>VALUE OF PROPERTY RISES.<br>COLLECT £500. | **OUT AND ABOUT**<br>DO YOU HAVE A CAR?<br>PAY £20 PETROL AND £15 SPEEDING FINES |
| **OUT AND ABOUT**<br>DO YOU WANT TO JOIN A STREET GANG?<br>INNER CITY: 1, 2, 3, TO JOIN<br>COUNTRY: 1, 2, TO JOIN.<br>IF YOU HAVE JOINED, PAY £60 FINE FOR DAMAGE TO PROPERTY. | **OUT AND ABOUT**<br>DRUNK.<br>PAY £20. | **OUT AND ABOUT**<br>CHILDREN NEED SCHOOL UNIFORMS.<br>PAY £50. |
| **OUT AND ABOUT**<br>YOU AND YOUR FRIENDS SHARE THE COST OF A PARTY.<br>YOU MUST PAY £20. | **OUT AND ABOUT**<br>CHEAP FLIGHTS TO JAMAICA AND DACCA.<br>PAY £100 IF YOU WANT A HOLIDAY | **OUT AND ABOUT**<br>WIN CROSSWORD COMPETITION<br>COLLECT £10.00 |
| **CHANCE**<br>BURGLERS IN YOUR HOUSE. THEY BREAK YOUR SOUND SYSTEM AND EAT YOUR FOOD. IF YOU HAVE NO INSURANCE, YOU MUST PAY £30 FOR FOOD. | **CHANCE**<br>UNEMPLOYED.<br>INNER CITY: THROW 1, 2 FOR A JOB.<br>COUNTRY: THROW 1, 2, 3, 4 FOR A JOB. | **OUT AND ABOUT**<br>YOU CAN BUY HOUSE INSURANCE IF YOU WANT.<br>£50 COUNTRY<br>£60. INNER CITY |
| **CHANCE**<br>RELATIVE DIES AND LEAVES YOU £50. | **CHANCE**<br>YOU SPILL TEA ON YOUR BEST CLOTHES. YOU MUST BUY SOME MORE AS SOON AS YOU CAN. | **CHANCE**<br>EMPLOYED?<br>YOUR COMPANY MUST LAY OFF WORKERS. TO KEEP YOUR JOB, YOU NEED TO TROW:<br>INNER CITY: 5, 6.<br>COUNTRY: 4, 5, 6. |

| | |
|---|---|
| YOU ARE<br>WHITE,<br>UNEMPLOYED,<br>LIVING IN<br>INNER CITY. | YOU ARE<br>BLACK,<br>UNEMPLOYED,<br>LIVING IN<br>INNER CITY. |
| YOU ARE<br>WHITE,<br>WORKING AND LIVING<br>IN THE COUNTRY. | YOU ARE<br>BLACK,<br>WORKING AND LIVING<br>IN THE COUNTRY. |
| CHANCE<br>UNEMPLOYED?<br>SPEND £10 ON BUS FARES AND STAMPS TRYING<br>TO FIND WORK. | CHANCE<br>UNEMPLOYED?<br>CHARITY GIVES YOU £5 AS CHRISTMAS PRESENT. |
| CHANCE<br>EMPLOYED?<br>PROMOTION<br>GET £200 BONUS. | CHANCE<br>YOUR SOUND SYSTEM BLOWS UP.<br>YOU HAVE NO MUSIC AT HOME. |
| CHANCE<br>WORKING<br>INNER CITY: THROW 1, 2, 3, TO KEEP A JOB<br>COUNTRY: THROW 1, 2, 3, 4, 5 TO KEEP JOB | CHANCE<br>UNEMPLOYED<br>EARN £10 ON PART TIME WORK. |
| CHANCE<br>UNEMPLOYED?<br>BLACK: THROW 1, 2, FOR A JOB.<br>WHITE: THROW 1, 2, 3, 4 FOR A JOB. | CHANCE<br>UNEMPLOYED?<br>SPEND £20 ON NEW CLOTHES FOR AN<br>INTERVIEW FOR A JOB. |

# CHAPTER 9

# Project Work

> *462: We also wish to draw attention to an extract from one of the submissions which has been made to us.*
>
> *Mathematics lessons in secondary schools are very often not about anything. You collect like terms, or learn the law of indices, with no perception of why anyone needs to do such things. As a result of this, school mathematics contains very little incidental information. A French lesson might well contain incidental information about France... but in mathematics, incidental information which one might expect (current exchange and interest rates; the rules and scoring systems of games, social statistics) is rarely there, because most teachers in no way see this as a part of their responsibility when teaching maths.*
> Mathematics Counts *(Cockroft 1982)*

Projects outlined briefly in this chapter offer scope to transfer mathematical skills learnt in a narrow, abstract, problem-solving approach to bigger, real-life investigations. Traditionally the majority of problems in a problem-solving approach are set by the teacher, their content carefully chosen to suit the particular part of the mathematical syllabus being covered. As described in *Pupil Projects* (1980) produced by The Mathematical Association, projects are often *chosen problems* contextualised in the immediate environment. The correct solution is known to the teacher. It is worked from the given data in the problem, using predetermined mathematical skills, usually in a given amount of time. Assessment of these *closed* problem-solving situtations is easy for the teacher. However, there is very little opportunity for the pupil to make decisions, to explore new ideas, to transfer mathematical skills to other areas of learning in a challenging way and to extend his/her knowledge of how maths is used by industry, economists, scientists and so on.

Project work based on open problems should extend student-centred, cross-curricular learning to the whole of the curriculum. A carefully chosen *open* project will maximise each pupil's involvement and endorse more than just mathematical skills. To allow issues of equality and justice to be raised, projects should be chosen against a predetermined set of criteria, given later in this chapter. Pupils are encouraged to choose global themes such as acid rain or the greenhouse effect, thereby building incidental learning into their mathematics. Solutions are not known at the beginning of an open project. Surprises will emerge, giving pupils ownership of their work and this may well motivate further investigations.

Planning and assessing such projects will require an open mind and considerable research. Trial and preparation by the teacher before a project begins will determine its success or failure. Pupils will need a good deal of guidance to ensure that mathematical skills are not being ignored for the sake of communication and cross-curricular skills. Teachers will have to find resources that provide accurate as well as interesting information. Initially teachers may say 'they aren't doing real maths' or 'we/they don't have enough resources' or 'what can we change anyway?'... but once they get used to doing broader investigation as part of their courses, pupils may involve teachers from other subject areas, take responsibility for their own research, and analyse information critically — with interesting results. Some useful lessons may be learnt from the experience of teachers in the primary sector. While secondary teachers rarely consider inter-departmental projects as a way of covering sections of the syllabus, primary school pupils are regularly exposed to a planned experience of whole-school, cross- curricular themes/topics, with features such as displays in the classroom and school foyer, quizzes and competitions. Secondary school timetables are not designed for teachers to meet and plan collaboratively; this will become very apparent now as the National Curriculum requires cross-curricular themes to be built into curriculum planning (3.8 and 3.9 from *Policy to Practice,* DES 1989).

In GCSE, projects consist of extended pieces of work which take up about 20% of the time spent on maths during these two years (with considerable variations between different examination boards). Whatever the percentage of continous assessment, well- planned projects will:

- enhance cross-curricular work (e.g. IT; Citizenship, Environmental Studies)

- permit greater pupil involvement and responsibility, so that pupils can build on their strengths without the teacher's constant talk or doing endless sums from textbooks.

- make more maths available to pupils, allowing pupils to see what others in the class have done.

- allow for the consideration of criteria, selection of appropriate study skills, application, analysis, reflection, evaluation, self-assessment and communication.

- allow a greater variety of assessment styles.

- create opportunity for collaborative, cooperative work in mixed ability and mixed gender groups.

- provide opportunities for both qualitative and quantitive work in mathematics.

- allow for outcomes which can be useful to pupils, the school and the community.

- encourage the popularization of mathematics.

- be easily adaptable for pupils with special needs (see Mathematics in Schools Vol.15 No.1 P 6-9).

Project work on issues of racial equality and justice receives little support. Leading journals in the field rarely encourage selection of topics which will develop such debate; the Mathematical Association and the Association of Teachers of Mathematics have both produced publications on projects and investigations that make no mention of social and controversial topics. Most of their ideas are based on pure maths. *Fifteen Starters for the Secondary Classroom* (A.T.M. 1973) for example, contains many good ideas but no real-life investigations which might appeal to less academic pupils or which might place mathematics in a global context. *Pupils' Projects: their use in secondary school* (M.A. 1980) gives a good introduction to the use of projects but the list of practical examples from the *G.C.E. Applicable Mathematics projects* (1980) has no societal content. *Sharing Mathematics with Parents: Planning School-Based Events* by The Mathematical Association is intended to encourage parental involvement but the whole exercise is concerned to advise parents on the delivery and organisation of school mathematics, offering little scope for parents to show how *they* use mathematics in their lives.

Encouraging only abstract projects may damage achievement, as pupils who are low attainers in maths will be further disaffected. Valuable opportunities may be missed, for example, by disregarding pupils who are not 'very able' at classroom maths but help out at the market stalls of families and friends. The opportunity is denied for them to show their skills in mental mathematics, decomposing numbers then putting them together, developed in contexualised situations full of meaning for the pupils concerned and demanding accuracy. This would be equally true for youngsters working in a market place in Milton Keynes or boys shining shoes in the streets of Delhi. An elaborate project on how teenagers around the world earn money could highlight how *The Rights Of The Child — UN Declaration,* 1959, works out in practice.

## Variety in project work

| | | |
|---|---|---|
| open-ended | — | closed |
| long | — | short |
| teacher directed | — | greater student control |
| for self | — | for the class, school or community |
| specific maths content | — | open |
| competitive | — | cooperative |
| skill-based | — | content-based |
| abstract | — | real world |
| one-off preject | — | built into maths |
| one-off project | — | scheme of work |

| | | |
|---|---|---|
| working on own | — in small group — | in whole class |
| not assessed | — self assessed — | teacher assessed |

aimed at making things happen (change)
using computers
using cross-curricular ideas
linking with other departments
practicals, students all doing same or circus rotation
using games
creating a display, working in folders,
exercise books, video, tape recorders, on
walls (mural), playground
using school and other libraries,
other outside resources
involving outside agencies, visits, speakers
parents, community groups

# Criteria for planning projects to raise issues of equality and justice in the maths classroom.

- Set out clear aims/objectives/approach at the start.

- Are you simply adding cultural content or are you seeking to equalize opportunities with specific issues of gender, race or class? Is it a skills or content based approach?

- Allow time for discussion on the moral issues raised: e.g. defence, GNP. Feelings will be touched, allow time to draw out and encourage personal opinions and sensitivities; open discussion is essential.

- Pupils must feel free to express views both in discussion and in written work. There must also be opportunities for black pupils, girls, and pupils with special needs to develop their own ideas without feeling embarrassed, intimidated or isolated. The work must at some level be valid to all pupils.

- Allow for pupils to engage in debate on possible solutions, encouraging collective decisions while valuing individual contributions.

- Topics chosen must have sufficient mathematical content and the opportunity to enhance mathematical skills.

- Integrate an appropriate range of assessment techniques into the planning to allow credit for a variety of skills being used and developed. Encourage pupils to see how certain actions, decisions, life styles affect the lives of others.

Such ideas are often new to maths teachers but advice and support are often inadequate. Teachers of history, geography, social studies have been engaged in teaching politically controversial and sensitive issues for years.

Projects must be programmed into the department scheme of work as well as into School Development Plans, so avoiding duplication. Collaborative planning and teaching produces a coherent understanding of the issues being raised, empowering and giving confidence to each member of staff to deal with any racist or sexist behaviour that might arise during the project. This chapter outlines some ideas for project work, short or long term, suitable for upper Primary and Secondary schools.

# Race and class issues will develop on and progress a spiral curriculum as follows (year stages are very approximate):

*Seeking solutions* — *Simulation and role play games;*
Writing to a local MP, supermarket, Minister,
Friends of the Earth, War on Want, Oxfam etc.

*Statistics* for unemployment, discrimination in housing etc, exploitation of young girls/children worldwide                    Year 11

Prejudice — apartheid — slavery — colonisation

*Land distribution and ownership*
How much land do black people, women and workers own?
Substainance and cash crops.
Role of multinationals.
Role of 'Education' in challenging and removing inequalities?    Year 10

*Sexual and racial segregation*
The population question? How much control do                     Year 9
women have over their own sexuality?
Institutional racism and sexism?                                 Year 8
Access to education, good food and healthcare?

*What is the 'class system'?* How is it created?                 Year 7
Why do living standards vary so much?
Surveys of living standards.

Awareness of the importance of Maths, English, Science as subjects.  Year 6
Recognition of racist and sexist bias in the curriculum.
Understanding terms: Third world — race — racism
Minorities — Blacks — Pakis — Immigrants.                        Year 6
Racist and sexist words and jokes in the media.

*Name-calling* in school, street, home surroundings             Year 5
How people live. Who has the best housing, the best jobs?
Where do our food, clothes, energy supplies etc. come from?     Year 4
An awareness of parental and teacher attitudes.

Celebrating Diwali, Id, —
Learn different ways of dressing, of eating, of praying —
Recognising a variety of cultural and religious patterns.        Year 3
How is this variety valued by society?
Awareness of own national community.                             Year 3

Awareness of variety of personalities in the class.
Co- operation or competition.

An awareness of own school community and school resources.        Year 2
Does it differ from a neighbouring school? How and why?
In-depth awareness of classmates — variety of backgrounds
An awareness of own town, village, city community —              Year 1
Rich, well-off, poor, white, black, mixed?

# MEASURING

Measure lengths, weights, volumes and time using material from a range of cultural backgrounds, past and present using traditional as well as modern methods, imperial and metric of measuring. Local museums, jumble sales, antique shops and attics in older properties may provide resources.

It is easy to provide differentiated tasks in measuring.

* How heavy is a piece of paper?
  How many ways can you think of estimating the volume of a piece of paper?
  How many grains of rice in a kilogram? How many potatoes in a Kg?

Sundials, stopwatches, pendulums, candle clocks, water-drip clocks, weights and measures — all have a cultural perspective. One class refused to believe that the teacher had not secretly arranged for the sundial to be moved during one lesson — it took some time to convince the year seven pupils that it was the sun that was moving!

# PACKAGING

This project looks at the cost of packaging to the consumer and the environment and the creation of designs which use less paper. It provides opportunities for inventing different ways of packing. Pupils may have noticed practices in other countries. Here's a popular method of packaging made from old newspapers in India. (from an OXFAM booklet — see figure on page 234).

Pupils could draw nets for different packets, plan the layout of complete nets for mass production thereby saving card, consider the area of card used in relation to volume, thinking also about the attractiveness and appearance of the packets in the shop, tessellate 3-d objects such as Toblerone and chocolate 'pyramids' (see *Design for the Real World*, by Victor Papanek Paladin 1978).

# SHOPPING

## Price and origin of our fruit and vegetables

Shopping for the home brings everyday mathematics to life and stimulates discussion on the countries connected with our food. Homework could be to shop around for fresh fruit and vegatables, checking seasonal prices and availability, climatic variations compared to Britain etc. A large map of the world on the classroom wall is helpful.

# HOW TO MAKE A PAPER BAG ARTWORK

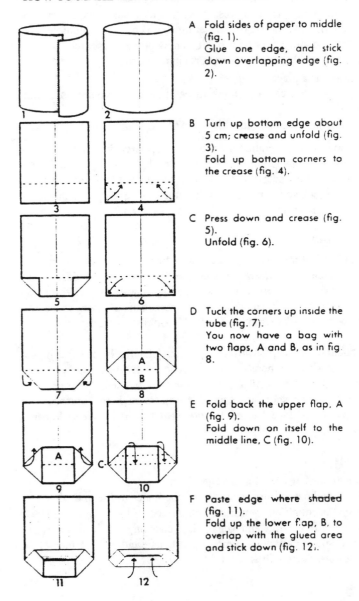

A   Fold sides of paper to middle
    (fig. 1).
    Glue one edge, and stick
    down overlapping edge (fig.
    2).

B   Turn up bottom edge about
    5 cm; crease and unfold (fig.
    3).
    Fold up bottom corners to
    the crease (fig. 4).

C   Press down and crease (fig.
    5).
    Unfold (fig. 6).

D   Tuck the corners up inside the
    tube (fig. 7).
    You now have a bag with
    two flaps, A and B, as in fig.
    8.

E   Fold back the upper flap, A
    (fig. 9).
    Fold down on itself to the
    middle line, C (fig. 10).

F   Paste edge where shaded
    (fig. 11).
    Fold up the lower flap, B, to
    overlap with the glued area
    and stick down (fig. 12).

# MATHS TRAIL

(Shape and space: Level 6, devising instructions for a computer to produce desired shapes and paths, using computer to generate 2D shapes, enlarging a shape by a whole number scale factor; Level 8 and 9)

Maths trails are an interesting way of teaching direction, mapwork, shapes and tessellations and the use of numbers in society (phone numbers, ages of houses, bus numbers and so on), as well as measuring and estimating (distances, heights for trigonometry or scale drawing). The trails can pass or visit churches, mosques, temples and a range of shops. Include some specific foci such as wheelchair ramps, slides in playgrounds, car parking facilities, heights of mosques and churches.

Trails can reveal informative patterns about living standards of local populations, links with local industry, employment patterns and so on. Here we give details of a school project in Birmingham which used the maths trail to look at progression and continuity concepts in racial equality and justice issues.

## Maths trail with year 6 pupils of Blakesley Hall Primary school, Birmingham

A predominently white school keen to introduce an awareness on issues of equality and justice, its staff noticed that where Yardley Green Road (the location of the school) changes to Green Lane, the nature of the area changes dramatically. The primary school in Green Lane has a predominantly Asian intake. The houses change gradually from country to town style; the shops are increasingly owned by Asians. There is considerable more dereliction in Green Lane.

Teachers were very keen for their pupils to experience this at first hand rather than in discussion. Maths Trail was designed to cover the entire length of Yardley Green Road plus Green Lane. Pupils who live in the immediate surroundings and know the road well helped to write a questionnaire. Pupils were asked to compare the prices in supermarkets and the smaller shops, note the language patterns on shop frontages, the state of housing and their impressions about the two schools, interviewing people along the way. The project was given an extra boost when BBC asked to come and film the trail. The outlines of mosques and churches were asked for exercises for learning angles (Level 4), understanding congruence of shapes, enlarging shapes using scale factors etc.

Yardley Green Road
Maths Trail

① What is the highest house number? ☐

② Give the numbers of the lamp posts.

③ Give the numbers of the telegraph poles.

④ Give your estimate of the distance between the telegraph poles. ☐

Measure the distance. ☐

By how much was your estimate wrong? ☐

⑤ Before the island how many houses are: —

Terraced? ☐

Semi-detached? ☐

Detached? ☐

Find the girth of the oak tree before the bridge by lamppost number 47. ☐

What shapes do you notice on the bridge?

What materials have been used to build the bridge?

Find the height of the wooden posts past the bridge. ☐

Find the circumference of these posts. ☐

How much taller are the concrete posts than the wooden posts? ☐

What is the name of the church? ☐

2) When was it built? ☐

3) How many years ago was this? ☐

4) How many services are there on Sunday? ☐

5) Give the times of the services. ☐

6) For how long does the parent and toddler group last? ☐

7) What colour is the danger sign on the substation by the church? ☐

8) What shape is it? ☐

9) What is the number on the hydrant outside house number 405. ☐

What is the number of the postal district on the Yardley Green Road sign? ☐

2) What are the signs on the island? (Sketch them)

3) How many windows in one door of the telephone box? ☐

4) Measure one row of glass to find the area. ☐

5) How much glass would you need to do the whole door? ☐

6) How many paces from the phone box to the next bus stop? ☐

7) How many times is the post collected? ☐

8) What is different about Saturday?

237

The children made a frieze of their photographs, drawings, questionnaires and the two roads were compared for:

- the variety of languages (and numbers) spoken and seen written on shop fronts;
- the variety of housing;
- price variation of food, petrol, clothes, housing, pharmeceuticals etc.
- landscaping

Pupils expressed their own feelings about race and class, e.g. 'There are lots of Pakis in Green Lane, Miss'; 'My dad never lets me come down Green Lane on my own Miss'; 'They are different to us, aren't they?' Such comments were not ridiculed. The children were encouraged to speak honesly about their source of information and what made them feel this way? Did they realise that such views are hurtful and racist?

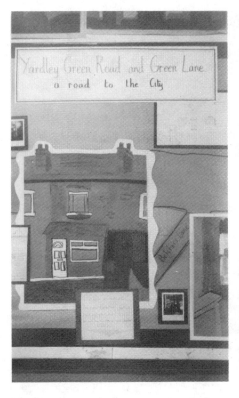

Marlborough School

?

Green Lane

First Avenue

Imperial Rd

Fourth Avenue

SOLD OUT

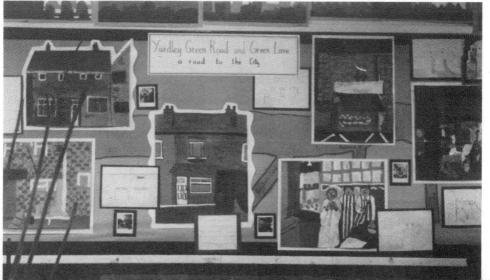

Yardley Green Road and Green Lane
a road to the City

Blakesley School's process-based approach to the curriculum is well suited to many of the projects that we have listed here for year 7 and 8 pupils. Portrayals on the media of violent confrontations with the police in urban disturbances, say, or the utter poverty and despair of famine can be upsetting, especially to younger children. If possible, teachers should begin from the local environment.

## Playground Games From Around The World

Many playground games involve basic rules of mathematics as well as calculating probabilities from simple to complex. Concepts such as even chances, good chances, 'fair' coins and dice, possible outcomes — more or less likely, combined events, subjective and objective estimates etc, are not easily understood by pupils of any age unless in the context of everyday situations. Transforming the playground into a large blackboard has become a very popular and practical solution to livening up and making real many such concepts. *Children's Games from Many Lands* by Nina Millen is a good source, though involving mathematics spanning only levels 1 to 3. Pupils could design some games for a local primary school play area for their GCSE coursework in Technology.

## CALENDARS FROM AROUND THE WORLD

Chinese, Hindu, Islamic, Jewish, Lunar do not fit readily into the National Curriculum. However, it is interesting identifying the difference. (From: *Mathematics Today* — India (February 1988)

## ENCHANTMENT OF MATHEMATICS

*(The entire spectrum of programmes of study for shape and space)*

Use ideas from chapters 5,6 and 7, to involve the whole school and create a panoramic display. Explore patterns in textiles — India, African and South American garments, carpets, shawls, baskets; in flowers, fruit, rock formations such as the Giants Causeway; in architecture, kites, floor designs, origami, calligraphy. Black paper on white, or vice versa, can show the symmetry of mosques, temples, churches against a skyline of the city.

# A CALENDAR TO THE YEAR 2000

Copy the lines, days, numbers and months from the diagrams. Use the razor blade to cut the heavy black lines.

Push the strips through.

To obtain your monthly calendar:

(a) put the Y under the year you want.
(i) Use B before Feb. 29.
(ii) Use A after Feb. 29.

(b) put the M under the month you want.

Can you discover how the calendar works?

Can you extend it past the year 2000?

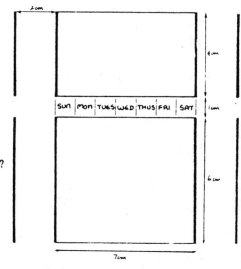

| | | | | | | |
|---|---|---|---|---|---|---|
| 79 | 80 ᴮ | 80 ᴬ | 81 | 82 | 83 | 84 ᴮ |
| 84 ᴬ | 85 | 86 | 87 | 88 ᴮ | 88 ᴬ | 89 |
| 90 | 91 | 92 ᴮ | 92 ᴬ | 93 | 94 | 95 |
| 96 ᴮ | 96 ᴬ | 97 | 98 | 99 | 2000 ᴮ | 2000 ᴬ |

| 2cm | | | | | 13 cm | | | | | | | 2 cm |
|---|---|---|---|---|---|---|---|---|---|---|---|---|
| 4cm | | | | | | Y | | | | | | |
| | JAN | | FEB | | SEP | APR | JAN | | FEB | | SEP | |
| | OCT | MAY | AUG | MAR | JUN | DEC | JUL | OCT | MAY | AUG | MAR | JUN | DEC |
| | | | nov | | | | | | nov | | | |

| 6cm | | | | | M 1 | 2 | 3 | 4 | 5 | 6 | 7 | |
|---|---|---|---|---|---|---|---|---|---|---|---|---|
| | 2 | 3 | 4 | 5 | 6 | 7 | 8 | 9 | 10 | 11 | 12 | 13 | 14 |
| | 9 | 10 | 11 | 12 | 13 | 14 | 15 | 16 | 17 | 18 | 19 | 20 | 21 |
| | 16 | 17 | 18 | 19 | 20 | 21 | 22 | 23 | 24 | 25 | 26 | 27 | 28 |
| | 23 | 24 | 25 | 26 | 27 | 28 | 29 | 30 | 31 | | | | |
| | 30 | 31 | | | | | | | | | | |

241

## Mathematics and Dance

In October '90, we had a unique opportunity to see an imaginative blend of theatre, movement and mathematics in Shobana Jeyasingh's Indian Dance Opera based on the beautiful mathematics of Ramanujan (See Chapter 5). With her permission, we have reproduced some extracts from the Teacher's pack accompanying her project, which gives many ideas for exploring mathematical patterns in dance.

## Correspondences:

A Bharatha Natyam dance opera based on the work and imagination of mathematician S. Ramanujan (1887-1920)

$$\psi(q) = 1 + q(1+q) + q^3(1+q)(1+q^2) + q^6(1+q)(1+q)(1+q^3)$$

$$\chi(q) = \frac{1}{1-q} + \frac{q}{(1-q^2)(1-q^3)} + \frac{q^2}{(1-q^3)(1-q^4)} + \frac{q^3}{(1-q^4)(1-q^2)(1-q^4)(1-q^5)}$$

$$F(q) = \frac{1}{1-q} + \frac{q^4}{(1-q)(1-q^3)} + \frac{q^{12}}{(1-q)(1-q^2)(1-q^3)}$$

*have got similar relations as above,*

*Mock θ-functions (of 7th order)*

$$(i) \quad 1 + \frac{q}{1-q^2} + \frac{q^4}{(1-q^3)(1-q^5)} + \frac{q^9}{(1-q^5)(1-q^5)(1-q^5)\dots}$$

$$(ii) \quad \frac{q}{1-q} + \frac{q^4}{(1-q^2)(1-q^3)} + \frac{q^7}{(1-q^3)(1-q^5)(1-q^5)\dots}$$

$$(iii) \quad \frac{1}{1-q} + \frac{q^2}{(1-q^2)(1-q^3)} + \frac{q^6}{(1-q^3)(1-q^5)(1-q^5)\dots}$$

*These are not related to each other.*

*Ever yours sincerely*
*S. Ramanujan*

Shobana Jeyasingh is an award-winning choreographer and exuberant dancer of this most vibrant form of classical Indian dance. She describes it thus:

Apart from dance (Nritta), Bharatha Natyam also encompasses the different but related technique of mime (Nritya) which in turn allows for stylised movement (Natya dharmi) and behavioural everyday movement (Lokadharmi).

In *Correspondences,* these techniques are combined to celebrate Ramanujan's lifelong love affair with mathematics. As he said: 'In mathematics alone one could have a complete realisation of God.' The problem of The Pearl Necklace from Bhaskara's *Leelavati* (See Chapter 5) is used to build an activity in mathematics.

A brother and sister were counting the pearls on their mother's necklace when the string broke in a playful struggle. Six pearls stayed on the string but the rest were scattered around the room. One third fell to the ground; one fifth rested on the arm-chair; one sixth were saved by the girl and a tenth were caught by her brother. Can you work out how many pearls were on the necklace before it was broken?

*A Scene of Correspondence*

The Teacher's pack explores the movements and lines further. Diagonal, circle and diamond patterns can be seen in Bharatha Natyam. The timing of jumps and arm movements is very precisely measured.

A Bharatha Natyam dancer uses his or her body to create precise geometric shapes.
The primary position of the dance divides the dancer's body into three sections which resemble three equilateral triangles.

**This is done in three stages:**

1. Pulling up the upper half of the body from the stomach; this immediately makes the dancer feel taller!
   This movement makes the first triangle.
2. Turning out the legs from the hips.
   This movement makes the second triangle.
3. Bending both legs from the base.
   This movement makes the third and final triangle.

The movement of the arms and legs are used to 'draw' beautiful clean lines in the space surrounding the dancer.

Diagonals, circles and diamonds are the patterns that can be seen in Bharatha Natyam dance.

A very special feature of Bharatha Natyam is the way that the fingers of the hands are used to make strong graceful shapes.

244

Each shape made by the fingers has a different name and these shapes add interest and decoration to the lines created by the arms.

The feet have their special positions; these are as follows:

The feet are used to create rythmns so that the audience hears as well as sees the dance. The music is set to rhythm 'cycles' which divide time into regular sections.

For example a five beat cycle has five beats to a bar of music.

The choreographer (the peson who designs the dance) creates interesting arithmetical patterns to be performed by the dancers feet within the ryhthm cycles.

Here are some examples of how a single bar of eight beats can be divided to make foot patterns.

```
1   2 3 4   5     6     7     8
1    1 1 1   11    11    11    11
```

Single beats for 4 and double time for 4
i.e. 123412345678

```
1    2    3    4    5    6    7  8
111  111  111  111  111  111  1  1
```

Four sets of 3 beats in double time followed by 2 single beats
i.e. 123123123123 12

```
 1   2   3   4   5   6   7   8
111/111/111/111/111/111/111/111/
```

i.e. Each beat is divided into 3.

## PROJECTS for YEARS 9/10/11

The following projects encompass a range of attainment targets and levels, and are whole-school, long term projects.

Students at this level are mature enough to consider more serious and advanced concepts as indicated on the spiral curriculum model. Year 9 is a good year to start, as students are not yet pressured by coursework and examinations. Positive titles like *Using maths to make things happen* from *Maths in School* (Vol. 14, No.2 March 1985), or Maths for All week can generate wider involvement of mathematics. Maths could be the basis for the school's contribution to events such as One World Week, sponsored every year by many organisations who produce materials for teachers.

Pupils can progress from an awareness level to more challenging ideas. In years 10 and 11, pupils who have been exposed to this kind of learning should be ready to seek solutions to some social and global inequalities using ideas from mathematics, science, geography and history. Such work gives a sense of continuity and achievement. Topic webs of the projects outlined here resulted from the concern of Year 9 pupils about the environment, particularly about energy and famine. Taking tea as an example of a cash-crop, the class traced its path from the producer to the consumer, looking also at the conditions of the workers. This coincided with the extensive coverage in the BBC Environment week on rainforests — Years 10 and 11, Science, Maths and Geography departments, all worked closely producing displays, discussions and workshops for parents. Videos such as *Battle for the Planet* (Channel 4) and *Man made Famine* (BBC2) generated discussions.

The project on famine began with a pupil's questions while they were collecting funds for Ethiopia: 'Is Africa really so poor, Miss?'. It produced this computer graphic display by Francis Khan.

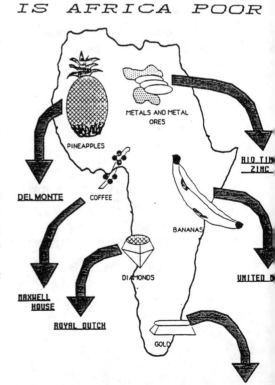

IS AFRICA POOR

We produced a list for each department to match the needs of the syllabus.

**Maths & Geography**
Energy requirements of people
Distribution of land.
Who owns what and how much?
Population and weather myths.
Cash crops/sustainence farming —
who grows them? who benefits?
Peter's/Mercator's projection?
Politics and Economics of food —
Do multinationals own the world?
Differential wages of men and women.
The Irish famine.

**Science**
Rainforests. How are deserts made?
Malnutrition/Overnutrition.
Homo exterminus or Homo sapiens?
Energy waste in manufacturing -
- industries
Simple cures for diarhoea.
Pesticides and fertilisers - at what cost?
Where do different elements in the periodic
table come from?
Watch: Battle for the planet.

**Technology and Design:**
water containers
water coolers
toilet using minimum
amount of water.
Keeping cool/keeping warm.

**ROOTS OF FAMINE A CROSS-CURRICULAR PROJECT FOR GCSE**

**Health Education**
Balanced diet.
Pulses and vegetables
Cost of packaged/unpackaged food.
Malnutrition/overeating.

**English**
Stories and poems about hunger from
Ireland/Ethiopia.
Empathy work on how damaging stereotypes on
famine can be Empathy work on how people
survive in famine times.

**Art/Music**
Design wall charts entitled:
FEED THE WORLD
Do a play on - 'Rights of children'
Hold Band Aid - style concert.

**Religious Education**
Does every one believe in God?
Religion around the world?
Religious stereotypes?

Projects on coffee, beef, rice, tea, rubber, wood or tin could be similarly developed, enhancing skills of information searching and handling.

## The Tea Growers

Tea growing is concentrated in warm regions with rainfall of 178 cm or more per year. The bushes grow best at higher altitudes. Tea plants mature in about 9 years. After the fourth year, leaves may be plucked. The same bushes may be cropped for over 50 years before replanting is necessary. (Nearly 2/3 of Sri Lanka's tea bushes are over 70 years old.)

India is the largest grower of tea — but over 2/3 of what is produced is drunk there. China is the next largest grower] but exports only about 1/5 of what is produced. Sri Lanka is the third largest grower and exports nearly all of what is grown. This makes Sri Lanka the largest tea exporter in the world. East African countries (Kenya, Malawi, Tanzania, Mozambique and Uganda) together sell about 1/5 of all tea in world trade. Indonesia, Bangladesh and Argentina are other countries that export much tea.

## COST OF MOST UK CUPPAS

25% to UK companies for blending and packaging in UK

transport, profit to retail shops, etc.

Over 50% to tea producing countries

# Who Produces Tea?

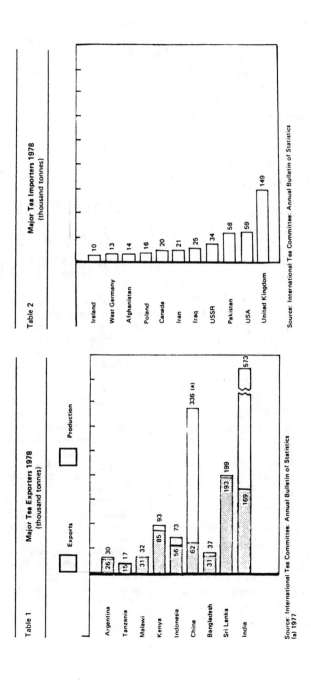

**Table 1**

Major Tea Exporters 1978
(thousand tonnes)

☐ Exports    ☐ Production

| | Exports | Production |
|---|---|---|
| Argentina | 26 | 30 |
| Tanzania | 15 | 17 |
| Malawi | 31 | 32 |
| Kenya | 85 | 93 |
| Indonesia | 56 | 73 |
| China | 62 | 336 (a) |
| Bangladesh | 31 | 37 |
| Sri Lanka | 193 | 199 |
| India | 169 | 573 |

Source: International Tea Committee: Annual Bulletin of Statistics
(a) 1977

**Table 2**

Major Tea Importers 1978
(thousand tonnes)

| | |
|---|---|
| Ireland | 10 |
| West Germany | 13 |
| Afghanistan | 14 |
| Poland | 16 |
| Canada | 20 |
| Iran | 21 |
| Iraq | 25 |
| USSR | 34 |
| Pakistan | 58 |
| USA | 59 |
| United Kingdom | 149 |

Source: International Tea Committee: Annual Bulletin of Statistics

**Surveys** Using and applying mathematics and handling data at various levels. Surveys can give interesting insight into people's understanding and opinions. Questions must be brief and clear, about 12 to 15 in number and have a precise purpose. Answers should be 'Yes/No' or 'Tick' boxes.

OXFAM produced an excellent leaflet called *Brass Tacks: What is the use of surveys?* For clarity on questionnaires dealing with development issues, see: *Teaching Development Issues.*

Design a survey to find out things like:

a) How many pupils know where the following countries are: Mozambique, India, Ghana, Thailand?

b) Where is the Third World?

c) What do pupils use home computers for?

d) How many teachers liked mathematics when they were at school? Why?

e) What name-calling goes on in school; who? why? when? what names?

f) Who does/doesn't enjoy maths? which kinds? why?

g) How many police per 100 in a crowd in a demonstration or a carnival?

How is this figure worked out?

h) How many pupils/teachers have heard of: Ramanujan, Abdus Salam....?

A survey on *Who are The Famous* revealed a peculiar patterning all subject areas (except sport and music). People could only name famous people long dead: dead mathematicians, dead scientists, historians and so on. Why?

# Pupils 'know little about Third World'

A survey of school children aged from 13 to 17 has shown that many of them are ignorant about Third World countries.

A the same time in-service courses on development education are being cancelled because of poor response by teachers.

The survey — which was carried out by seven sixth-formers at Banbury School among 237 youngsters at school and youth groups in Oxfordshire found 81 per cent felt they knew little or nothing about the Third World. A further 90 per cent professed ignorance about the Caribbean and the Far East: Latin America and the Middle East did not do, much better — 85 per cent knew nothing or little about them.

Africa fared best with 77 per cent admitting to knowing at least something about it.

Geography apparently gives most coverage to the Third World. Nearly 60 per cent felt they had learnt little or nothing about other countries in religious education classes.

Do a survey based on if there were 100 people in the world...
(From: *Learning For Change in World Society,* page 40, 41)

    A.  How many would be Chinese? Indian? American? Japanese? Others?

    B.  How many would speak Hindi? Chinese? English? Japanese?

Do the same with if there were 100 people in Birmingham (your own city):

    A.  How many would be white? black?

    B.  How many Indians, Pakistanis, Afro-Caribbeans, Irish, English?

    C.  How many employed, unemployed?

       First draw a series of pie charts using your own ideas. Then find the real proportional figures. What do they reveal?

The preparation of graphs that allow for international comparisons frequently supplies students with striking visual evidence of global problems while also encouraging the sharpening of their mathematical skills.

Compare the energy use of different countries

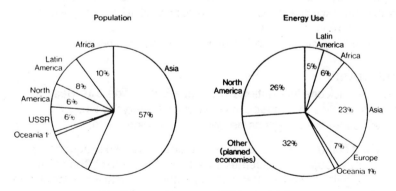

Fig 2 Compare the energy use of different populations

## Data Management

In Years 10 and 11 specific and selected data on multinationals, industrialised nations, world trade rules, 'Third world' debt, etc. can be used to:

*   analyse information generated by the database
*   reproduce visually on the world map — show disparities of wealth and power.
*   consider concepts like interdependence, standard of living, overpopulation, developing, developed, monopoly, free market system, green investment etc.
*   draw conclusions on the urgent necessity and feasibility of redistributing earth's resources.

Using QUEST or GRASS or any suitable database, pupils can create Visual Data Charts — their own display of world maps showing military expenditure by different nations concerning, for instance: Health, Energy production and consumption, socio-economic indicators, 50 largest foreign investments in the UK and 50 largest multinationals in the world, 50 largest UK multinationals — their income, assets, resources etc. Mathematical illustrations have more impact than columns of figures. The databases are easy to use and contain recent 'official' data. They can help students to understand how technological 'innovations' do not always give people a better quality of life. Many jobs are lost — what are the ramifications of this on the mental and physical health of people, on the resources for health care? When expenditure is studied alongside UN world statistics, on aspects of life such as infant mortality, life-expectation and gross national product, it becomes possible to understand how they connect.

Two smaller projects developed by pupils are outlined below:

## Best Buys

Objective: Pick one international product and investigate its 'Best Buy' value, its power and connections to your own everyday life.

The idea for the project came from the following quote:

I had commented that some of the brushes being produced by a nearby cooperative seemed a bargain. 'No,' he said, 'they are not a bargain. They are cheap because the people are desparate to make a sale.' 'For us though,' I insisted, 'that means they are a bargain.' 'What a peculiar idea of a bargain you have in England,' Sujoy replied 'For me, a bargain is an agreement where both parties are happy that they have got the best deal'.

Conversation between Richard Adams (Traidcraft) and Sujoy Srimal of Equitable Marketing Association in Calcutta (*Who Profits*, by Richard Adams (1989) Lion, page 74)

COFFEE: Which is the best buy?
The usual maths question concerns only value for money on a strictly numerical basis. We considered the usual 'best buy' scenario, different sizes of jars, amount, quality etc. but also:

— the usefuless of the container after the coffee has been consumed.
— whether the jar can be reused or recycled.
— the wages paid to workers in the coffee plantations.
— links between the coffee company and other matters such as baby milk products. Bottle-fed babies in the developing world are twice as likely to die as breast-fed babies. Who supplies this dried milk? What's the connection? UNICEF claims that: 'If all women breast-fed instead of bottle feeding, you would save one million lives a year!

Students found that Nestlé has the largest share of the baby milk market in developing countries, selling £24 of baby milk every second.

# COFFEE
After oil, coffee is (in most years) the most valuable commodity in world trade. All coffee is grown in the poorer countries of the SOUTH, but about 4/5 is drunk in the richer countries of the NORTH...

## Prices for coffee
Overall, coffee prices tend to move in cyles. There are short periods of boom. But these are often followed by long periods of over-supply and low prices. The real prices of coffee (and many other Third World commodities) have tended to decline. 'Real terms' refers to what can be bought in return for the money earned. The picture below shows what a coffee producing country needed to sell in 1969 to buy one 16-ton truck — *and how much more was needed in 1979 to buy the same truck...*

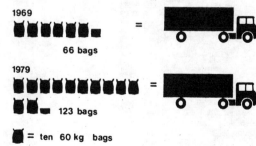

1969
66 bags

1979
123 bags

= ten 60 kg bags

## Cut out Nescafé

□ I pledge not to buy Nescafé until Nestlé abides by the letter and spirit of the WHO/UNICEF Code on the marketing of baby milk.

Name

Address

□ I enclose £5 cheque/PO for a boycott pack.

□ I wish to join BMAC. I enclose a cheque for £10. (£2 unwaged)

□ I enclose a donation of £.........

Please return to Baby Milk Action (BMAC)
6 Regent Terrace, Cambridge CB2 1AA.

## and join the boycott

**Every three minutes,** Nestlé spends £18 persuading you to buy Nescafé. In the same time another baby dies from unsafe bottle feeding.

**Nestlé,** the world's largest producer of baby milk, floods Third World hospitals with enough free baby milk to ensure that newborns are routinely bottle fed. This practice is condemned by the World Health Assembly because it places babies at risk of life-threatening infections.

**Breastmilk is free and safe -** but companies know that unless they get babies on the bottle, they don't do business. **We can't let them get away with it.**

### Wake up to the facts. Not Nescafé.
Baby Milk Action (BMAC) 6 Regent Terrace, Cambridge, CB2 1AA.

# Over 100 coffee brands to choose from....

## so why go for one that profits from this?

## *What is a living wage?*

Objective: To understand the meaning of this much-used phrase in the context of living conditions of the workers.

Here is a quote from a worker in a Thai sportswear factory:

'People in Britain should ask about the conditions in the factories and not support the bad ones.'

Clothing, televisions, videos: many consumer goods are often not made in the country of purchase. Efficient communications and transportation allows large companies to move their operations to places where labour is cheap. It is a good question to ask how much the people who make the goods receive. Is it a living wage? Are we willing to pay more so that they can live with dignity and reasonable comfort? If not, why not?

* Consider this cost of everday requirements in Bethany,:

| | |
|---|---|
| rice | Rs 7.00 per kg |
| lentils | Rs 6.50 per kg |
| eggs | Rs 8.40 per dozen |
| tomatoes | Rs 3.00 — 8.00 per kg (seasonal) |
| buffalo milk | Rs 2.00 per pint |
| mutton | Rs 40.00 per kg |
| bananas | Rs 3.50 per dozen |
| peanut oil | Rs 23.00 per litre |

The aid worker sending this information has calculated the minimal cost of adaqately feeding one person per day as Rs 10.00. The wages for women who weave in the workshop are Rs 12.00 per day. Show how a family of two (working) adults and three children would plan meals for a week.

Do the same calculation for a family on a multinational tea plantation in Kenya. (The advertisement would have you believe that the company cares for its workers and gives them education and health care). Ref: The Tea Trade published by the World Development Movement.

| | |
|---|---|
| maize flour | sh 3.10 per kg |
| sugar | sh 4.50 per kg |
| bread — small loaf | sh 2.25 |
| beer — litre bottle | sh 4.15 |
| rice | she 4.60 per kg |
| vegatables | sh 1.50 — sh 5.00 per kg |

255

tea 'siftings'              sh 12.30 per kg
clothes — shirt             from sh 40.00
— T shirt (3-5 yr old)      sh 15.00
clinic (cost for childbirth) sh 15.00 plus food

*Tea Workers' Wages in Kenya (1.1.79 — 1.1.80)*

| Job | Daily Rate | | Monthly Rate | |
|---|---|---|---|---|
| | (Ksh) | (Pence) | (Ksh) | (£ sterling) |
| Field Labourer | 7.50 | 45p | 195 | £11.70 |
| Pruners, Sprayers | 8.00 | 49p | 208 | £12.50 |
| 'Female Task' Juveniles | 5.95 | 36p | 155 | £ 9.30 |
| Factory — Male | 7.70 | 47p | 200 | £12.00 |
| Female | 6.10 | 37p | 158 | £ 9.50 |
| Supervisor | 8.30 | 51p | 216 | £13.00 |
| Pickers | Piece work sh 0.34 per Kgf. (2p per Kg.) | | | |
| In above 1 month = 26 working days £1 sterling = Ksh 16.50 (24.8.79) | | | | |

Several companies, like Traidcraft, have set up fairer ways of trading. Their policies encourage all workers to receive a fair minimum wage, have legally enforceable contracts of employment, and join independent workers' organisations.

# Extracts from Traidcraft booklet: *People Friendly Clothing — Campaign briefing*

The women at XYZ Garment Ltd in Bangladesh (98% of the workforce) work 10 hours a day plus 3 hours compulsory overtime. They are frequently paid months late and workers appointed after 1984 were given no letter of appointment, so they can be dismissed without any reason. In February '86, 4 union leaders were beaten up.
*Bangladesh justice and Peace Newsletter (1987)*

The management of ABC Garments, Dhaka, sacked the union leaders when they heard of the union's registration. They then declared a lay-off and subcontracted the works to another factory. The dismissed workers were not given their due pay.
*Bangladesh Garments Sramik Federation (1987)*

Manike works in the Colombo Free Trade Zone, Sri Lanka, for a Hong Kong shirt factory. When a needle broke and damaged her eye, the management tried to pressurise her into signing a declaration that it was a birth defect. She refused and was offered $2 compensation. A campaign resulted in compensation of $156.
*Asia Women Workers' Newsletter (1988)*

At LMN Garments Corporation, Philippines, the workers are paid the minimum wage only if they meet a production target. If they don't they have to work overtime. The company keeps pressure on the employees by sub-contracting work to other factories. The factory supplied baby dresses to Europe.
*Young Christian Workers*

A European-owned factory in the Philippines, considered a comparatively good employer, operated a 6 month 'apprenticeship' scheme (even for skilled machinists) on lower pay and without the right to join a union. Often they laid workers off at the end. Married women had to sign an agreement that they would not get pregnant for 6 months. Women with small children would not be taken on.
*United Nations study (1987)*

The Chairman of a UK Hosiery company, on homeworkers working for him: '...If the women were not disturbed they should earn at least £1.60 an hour.' Homeworkers have to pay for their own heating, lighting, rates.
*Observer (1988)*

A UK homeworker. 'I used to work a 90-hour week to get the money I needed...I challenge anyone to check, sew and label a dozen sweaters at the rate they set and earn more than 66p an hour.
*Observer (1988)*

'Tights work i.e. examining, straightening and bagging of tights and stockings...has a pay rate of approximately 80p per hour, or...6p — 18p per dozen.
*Leicester Outwork Campaign (1988)*

'The pay is low, the work is hard. It ruins your health'. Homeworker in Swindon, where a survey revealed blouse workers earned 75p — £1.30 an hour.
*Thamesdown Law Centre (1989)*

# UK

Most clothing manufacturers are small scale — well over 90% employ less than 100 people and 72% of women's fashionwear manufacturers employ less than 10! The ethnic minorities are a major part of the workforce, often employed in the smaller workshops on unfavourable terms: their isolation and fear of racial harassment make them a vulnerable group.

Manufacturers are often quite dependent on just one or two big retailers; in many cases the retailer in effect controls production. When a retailer changes supplier, manufacturers go to the wall.

Low pay is a universal feature — it is second only to hotels and catering for this. Union membership is low. The Department of Employment estimates wages in the clothing industry are only 77% of the average for manufacturing.

## Consider food in Britain

Why is it difficult to change people's habits from junk food to healthy food? Is it only the covenience factor?

The figures shown on pages 259/260 (The Guardian 18.10.86) compare the costs of a typical shopping list for a family of four compared to another list for a healthy diet for the same family. The article uses official diet information and points out that it is not cheap to buy healthy food. No wonder some families on low income find it difficult to buy good food for themselves and their children.

There is much material which will support the teacher in this work. One book which has been very widely read is *How the other half dies* by Susan George (1977). A video is available from Channel 4. 80-slide pack with written commentary (13 mins) or video-cassette called *The Financial Famine — the human cost of the debt crisis* (UNICEF-UK and the World Development Movement) gives a good introduction to the 'Third world Debt' problem.

Databases can of course be used in racist ways: for example, by locating the financial poverty of 'developing' countries is their own caste, class and cultural system and totally disregarding the imbalance of power. Accurate explanations of the causes of 'Third world' debt, Aid and Trade structures can give pupils critical insight into matters such as the real relationship between rich and poor countries.

# Shopping list for a typical diet

|  |  |  |
|---|---|---|
| Milk, whole | 21 pints | £4.41 |
| Eggs | 1 dozen | 87p |
| Margarine | 2 x 500g | £1.10 |
| | 1 x 250g | 27p |
| Cheddar cheese | ½lb | 50p |
| Cornish pasties | 4 | £1.20 |
| Tinned ham | ½lb | 45p |
| Chicken | 1, small | £2.15 |
| Fish fingers | 10 | 45p |
| Pork sausages | ¾lb | 60p |
| Tinned corned beef | ½lb | 75p |
| Steak and kidney pie | 1lb | 79p |
| Bacon (streaky) | ½lb | 65p |
| Mince | 1lb | £1.15 |
| Beefburgers | 4lb | £3.96 |
| Bread, white | 5 large loaves | £1.85 |
| Cornflakes | 1 x 500g box | 58p |
| Weetabix | box of 12 | 40p |
| Biscuits, plain | 3 packets | 63p |
| Pudding rice | 1 small packet | 49p |
| Carrots | 1½lb | 22p |
| Swede | 1½lb | 26p |
| Frozen peas | ¾lb | 33p |
| Cabbage | 2lb (approx) | 36p |
| Baked beans | 1 440g tin | 16p |
| Tomatoes | 1 small tin | 12p |
| Potatoes | 10lb | £1.10 |
| Apples | 2lb | 60p |
| Pears | 1lb | 32p |
| Onions | 2 | 18p |
| Ice cream | ½ litre | 49p |
| Sponge cakes | 2 | 88p |
| Apple tarts | 1 pack of 6 | 48p |
| Chocolate biscuits | 1 pack of 6 | 29p |
| Jellies | 2 | 31p |
| Instant whip | 1 | 16p |
| Crisps | 12 packets | 95p |
| Sweets, chewy variety | 4 packs | 35p |
| Tomato sauce | 1 medium bottle | 33p |
| Cooking oil | ½ litre | 36p |
| Jam | 2 x 340g jars | 82p |
| Sugar | 1 kilo | 46p |
| Tea bags | 160 | £1.37 |
| Squash | 2 litres | 63p |
| Oxo cubes | 1 pack | 22p |
| Soup | 1 800g tin | 48p |
| Beer | 2 pints | £1.39 |
| Flour, white | 1 small packet | 22p |

TOTAL £37.09

# Shopping list for a healthy diet

|  |  |  |
|---|---|---|
| Milk, whole | 5 pints | £1.05 |
| Milk, skimmed | 16 pints | £3.20 |
| Cheese, Edam | 5oz | 32p |
| Cheese, Cheddar | 5oz | 29p |
| Beefburgers | 10 | 99p |
| Pork chops | 4 medium | £2.82 |
| Bacon (lean) | ¾lb | £1.70 |
| Chicken, whole | 1 small | £2.15 |
| Chicken, breast | 5oz. | 75p |
| Sausages, beef | 1½lb | £1.09 |
| Mackerel, tinned | 1½lb | £1.60 |
| Fish fingers | 6 | 30p |
| Pilchards | 2 cans | 50p |
| Eggs | 1 dozen | 87p |
| Butter | 250g | 48p |
| Margarine, sunflower | 700g | 78p |
| Vegetable oil | ½ litre | 40p |
| Sugar | 1 kilo | 46p |
| Potatoes | 11lb | £1.21 |
| Green veg, fresh | 1¾lb | 32p |
| Root veg | 3lb | 45p |
| Frozen peas | 1lb | 44p |
| Tomatoes, fresh | ¾kg | 67p |
| Lettuce | 1 medium | 20p |
| Cucumber | 1 medium | 45p |
| Baked beans | 3 x 44pg tins | 48p |
| Apples | 28 (1 each day) | £2.79 |
| Oranges | 28 (each day) | £3.36 |
| Dried fruit (raisins) | 1½lb | 82p |
| Bread, wholemeal | 7 large loaves | £3.22 |
| Muffins | 4 | 34p |
| Flour, white | 1 small pack | 22p |
| Flour, wholemeal | 1 small pack | 22p |
| Doughnuts | 4 | 52p |
| Biscuits, digestive | 2 packets | 52p |
| Cornflakes | 1 x 500g pack | 58p |
| Muesli | 1 340g pack | 47p |
| Spaghetti, wholemeal | 1lb | 22p |
| Pudding rice | 1small packet | 49p |
| Semolina | 1lb | 36p |
| Red kidney beans, dry | 200g | 30p |
| Tea | 8oz | 51.20 |
| Instant coffee | 1 small jar | £1.19 |
| Squash | ½ large bottle | 32p |
| Canned drinks | 2 | 64p |
| Wine | 1 bottle | £2 |
| Beer | 2 pints | £1.39 |
| Ice cream | ½ litre | 49p |
| Chocolate | 1 med bar | £1.35 |
| Toffees | 1 packet | 59p |
| Crisps | 6 packets | 47p |

TOTAL £48.04

An important change in world industry is <u>where</u> it is and will be taking place. Between now and the year 2000, more and more of the world's industrial production is likely to take place in the South, the poorer countries of Asia, Africa, and Latin America . . .

# We're in this changing scene now

## 1970

The OECD* countries with just 👤👤👤👤👤 👤👤👤👤👤 **20%** of the world's people had 🏭🏭🏭🏭🏭 🏭🏭🏭🏭🏭 **69%** of the world's industrial production

*Organisation for Economic Co-operation and Development member countries:
Australia, Austria, Belgium, Canada, Denmark, Finland, France, Germany, Greece, Iceland, Ireland, Italy, Japan, Luxembourg, Netherlands, New Zealand, Norway, Portugal, Spain, Sweden, Switzerland, Turkey, United Kingdom, United States.

The developing countries (including China) with 👤👤👤👤👤 👤👤👤👤👤 **70%** of the world's people had just 🏭🏭🏭🏭🏭 🏭🏭🏭🏭🏭 **12%** of the world's industrial production

The UUSR and East European countries with 👤👤👤👤👤 👤👤👤👤👤 **10%** of the world's people had 🏭🏭🏭🏭🏭 🏭🏭🏭🏭🏭 **19%** of the world's industrial production

# estimates for the year 2000

(from an OECD Interfutures Analysis, 1979'

The OECD countries with just 👤👤👤👤👤 👤👤👤👤👤 **15%** of the world's people may well have 🏭🏭🏭🏭🏭 🏭🏭🏭🏭🏭 **50%** of the world's industrial production

The developing countries (inc China) with 👤👤👤👤👤 👤👤👤👤👤 **78%** of the world's people may well have 🏭🏭🏭🏭🏭 🏭🏭🏭🏭🏭 **27%** of the world's industrial production

The USSR and East European countries with 👤👤👤👤👤 👤👤👤👤👤 **7%** of the world people may well have 🏭🏭🏭🏭🏭 🏭🏭🏭🏭🏭 **23%** of the world's industrial production

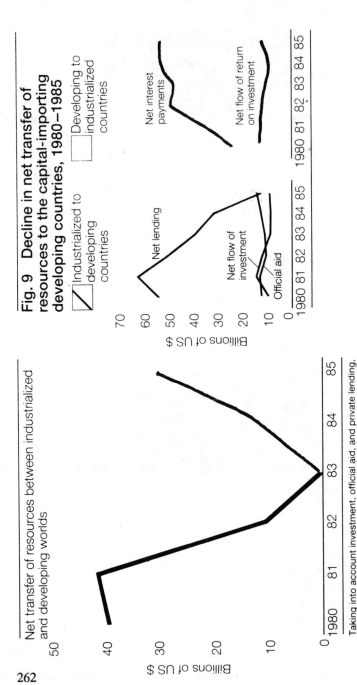

Fig. 9  Decline in net transfer of resources to the capital-importing developing countries, 1980–1985

Net transfer of resources between industrialized and developing worlds

Taking into account investment, official aid, and private lending, and subtracting repayments of interest and capital, the net flow of resources is now from the developing world to the industrialized world.

Source: United Nations Department of International Economic and Social Affairs, 1986.

*From: State of the World's Children*

For pupils interested in statistical indices, the database can provide an excellent start to the design of an 'index for life' which will attempt to rank quality of life across the world. The 'human development index' in *Human Development Report* produced by U.N.D.P. (1990) gives more adequate figures relating to 'quality of life' than mere G.N.P.

## The World's children

No project could better raise the awareness of children *about* children than an in depth study of how much care the world's children receive.

- What happens to children in a state of war?
- What happens to public services spending under a debt crisis?
- What is the effect of pollution on young children? (Timberlake and Thomas, 1990)
- Why is it becoming increasingly important for charities like 'Save The Children' and UNICEF to raise their own funds through Band Aid/Sports Aid? What is happening to the International aid programme?

*The State of the World's Children,* a UNICEF book, is an excellent source of data and visual charts. It will help pupils to understand one particularly difficult concept: that where there are less deaths in infancy and better health care for mother and child, there are fewer births. It is the fear that their babies won't survive that makes people have more children.

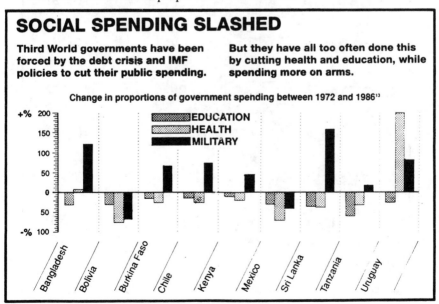

**SOCIAL SPENDING SLASHED**

**Third World governments have been forced by the debt crisis and IMF policies to cut their public spending.**

**But they have all too often done this by cutting health and education, while spending more on arms.**

Change in proportions of government spending between 1972 and 1986[13]

EDUCATION
HEALTH
MILITARY

Bangladesh / Bolivia / Burkina Faso / Chile / Kenya / Mexico / Sri Lanka / Tanzania / Uruguay

# MISERLY AID

**Western countries are giving less in overseas aid now than in 1965. Only four countries now meet the UN target of 0.7% of GNP: Norway, Holland, Denmark and Sweden.**

Official development assistance as % of GNP, 1965 and 1987.[6]

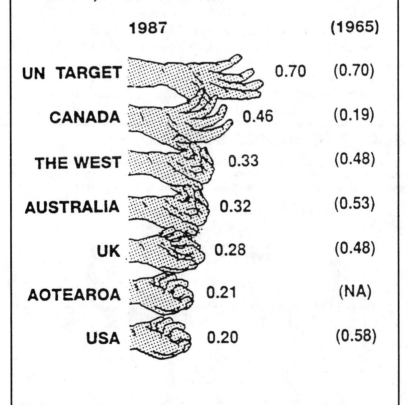

| | 1987 | (1965) |
|---|---|---|
| UN TARGET | 0.70 | (0.70) |
| CANADA | 0.46 | (0.19) |
| THE WEST | 0.33 | (0.48) |
| AUSTRALIA | 0.32 | (0.53) |
| UK | 0.28 | (0.48) |
| AOTEAROA | 0.21 | (NA) |
| USA | 0.20 | (0.58) |

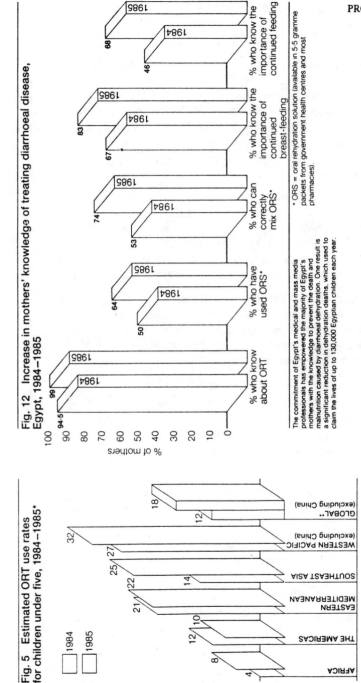

Fig. 12  Increase in mothers' knowledge of treating diarrhoeal disease, Egypt, 1984–1985

* ORS = oral rehydration solution (available in 5·5 gramme packets from government health centres and most pharmacies).

The commitment of Egypt's medical and mass media professionals has empowered the majority of Egypt's mothers with the knowledge to prevent the death and malnutrition caused by diarrhoeal dehydration. One result is a significant reduction in dehydration deaths, which used to claim the lives of up to 130,000 Egyptian children each year.

Fig. 5  Estimated ORT use rates for children under five, 1984–1985*

265

Oral rehydration therapy (ORT) can be used to prevent or correct the diarrhoeal dehydration which is the most common cause of deaths to young children. In the 1980s the promotion sachets of oral rehydration salts (ORS), or salt and sugar solution, or other kinds of home-made rehydration fluid, has put this therapy at the disposal of approximately 20% of the world's parents and is now saving an estimated 6000,000 lives a year.

Use rates refer to the percentage of diarrhoeal episodes in children under five years of age treated with ORT. When estimates for both were available for a country the midpoint between the sum and the greater of the two values was used as the ORT. All numerators were calculated assuming no use of ORT in countries for which no data were available.

When estimates of the use of ORS, salt and sugar solution and any type of household fluid were available, and the greater of the three was used, a global minimum of 24% of episodes was estimated to have received some form of oral rehydration fluid in both 1984 and 1985.

*Source...'Interim Programme Report 1986' World Health Organisation Programme for Control of Diarrhoeal Diseases. Who/CDD/87.26.*

# Mathematics of women's work
## *(Handling data, Level 9)*

Women all over the world including the West provide significantly cheaper labour than men. Their educational opportunities are poorer. Conditions of workers in clothing industries, at airports, railway stations and hospitals cleaning and nursing jobs in hospitals are interesting areas for investigating racism and sexism. Although wages, holidays and overtime are set as a legal entitlement, black women workers in Britain continue to suffer poorer conditions and pay.

To start with consider the situation of female workers for this project. Compare and contrast wages per hour of, for example, a 'dinner lady', office cleaner, a cleaner at the railway station, airport, or hospital. You should be able to find these out by writing to different employers.

Now do the same with male employees in each of the above. Present this information pictorially.

In all the areas of service-related employment listed above, an excessive concentration of black women workers can be found in Britain. 'Racism: The Great Divide' (*Nursing Times* June 1987) highlights the discrepancy between promotion prospects of black nurses and white.

## PAID AND UNPAID WORK OF HUSBANDS AND WIVES

**MAN with a job**

49    34

**WOMAN with a job**

40    24

**WOMAN housewife**
1

33

☐ Paid working hours per week

■ Unpaid working hours per week

▨ Free time per week

Data from 12 countries in 1975: Belgium, Bulgaria, Czechoslovakia, France, Federal Republic of Germany, German Democratic Republic, Hungary, Peru, Poland, United States, USSR, Yugoslavia.

267

| Table 1. RGN and RMN trainees | | |
| --- | --- | --- |
| | Number | Percentage |
| Total white | 7765 | 96.6 |
| Total black | 245 | 3.1 |
| Afro-Caribbean | 97 | |
| African | 26 | |
| Asian | 104 | |
| Other | 18 | |
| Table 2. RGN trainees | | |
| | Number | Percentage |
| Total white | 6770 | 97 |
| Total black | 209 | 3 |
| Afro-Caribbean | 89 | |
| African | 19 | |
| Asian | 91 | |
| Other | 10 | |
| Total 3. RMN trainees | | |
| | Number | Percentage |
| Total white | 1015 | 96.6 |
| Total black | 36 | 3.4 |
| Afro-Caribbean | 8 | |
| African | 7 | |
| Asian | 13 | |
| Other | 8 | |

Statistical surveys are used to follow the case of two nurses, one black and one white. Andrew Cole looks at the 'real reason' behind the declining numbers of black nurses in the NHS as shown in the CRE, 1987 survey.

Pupils can collect statistics of employment by writing to large companies and the local hospital, railway station, council etc. Find out which organisations monitor their own employee statistics in accordance with the guidance provided by the Council for Racial Equality.

Employment is one area of modern life in which racism can flourish and pupils should know how it operates.

# ASIANS 'LOSERS' IN JOBS EFFORT

by LIAM TULLY
Ethnic Affairs Reporter

ASIANS are the biggest losers when it comes to finding jobs and getting training, a skills survey in East Birmingham has revealed.

The worrying picture also shows nearly eight out of every ten people not working in Nechells and Washwood Heath did not even want to go on training courses and nine out of every ten who had never worked did not want training.

It indicated a disappointing level of aspiration and ambition and a lack of knowledge of job opportunities becoming available in the area, said the survey commissioned by the East Birmingham Task Force.

It is particularly worrying for the Task Force — set up by the government to regenerate the inner city area — because it could mean local people, especially Asians, missing out on jobs created at Heartlands.

But Christine Heard, leader of East Birmingham Task Force, said since the survey was completed last year a lot of work had been done to improve training and get local people jobs.

Less than half the people interviewed in the survey of 1,267 residents in Washwood Heath and Nechells were working full-time.

It found the Asian community had the largest numbers of long-term unemployed and those who had not worked at all.

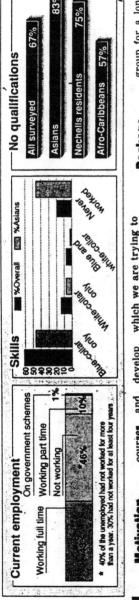

**Current employment**

Working full time — Working part time — On government schemes — Not working

* 40% of the unemployed had not worked for more than a year. 30% had not worked for at least four years.

**Skills**

%Overall — %Asians

Blue-collar only — White-collar only — White-collar and Blue and — Never worked

**No qualifications**

| All surveyed | 67% |
| Asians | 83% |
| Nechells residents | 75% |
| Afro-Caribbeans | 57% |

Mail graphic

## Motivation

And few had qualifications or skills which could lead to them finding work. Hardest hit were Asian women who made up the majority of people who had never worked.

The survey, exclusively revealed in the *Evening Mail* last December, said motivation and aspirations were low, there were poor levels of training and educational qualifications, communication skills particularly among Asians needed improving and many people needed to have their confidence built up.

But Christine Heard said: "Since the survey, we have done a lot of work in the area with the city council to get people on training courses and develop their skills. We are slowly overcoming the problems and are very optimistic about the future.

"Heartlands is half of our area and it is the greatest opportunity we are going to have.

"We need jobs in East Birmingham and the companies need workers and we are confident we can match up the two.

"Heartlands has accepted criticism over a poster campaign which was not translated into the appropriate languages and I don't think they will repeat that mistake.

## Improve

"Many women do want to work but can't because of the lack of child care facilities which we are trying to improve," she said.

"Many people in the area only have very basic skills and the task force is helping to improve those job skills, basic literacy and communication skills. We have also got quite a number of people onto access courses," she added.

"We have even set up a multi-lingual job club in Alum Rock which is helping to find jobs for Asian men and women.

"But you have to remember it takes time to change the attitudes of people and that can be a slow process."

Mr Mohammad Nazir, from the Gate recruitment agency, said: "This survey paints a very realistic picture but it is also extremely worrying.

group for a long time.

"I fear that with the creation of Heartlands many companies will move into the area and bring their existing workforce with them or employ workers from outside East Birmingham so the local people will lose out," said Mr Nazir.

## Package

"In an area like this where people's aspirations are very low instead of being constructive and positive about their area they become passive and destructive and lose hope for the future.

"To overcome the problems in the area we need to have a whole package to deal with jobs, training, education, housing, the environment and many other problems.

"You can't just throw money at something and hope the problem will go away, you need to get to the root cause.

"The situation is particularly bad for Asian people, especially women, and we have been urging for help for this disadvantaged

"I would expect Heartlands to come up with training packages for Asians and explain them in the necessary language."

*Chapter 10*

# Inservice Training for Mathematics Teaching

> *Our investigations have left us in no doubt about the fragmentary nature of in-service education for a multicultural society, Indeed it appears non-existent in many areas and in none does it seem wholly adequate.*
> J. Eggleston, D, Dunn and A, Purewel, *In-service Teacher Education in a Multicultural Society, Keele, (1980)*

This chapter offers some checklists for examining INSET for a mathematics department wishing to develop a teaching approach which raises issues of equality and justice. Their aim is to eliminate the blockages to learning caused by racism or sexism, and to enhance motivation, enjoyment and achievement. Accordingly issues of equality and justice have been given a high profile.

Schools vary enormously in their organisation and structure, so not all our checklists will be applicable to all schools, for instance regarding language. Most are relevant and transferable to many situations — and particularly to schools where pupils are white:- these are the schools most likely to provide an anachronistic education based only on white eurocentric values and attitudes.

The recommendations are set in the context of the National Curriculum and the categories defined in consultative documents for mathematics teaching and assessment from the Schools Examinations and Assessment Council — SEAC — and TGAT, the Task Group on Assessment and Testing, namely:

1. Aims of the Department
2. Teaching attitudes.
3. Cross-curricular issues (Skills, Themes, Perspectives)
4. Community involvement. (Parents, Governors —)
5. Syllabus matters.
6. Assessment.
7. Resources.
8. Maths within the school.
9. Role of the Head of the Department.

However, the concerted attack on anti-racist/multicultural teaching approaches to mathematics by the Prime Minister Margaret Thatcher and Mr. Baker, the Secretary of State for Education (1988) cannot be disregarded. At the 1988 Annual Conservative Conference, Mrs Thatcher observed that:

> Instead of learning to count and multiply, the children seem to be learning anti-racist maths, whatever that means.

Paragraph 10.22. of the Proposals of the Secretary of State for Education and Science in *Maths 5 to 16* states:

> We have not included any multicultural aspects in any of our attainment targets.
>
> There are many of those who argue for a multicultural approach to the mathematics curriculum on the basis that such an approach is necessary to raise the self-esteem of ethnic minority cultures and to improve mutual understanding and tolerance between races. We believe that this attitude is misconceived and patronising.

Teachers who have been attempting to put maths in its natural world-wide context may regard the official position as condescending and patronising. *Their hope is that students will use the skills of making conjectures, analysing problems, devising and verifying solutions, to sharpen their own logical reasoning, making critical sense of the world and demolishing stereotypes.*

With frequent changes causing pressure on departments, it is easy to put multicultural/anti-racist perspectives aside to deal with later, which leads to marginalisation and tokenistic input whatever the intentions. The reorganising and reviewing that implementing the National Curriculum demands creates an opportunity to incorporate a holistic approach to issues of equality and justice. It fits into an appraisal along these lines:

> - where is the department now?
> - what innovations are needed/worth exploring?
> - along what lines do we want the department to develop?

To achieve effective teaching, we will have to take constant trips around the loop, planning, sharpening our focus, trying out new ideas, testing them and rethinking. It will keep us fresh or it will wear us out, depending on how we meet our own INSET needs. We have to take account of forces at work in the education of our students outside of those between teacher and pupil, or teacher and the whole class. We can help ourselves by extracting and using the best of these other influences, creating opportunities for transferring skills learnt in mathematics to other areas of knowledge, examining bad teaching and poor learning.

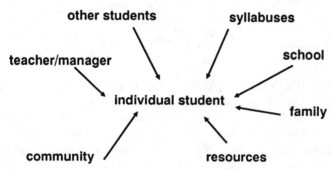

The teacher's role is increasingly faciliatative, using and manipulating a variety of activities which go into the learning experience of the students. The Head of the mathematics department has the key responsibility for management.

All-white schools in rural England or Grammar schools in urban areas could easily claim to provide an appropriate education for their students without ever widening the horizons from which they pick the content of the curriculum. But do they provide students with an awareness of culture other than their own? If students are given a sense of control over their lives, should they not also be given a sense of responsibility for combating inequality and injustice?

273

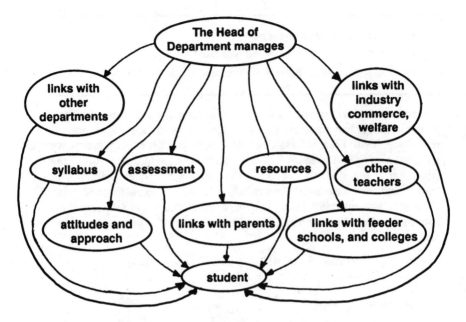

## Checklist 1: Department Aims & Objectives

The questions which follow do not set out to be a full departmental list of aims and detailed objectives, but should be asked (and answered) by departments interested in incorporating issues of race and gender into mathematics teaching. Determining aims and objectives must involve a critical process which includes dialogue between and with all participants in the teaching and learning environment.

a)   Do our aims include clear statements on equal opportunity relating to race and are they supported by appropriate INSET and organisational change to ensure implementation?

b)   Will our objectives ensure that the department gives time, energy and resources equally to all pupils in the school, ensuring both progression and differentiation?

c)   Does the department aim not only at optimum exam results, but also at the active involvement of pupils in mathematics, pure and applied?

d)   Are we creating opportunities for choice of topic, approach, method of presentation, mode of working (individual or group), self-assessment and for the use of wide range of resources?

e) Do we offer lessons that allow oral work, language development, discussion and argument on issues the students wish to address? Does the department present previously agreed positive values and attitudes on issues of race and gender?

f) Do our aims include links with parents, feeder schools, colleges, industry, community?

g) Do our aims reflect the idea that teachers are not just teaching maths but are empowering students to take charge of their lives and play an active part in the society?

## Checklist : Teacher Attitudes

Teachers are all individuals but have certain responsibilities in their professional role. Research has shown that teacher attitudes play a significant part in motivating or demotivating students (Booth and Colby, 1987). If race and gender issues are to be given a positive place in lessons, certain attitudes should be evident.

a) Are the members of the department knowledgeable about the many cultures which make up our country and do they take this into account in their teaching? What images do they present of them?

b) Has the school determined unequivocal disciplinary measures for racist/sexist remarks, jokes and behaviour? Are racist/sexist comments by colleagues dealt with?

c) What are the attitudes of maths teachers to pupils who continually fail in the system? Does it lead to a re-evaluation of professional practice or are they dismissed as 'trouble makers, disaffected, disruptive, not very bright, slow learners' etc.?

d) Do members of the department know each pupil in their charge, their background, character, abilities and aspirations? Is this knowledge observable in classroom practice; do we take the time to differentiate activities in the same lesson, recognise and reward positive achievement, ensure active involvement of all pupils in projects and discussions? Are teachers willing to put in the time needed to develop this approach?

e) Do maths teachers take a positive line in involving parents in the education of their children, in planning projects that show commitment to the community? Do we reveal society's unequal treatment of blacks and women in regard to employment, salaries etc.?

f)   Who owns the classroom discourse: teacher or pupils? How does the teacher ensure student participation and responsibility?

g)   Do teachers actively complain to publishers, examination boards, and the D.E.S. about inaccuracies, stereotyping, patronising and tokenistic portrayals of black people and women in learning materials?

h)   Are teachers concerned about the learning environment (atmosphere, desks, equipment, displays, materials) and relationships in the class (teacher/pupil and pupil/pupil) and for the outcome of learning (fostering co-operation, acquiring knowledge, critical evaluation and personal growth)?

## Checklist 3: Cross-curricular issues: Skills/Themes/Perspectives

The National Curriculum includes cross-curricular issues/skills/perspectives, spelt out in the DES document *Policy to Practice*

The whole curriculum for all pupils will certainly need to include at appropriate (and in some cases all) stages:

*   careers education and guidance.
*   health education.
*   other aspects of personal and social education.
*   coverage across the curriculum of gender and multicultural issues.
    — A great deal of learning related to these themes can and should be covered for all pupils in the context of the foundation subjects,

a)   Is the mathematics department insular and elitist? Does the department actively contribute to cross-curricular inititatives such as environmental education, health education, IT, economic awareness, oracy and other current issues?

b)   Does the department encourage the teaching and assessing of some maths topics either solely or jointly by non-maths teachers, say science or geography teachers?

c)   Does the maths department support and use services provided by the special needs department to help not just pupils with special needs but also those with, for example, behavioural, linguistic, numeracy difficulties?

d) Does the department have representatives on working parties on matters such as school aims, equal opportunity, school/parent links, school/industry links, TVEI etc?

e) Does the department work with other departments to develop projects and initiatives that go across curriculum areas?

## Checklist 4: Community

Giving value to each pupil means acknowledging the community in which that pupil lives. For 'parent power' to become a reality — and many teachers are also parents — we need an active support system *for* and *from* parents. Understanding between governors, parents' groups and between schools and individual parents is essential to for work of the department and its policies. This checklist explores the community as a resource. Schools situated in monocultural areas will need to develop broader community links.

a) What structures exist in the department to facilitate regular contact between parents and teachers? Are parents' evenings inviting, friendly and encouraging? Is a creche provided? Is there a good display that shows the department's attitudes to work, culture, and values? Are parents welcome into lessons? Is there a two-way exchange of information and ideas at parents' evenings?

b) Does the department try to gain active support from school governors for their policies on race, culture and learning? Are governors invited into lessons and do they take part in development of departmental theory and practice?

c) Has the department considered creating opportunities such as *Family Maths* workshops where parents and children can work together on maths? Should ancillary workers such as cleaning staff, dinner supervisors, technicians, kitchen staff be given a similar opportunity?

d) Can the maths department contribute to the project which other departments may have developed for involving the community?

e) Do students work at the local library for their project research? Do they visit factories, trade union offices, television and radio stations, environment projects? Is use made of the student's work experience? Are adults from various sections of the community invited into schools?

f)   What links are there with feeder schools? Do pupils take part? Do teachers and parents at the feeder schools know and understand the aims and work of the school and department?

g)   Are there links and visits between the high school and local colleges? Are pupils followed through?

h)   Are members of the department informed about how local industry makes use of mathematics? This would help students understand the potential of mathematics in careers. For example, access to some careers demands knowledge of calculus rather than computation; others may require skills of scale drawing and geometry.

## Checklist 5: Syllabus matters

The statutory orders contain details of mathematical content. As John Eden, Midlands Co-ordinator of the Raising Achievement in Mathematics Project, (RAMP) observes:

> Apparently dry 'Statements of Attainment' could be translated into dry classroom practice. This must not be allowed to happen.'

The following checklist seeks to ensure that departmental schemes of work are not dry and lifeless.

a)   Does the department keep up to date with projects such as RAMP, and with documents such as the Cockroft Report and *Better Mathematics?*

b)   Does the department follow one teaching scheme or does it use a variety of commercially produced material? Is this material examined critically for bias?

c)   Are staff expected to explore the nature of mathematics, its history, the use of cultural associations in the teaching of geometry, the manipulation of statistical figures to distort reality? Do the departmental guidelines promote permeation of issues of race, gender and class through lesson content as well as process?

d)   Do the guidelines suggest appropriate lesson styles for skills such as exposition, group discussion, investigation, problem solving?

e)   Are projects and extended pieces of work listed in the syllabus? Is advice on methods of working and resources given? Do some projects provide opportunities for students to express their feelings and critical comments?

f)  Are there clear strategies for sharing attainment targets across all levels to facilitate cross-curricular connections?

g)  Are schemes of work differentiated to take account of the range of pupil ability in each class? How is this ability decided upon?

h)  If pupils are set, is there movement between sets? How often is this monitored? What measures are there to minimise the ability connotations which may lead to low self-esteem? Are words like 'bottom group' and 'top group' avoided or encouraged?

i)  Does the choice of GCSE syllabus take into account the opportunities for pupil involvement in their 4th and 5th year course and in its coursework? Is the coursework passive and abstract, or does it contain both abstract as well as practical maths relating to current national and international situations?

## Checklist 6: Assessment

a)  Have the purposes and processes of assessment as outlined in the National Curriculum documents been examined and discussed by the department as a whole?

b)  Is there a whole school policy on assessment? Who co-ordinates assessment procedures? Who assesses? Are monitoring, review and evaluation built into the process of implementation?

c)  Are standardised tests used and for what? Are they up to date? Are they culture-free? Do they show attainment or potential? If they are diagnostic, how has reliability been verified?

d)  Is there departmental consensus on assessment strategies, profiling techniques, mathematical skills development etc? Is assessment continuous,part of teaching or is it like a test at the end of a topic? Have the following matters been resolved?

- Do assessment strategies allow students to respond in various modes as suggested by TGAT?
- Do students have opportunity to use OHPs, videocameras, tape recorders, computers and other equipment in maths lessons? Can they be used as evidence for attainment?
- Are there interim reports for pupils on their progress?
- Are there clear agreed methods for both formative and summative recordings?
- Is there systematic, regular pupil self-assessment to identify pupil needs and attainment/achievement?

- What disadvantages are developing bilingual pupils likely to encounter?

e) Are tests used for setting? Do they mainly test numeracy? How much of the formative assessment forms a part of the summative result or does only the yearly examination result count? What measures are taken to avoid behavioural impressions being used as a judgement on pupil performance and ability?

f) Which tests are used by the department for diagnosing pupil weaknesses? What actions are taken to correct those weaknesses?

g) Is policy on marking clear? Is it reviewed regularly and by whom? What does marking tell the teacher about:-

- his/her own teaching style, content and process?
- the pupil's weaknesses/strengths?

Do marking strategies:-

- inform the pupil constructively about his/her weaknesses/strengths and what to do about them?
- inform the future work of the department?
- allow pupils to express opinions, both positive and negative about the marking of their work?

Does the department support language development and take care not to mark down mathematics work for poor English?

h) Are pupils sometimes allowed to set targets? Are they allowed to assess each other's work, particularly project work containing material relating to the outside world, and in which the students may be able to offer experience?

i) Do all pupils have access to public examinations? What are the criteria to exam entry policy?

What alternatives are offered to non-exam students?

j) Is the full range of teaching and learning styles such as class, group, individual work matched with classroom management and assessment techniques being used?

k) Are reports to parents purposeful, informative and accurate? How often are parents informed of assessment? How often are they involved in assessment? Are parents invited to comment? Are their comments noted?

l) Are all assessments, particularly examination results, tracked carefully for the progress of each pupil (pointing out drops in performance as well as improvement), for variation in performance between boys and girls, between schools across an LEA, between students of different cultural as well as economic backgrounds? If examination papers are found to be biased, what is done about it?

# Checklist 7: Resources

Teachers, pupils, parents and community, local industry, colleges and the complete spectrum of commercially produced materials are all resources. Aims and objectives cannot be implemented efficiently if the tools of implementation are not evaluated and monitored. Teachers, more than most professionals, need thinking time, a space in which to reflect critically upon day-to-day practice as well as long-term issues, but time is seldom allowed for reflection.

a) Is there a strategy for Time Management?

The teacher's class contact time may be totally taken up by 'teaching' and she may feel that pupils are achieving a good deal — but is there time for pupils to talk about matters other than mathematics, time for new ideas to be generated together; time to have a laugh with pupils?

Is there collaborative teaching and planning?

If a withdrawal scheme operates, is there a clear procedure for returning pupils to mainstream lessons? What measures are taken to continue support for the pupil?

b) Have all resources been checked for pejorative bias, for readability, for language, for appropriate maturity level etc.?

c) Does the department make use of and support the school library, ordering books and materials for the library, and contributing to the development of the library as a resource centre for project work?

d) Are resources borrowed from the local Teachers' Centre or support service? Does the department make use of resources from the local university or teacher training college or other LEAs? If teachers go abroad on a working holiday or exchange, do they make a point of looking for new resources for maths lessons?

g) Are there structures for parent and the community to be a source of resources? Some parent-teacher associations are actively involved in the working environment, helping with furniture repairs and maintenance. But rarely are parents — black or white — acknowledged as equal partners in their children's education or recognised for their own expertise. Parents who question and challenge are often seen as threatening, pushy or over-ambitious.

## Checklist 8: Maths across the school curriculum
As one of the core subjects of the National Curriculum, the mathematics department can influence the whole curriculum, formal and informal.

a) Does the maths department ensure that the use of statistics and graphical representation in Geography, Science etc. is accurate and thorough?

   Do the statistics used demonstrate only eurocentric and white male perspectives or a world view, showing that there is not one 'reality' but a choice of interpretations?

   Does the maths department deliberately offer assistance to teachers and pupils using mathematics in other subject areas?

b) Does the maths department encourage positive use of maths in non-curricula aspects of school life such as fundraising, plays, outings, pensioners' lunches, variety shows?

c) Does the department make the use of display boards in the entrance hall?

d) Is the department represented on working parties and sub-committees on relevant initiatives such as TVEI, oracy, education & industry, economic awareness etc? And do they offer support on matters relating to equality issues?

e) Does the department take part in cross-curricular initiatives?

## Checklist 9: The Role of Head of Department
The role of the Head of Department is crucial in promoting ideas outlined in this book. Achieving harmony, shared purpose and agreement over issues of culture among group teachers requires insight, clear knowledge, sensitivity and commitment. To ensure the personal and professional development of members of the department will require negotiations all around. Going down this road is not easy, but, in our experience, those who have livened up their mathematics with a perspective of equality and justice have never returned to a monocultural, eurocentric teaching style.

An enthusiastic deputy can be given responsibility for monitoring, reviewing and evaluating developments. Liaising with heads of department in other schools who are also trying to widen their perspectives can be very supportive, particularly in In-service training, where this checklist may help in exploration of roles:

a) Do you want to introduce issues of race and culture because:-
   - there are black kids in your class.
   - black kids are underachieving.
   - pupils are finding maths boring.
   - the authority policy and the national curriculum documents require that you look at multicultural issues?

b) Do you feel able to put these ideas into practice, or will you first read up on, talk about and find out more?

c) Do you plan for staff development within the work of the department in discussions, at meetings, during team teaching?

   Do you encourage staff to read relevant books and materials (which you borrow or buy, and facilitate visits and the attendance of courses outside the school?

d) Is your leadership style appropriate to equal opportunities?

   Positive leadership should allow for discussion and expression of opinion while expecting professional competence, but not be doctrinaire.

   Have you a management qualification?

   Does your planning maximise the use of staff time, taking account of each teacher's responsibilities and experience?

e) Is the department policy clearly set out and available to all members of staff? Will it give a probationer or cover staff sufficient guidance?

f) Do your interview procedures ensure equalising of opportunities?

   Do you ensure that candidates for new posts are aware that they expected to support the equality aims of the department?

g) Do you plan one-off events designed to highlight matters such as 'Geometry around the World Week', or 'Family Maths'?

It is unlikely that any school in Britain could fulfil all the ambitions of these checklists. The checklists are designed for the future — hopefully not too far distant — setting some goals, directions and steps to be taken to teach our students well and to encourage motivation. Many schools that we know are well on their way to achieving much on the list, having found that once they start on some ideas, others follow. When teaching staff and pupils start to think in a culturally open way, new opportunities are presented and may lead to deep permanent changes in the life of the department and, almost certainly, the whole school.

# Acknowledgements

## Chapter 2

page 27: *Better Mathematics: A Curriculum Development Study* © Crown copyright 1987. Reproduced by permission of the Controller of HMSO.

## Chapter 3

page 41: Kaner, Peter (1984) *Integrated Mathematics Scheme IMS L2*, Bell & Hyman.

page 42: Glen, Robert (1987) *Foundation Maths for GCSE and Standard Grade*, Heinemann Educational Books

page 43: *General Certificate of Secondary Education, Statistics, Specimen Examination Papers,* NEA (Northern Examining Association).

page 46: (i) *Smith, Mike and Jones, Ian (1987) Central Maths for GCSE and Standard Grade*, Heinemann Educational Books.
(ii) Graham, Duncan and Christine (1983) *Maths for You 2*, Hutchinson.
(iii) Holderness, Jean (1987) *GCSE Maths Foundation Level*, Causeway Books.
(iv) *SMP 11-16 G2* (1985) Cambridge University Press.
(v) *Mathematics in Action 3A*, Blackie, Chambers.
(vi) *SMP 11-16 R3* (1987) Cambridge University Press.
(vii) *Mathematics in Action 3A*, Blackie, Chambers.

page 47: (i) *SMP 11-16 R3* (1987) Cambridge University Press.
(ii) *SMP 11-16 G3* (1985) Cambridge University Press.
(iii) *SMP 11-16 B5* (1987) Cambridge University Press.

(iv) Elvin, R, Ledsham, A, Oliver, C (1979) *Basic mathematics: revision and practice with answers*, Oxford University Press.

page 48: (i) Elvin, R, Ledsham, A, Oliver, C (1979) *Basic Mathematics: revision and practice*, Oxford University Press.

(ii) Solomon, R C (1987) *GCSE Mathematics*, The Guernsey Press Company Ltd.

(iii) *SMP 11-16 Negative numbers* (1983) Cambridge University Press.

(iv) SMP 11-16 B5 (1987) Cambridge University Press.

page 49: (i) *SMP 11-16 Whole numbers 4* (1983) Cambridge University Press.

(ii) Smith, Mike and Jones, Ian (1987) *Central Maths for GCSE and Standard Grade*, Heinemann Educational Books.

page 50: (i) *Mathematics in Action 3A* (1987) Blackie, Chambers.

(ii) Graham, Duncan and Christine (1983) *Maths for You 2*, Hutchinson.

(iii) *Mathematics in Action 3B* (1987) Blackie, Chambers.

(iv) Elvin, R, Ledsham, A, Oliver, C (1979) *Basic mathematics: revision and practice*, Oxford University Press.

page 51: (i) *Mathematics in Action 3B* (1987) Blackie, Chambers.

(ii) Holderness, Jean (1987) *GCSE Maths Foundation Level*, Causeway Books.

page 52: (i) Rayner, David (1987) *Mathematics for GCSE 2*, The Oxford University Press.

(ii) *Mathematics in Action 3A* (1987) Blackie Chambers.

(iii) *Mathematics in Action 3B* (1987) Blackie, Chambers.

(iv) Holderness, Jean (1987) *GCSE Maths Foundation Level*, Causeway Books.

page 53: (i) Rayner, David (1987) *Mathematics for GCSE 2*, Oxford University Press.

(ii) *SMP 11-16 R2* (1986) Cambridge University Press.

(iii) Farrow, L and Llewellyn, S (1987) *Mathematics Using the Basic Skills*, Stanley Thorne.

(iv) *SMP 11-16 G5* (1986) Cambridge University Press.

(v) Hollands, Roy (1983) *Success with Numbers*, Macmillan Education.

(vi) Farrow, L and Llewellyn, S (1987) *Mathematics Using the Basic Skills*, Stanley Thorne.

(vii) Mathematics in Action 3A (1987) Blackie, Chambers.

page 54: (i) *SMP 11-16 G5* (1986) Cambridge University Press.

(ii) *SMP 11-16 G2* (1985) Cambridge University Press.

(iii) Glen, Robert (1987) *Foundation Maths for GCSE and Standard Grade*, Heinemann Educational Books.

(v) Farrow, L and Llewellyn, S (1987) *Mathematics Using the Basic Skills*, Stanley Thorne.

(iv) Bental, Lila (1986) *Mathematics with meaning*, Stanley Thornes.

(vi) Smith, Mike and Jones, Ian (1987) *Central Maths for GCSE and Standard Grade*, Heinemann Educational Books.

(vii) *Mathematics in Action 3A* (1987) Blackie, Chambers.

(viii) Graham, Duncan and Christine, *Maths for You 2*, Hutchinson.

(ix) Graham, Duncan and Christine, *Maths for You 1*, Hutchinson.

page 55: (i) *Mathematics in Action 3A* (1987) Blackie, Chambers.

(ii) Kaner, Peter (1983) *Integrated Mathematics Scheme IMS M1*, Bell & Hyman.

(iii) Kaner, Peter (1985) *Integrated Mathematics Scheme IMS M2*, Bell & Hyman.

page 56: (i) Kaner, Peter (1987) *Mathematics Revision for GCSE*, Unwin Hyman.

(ii) *Mathematics in Action 3B* (1987) Blackie, Chambers.

(iii) Smith, Mike and Jones, Ian (1987) *Central Maths for GCSE and Standard Grade*, Heinemann Educational Books.

(iv) *Mathematics in Action 3A* (1987) Blackie, Chambers.

page 57: (i) *Pupil Poll* (1981) Schools Council Publications.

(ii) Graham, Duncan and Christine *Maths for You 2*, Hutchinson.

(iii) *Mathematics in Action* (1986) Blackie, Chambers.

(iv) Graham, Duncan and Christine *Maths for You 1*, Hutchinson.

(v) *Mathematics in Action* (1986) Blackie, Chambers.

# Chapter 4

page 65:    Smith, D E, (1953) *History of Mathematics Volume 1*, Dover Publications.

page 69:    Boyer, Carl (1968) *A History of Mathematics*, Wiley International.

page 70:    Smith, D.E. (1953) *History of Mathematics.* Volume 1, Dover Publications.

page 71:    Zaslavsly, Claudia (1973) *Africa Counts*, Lawrence Hill.

page 73:    Zaslavsky, Claudia (1973) *Africa Counts*, Lawrence Hill .

page 76:    Smith, D E, (1953) *History of Mathematics Volume 2*, Dover Publications.

page 77/78:    Zaslavsky, Claudia (1973) *Africa Counts*, Lawrence Hill.

page 81:    Barrs, John, *The Game of Go*, Philmar.

page 86/87:    Gill, V and Hildyard, E (1981) *Caribbean Home Economics 2*, Macmillan.

page 90:    *Longmans School Caribbean Atlas* (1982) Collins-Longman, Jamaica.

# Chapter 5

page 95:    *Mathematics*, Obunsha. Japan.

page 96/97:    *Matematika* (1986) Tankönyvkiadó, Budapest.

page 98:    Hogben, L (1955) *Man Must Measure*, Rathbone Press.

page 99:    Meninger, C. *Number Words and Number Symbols,* MIT Press, Cambridge, Massachusetts, USA.

page 100:    Hogben, L (1955) *Man Must Measure*, Rathbone Press.

page 101:    Smith D.E (1953) *History of Mathematics*, Dover Publications.

page 106:     Pennick, N. *The ancient science of Geomancy,* Thames and Hudson, London.

page 108:     Shap Calendar — The National RE Centre, Kensington Square, London W8 5HN.

page 109:     *Mathematics Teaching,* March 1987, Association of Teachers of Mathematics.

page 110:     *Mathematics in School,* September 1988.

pages 111/112: Gerdes, P. (1988) *For the Learning of Mathematics* (8.1)

page 114/115: Gerdes, P. (1988) *Reconstruction and extension of lost symmetries.*

page 122:     Harris, Mary, *Maths in Work* © Crown copyright. Reproduced by permission of the Controller of HMSO.

# Chapter 6

page 124:     *Aramco World* Volume 40 Number 5, September-October 1989, Aramco Services Company.

page 125:     Mustafa, Ahmed (1979) *The Scientific Construction of Arabic Alphabets.*

page 126/127: *Armaco World* Volume 38 Number 6, November-December 1987, Aramco Services Company.

page 128:     *Arts & The Islamic World* Volume 1 Number 3, Summer/Autumn 1983, Islamic Arts Foundation.

page 130-133: Critchlow, Keith (1976) *Islamic Patterns,* Thames & Hudson.

page 134/135: *Visual Elements — World Traditional Folk Patterns* (1988). Rockport Publishers, Rockport, Massachusetts, USA.

page 136:     *Aramco World* Volume 37 Number 6, November-December 1986, Aramco Services Company.

page 155:     *Arts & The Islamic World* Volume 3 Spring 1985, Islamic Arts Foundation.

# Chapter 7

page 157:   *Tools for Self-Reliance*, Netley Marsh Workshops, SO4 2GY.

page 160:   *Young People Now*, June 1989.

page 163:   Friends of the Earth.
Sally Zalewski, International Centre for Conservation Education, Guiting Power, Cheltenham.

page 164:   Friends of the Earth.

page 165:   UNESCO 'World problems in the Classroom'. Educational Studies and Documents No. 41. © Unesco 1981. Reproduced by permission of UNESCO.

page 168:   Teaching Development Issues, Section 4 Health(1986), Development Education Project. Manchester Polytechnic M20 8RG.

page 169:   UNICEF News, 1981.

page 172:   Diagram by Frances Khan based on 'Facts on Food' from Centre for Social and Economic Information, Geneva; data based on paper by J.S. and C.E. Steinhart in Science (19 April 1974).

page 174:   Drawn by Francis Khan.

page 175:   *Time Educational Supplement*, 1988.

page 176:   *Spur* WDM (1986)

page 177:   Photo from *Catholic Pictorial.*

page 182:   *Third World Atlas* (1983) The Open University.

page 185:   *Third World Atlas* (1983) The Open University.

page 186-188: *New Internationalist*, March 1985.

page 189:   Macauley, David (1984) *Pyramid*, Collins.

# Chapter 8

page 195:     *Young People Now.* November 1989.

page 196:     *Third World Atlas* (1983) The Open University.

page 198/199: *Teaching Development Issues, Section 7: Aid and Development* (1986) Development Education Project, Manchester Polytechnic M20 8RG.

page 200:     Seager, Joni and Olson, Ann (1986) *Women in the World*, A Pluto Press Project.

page 208:     'So you love animals? For school dinner?' SCREAM, The Vegetarian Society.

page 209-214: Assistance from Terry Thomas and Department of Engineering, University of Warwick, is gratefully acknowledged. The department offers B.Eng (Design and Appropriate Technology).

page 210:     New International Publication

page 212:     *Third World Atlas* (1983) The Open University.

page 213:     *Visitors' Guide,* Centre for Alternative Technology.

page 214:     Dunn, P D (1978) *Appropriate Technology*, Macmillan Press.

page 215:     *Guardian* 22nd December 1989.

page 216/     *The Little Green Book,* Vole.
217/219

# Chapter 9

page 241:     *Mathematics Today*, February 1988, Dhanpat Rai & Sons, Delhi.

page 242:     *Ramanvjan's notebooks*, printed in 'Correspondences' by Shobana Jeyasingh.

page 243/     *Correspondence* by Shobana Jeyasingh.
244/245

page 248:     World Development Movement booklet.

page 249:     *The Tea Trade,* World Development Movement booklet.

page 250:     *Times Educational Supplement,* 7 September 1984.

page 253:     *The World in Your Coffee Cup,* Revised Edition 1980. Campaign Co-op (London), 172 Lavender Hill, London SW11.

page 259/260: *The Guardian* Saturday October 18th 1986.

page 261:     *CWDE Cartoon Sheet 2: Employment*
              *Technology Fact Sheet 4 T*hird World First.

page 262:     *State of the World's Children,* UNICEF

page 265:     National Surveys reported in draft MOH/USAID/-UNICEF/WHO Evaluation Report, 1986.

page 267:     Worldwatch Paper 37, May 1980.

page 268:     From *The Nursing Times,* June 1987.

page 269/270: *Evening Mail* (Birmingham) Saturday 10th, 1990.

# Bibliography

Adam, R. (1989) *Who profits?,* Lion Publishing plc, Oxford.

Ahmed, N. and Mills, P. (1987) in *Black Voices* An anthology of ACER's Black Young Writers Competition, Edited by Paul McGilchrist, ACER.

Arora, R. and Duncan C. (1986) *Multicultural education: towards good practice* Routledge and Kegan Paul, London.

Assistant Masters and Mistresses Association (1987) *Multicultural and Antiracist Education,* AMMA, London.

Association of Teachers of Mathematics (1973) *Fifteen Starters for the Secondary Classroom,* Derby.

Baby Milk Action (1989) leaflet, 6 Regent Terrace, Cambridge CB2 1AA.

Ball, J. (1989) *Games from around the world,* produced in association with SMARTIES for the Pop Maths Roadshow.

Basham, A. L. (1985) *The wonder that was India,* Sidgwick and Jackson, London.

Beckles, E. (1990) *Multicultural Teaching* Vol.8 No.2.

Bowles and Gintis (1976) *Schooling in Capitalist America*

Buccheri, S. (1989) *Young People Now,* June.

Bullock Report (1974) *Language for Life* p143.

Burton, L. (1986) *Girls into maths can go* Holt Education.

Centre for World Development Education (1988) *World development database,* CWDE London.

Coard, B. (1971) *How the West Indian Child is made Subnormal in the British School System,* New Beacon Books, London.

Cockcroft Report (1982) *Mathematics Counts* (Report of the Committee of Inquiry into the Teaching of Mathematics in Schools). HMSO.

Commission for Racial Equality (1988) *Learning in Terror,* London

Crawford, K. P. (1986a) *Simultaneous and succesive processing, executive control and social experience: Individual differences in educational achievement and problem solving in mathematics* (Unpublished thesis) Australia.

Crawford, K.P. (1986b) *Cognitive and social factors in problem solving behaviour* in 'Proceedings of the 10th Annual Conference on the International Group for the Psychology of Mathematics Education', London.

Critchlow, K. (1976) *Islamic Patterns —an analytical and a cosmological approach,* Thames and Hudson, London.

D'Ambrosio, U quote in Chapter 1 from a paper delivered at ICME-6 1988, and Chapter 2 from ICME-6 1988: *Ethnomathematics and its place in the History and Pedagogy of Mathematics* —For the Learning of Mathematics.

Dawe, L. (1983) 'Bilingualism and mathematical reasoning in English as a second language' in *Educational Studies in mathematics.*

DES (1985) *Education for all* (Swann Report) HMSO.

DES (1987) *Better mathematics,* HMSO.

DES (1988) HMI *Maths from 5 to 16.*

DES (1989) *The National Curriculum: From Policy to Practice,* HMSO.

Datta and Singh, *History of Hindu mathematics* Asian Publishing House, India.

Development Education Project (1986) *Teaching development issues,* Sections 1-7, c/o Manchester Polytechnic, 801 Wilmslow Road, Manchester M20 8RG.

Devi, S. (1977) *Figuring: The Joy of Numbers,* Hodder and Stoughton, Sevenoaks.

Dickson, L. Brown, M and Gibson, O (1984) *Children learning mathematics —a teacher's guide to recent research,* Cassell, London.

Dixon, B. (1977) *Catching them young 1: Sex, Race and Class in Childrens' Fiction; 2: Political Ideas in Childrens' Fiction.* Pluto Press, London.

Eggleston, J. Dunn, J Anjali, M (1986) *Education For Some,* Trentham Books, Stoke on Trent.

Ernest, P. (1986) 'Social and Political Values' in *Mathematics Teaching* Vol.16.

Francis, M. 'Transcript of a discussion between a teacher and a group of children' in *Everyone Counts* ILEA (Harcourt, Brece, Jovanowitch)

Friends of the Earth *Rainforest,* London.

Friends of the Earth *Recycling,* London.

Friere, P. (1985) *Pedagogy of The Oppressed,* Penguin Books.

Gaine, C. (1987) *No Problem Here —A Practical Approach to Education and Race in White Schools,* Hutchinson.

George, S. (1987) *How the other half dies,* Penguin Books.

Gerdes, P. (1988) 'A widespread Decorative motifs and the Pythagorean Theorem' *For the Learning of Mathematics,* 8(1).

Gerdes, P. (1986a) *On culture, mathematics and curriculum development in Mozambique;* in Mellin-Olsen and Johnsen Hoines.

Gerdes, P. (1986b) How to recognise hidden geometrical thinking: a contribution to the development of anthropological mathematics, *For The Learning of Mathematics,* 6(2).

Gibson, J. R. (1983) The Aga Khan Award for Architecture — An Architect's overview in *Arts and The Islamic World,* ARAMACO magizine Vol.1 No.3.

Gill, D. 'Politics of Percent' in *Mathmatics Teaching.* Vol.114.

Gooneatilake, S. (1984) *Aborted Discovery — science and creativity in the Third World,* Zed.

Graham, J. and Lynn, S. (1989) *Children's images of the Third World countries,* South Bank Polytechnic, London.

Halliday, M.A.K. (1977) *Language and Social Man,* Longman.

Hargreaves, D.H. (1967) *Social relationships in a secondary school* RKP.

Hardy, G H (1941) *A Mathematician's Apology* University Press, Cambridge.

Harris, M *Maths in Work* University of London, Institute of Education.

Haylock, D Blake, G and Platt, J 'Using Maths to make things happen' in *Mathematics in schools* March 14 (2).

Health Education Council (1987) *The Health Divide.*

Hicks, D. (1981) 'Bias in School Books: messages from the ethnocentric curriculum' in *The School in the Multicultural Society,* James, A and Jeffcoate, R (Ed), Harper and Row.

Hogben, L (1955) *Man must measure,* Rathbone Books.

Home Office (1981) *Racial Attacks — Report of a Home Office study,* HMSO London.

Home Office (1989) *Response to Racial Attacks and Harassment/Guidance for Statutory Agencies,* Report of Interdepartmental Racial Attacks Group.

House of Commons — Select Committee Report (1986) *Racial Attacks and Harassment,* HMSO, London.

Hudson, B (1987) *Global statistics,* Centre for Global Education, University of York.

Hudson, B (1987) *Global problems — Mathematics exercises involving the use of social and economic statistics,* Centre for Global Education, University of York.

Jaggi, O.P. (1981) *History of Science and Technology in India*, Atma Ram and Sons, India.

Joseph, G.G. (1981) 'History of Mathematics: a non-Eurocentric approach' in *Race and Class* 28(3).

Kawaguchi, T (1988) *Mathematical Thoughts being latent in various Artistic Activities* Fifth Day Special, ICME6 — Hungary.

Khyyam, Omar *Rubaiyat*

Klein, G (1986) *Reading into Racism, RKP, London.*

Lawton, C (1989) *Shap Calendar of Religious Festivals,* Shap, The National Society's RE Centre, 23 Kensington Square, London W8 5HN.

Leeds Community Relations Council (1987) *Racial Harassment in Leeds 1985-86.*

Macawley, D (1975) *Pyramid,* Collins, London.

Mathematical Association (1980) *Pupil Projects: their use in secondary school,* Leicester.

Mathematical Association (1987) *Sharing Mathematics with parents: planning school-based events,* Stanley Thornes, Cheltenham.

*Mathematics Pie* (1984) No. 103 from The Mathematical Association, Leicester.

Maxwell, J 'Hidden Messages' in *Mathematics Teaching,* Vol.3.

McDiarmid and Pratt (1971) *Teaching Prejudice.* Ontario Institute for Studies in Education, Toronto, p2.

Meninger, K *Number words and number symbols,* MIT Press.

Metropolitan Police (1987) *Racial Harassment Action Guide.*

Midland Examining Group (1985) *Equal Opportunities and the GCSE — a policy statement,* TWMEB, Birmingham.

Mikami, *Mathematics in China and Japan.* Chelsea.

Milne, A (1986) *The cost of healthy eating,* The Guardian 18 October.

Mustafa, A (1979) *The Scientific Construction of Arabic Alphabets.*

Nash, I (1973) *Classroom observed,* Routledge Kegan Paul, London.

National Association of Head Teachers *A School Policy on anti-racism.* NAHT, Haywards Heath, West Sussex.

National Association of Schoolmasters and Union of Women Teachers (1989) *Developing a School/College Based Policy on Racist Behaviour,* NASUWT, Birmingham.

National Union of Teachers (1989) *Anti-Racism in Education,* NUT, London.

Nelson, P (1988) 'Sand drawings of the Vanatu' in *Mathematics in schools* 17(4).

New Internationalist (1986) (figures on population in South Africa) Third World Atlas Calendar.

Nicholas A P and Williams K R *Discover Vedic Mathematics.* North London Polytechnic.

Nicholas A P Pickles and Williams K *Introductory Lectures on Vedic Mathematics* North London Polytechnic.

Nicholas, A P Pickles and Williams *Vertically and Crosswise*. North London Polytechnic.

Nobre, S R (1986) *The Animal Lottery and Mathematics Education.*

Northern Examining Association (1987) *Instructions to Chief Examiners in the preparation of GCSE question papers,* J.M.B., Manchester.

Open University (1983) *Third World Atlas,* Open University Press, Milton Keynes, prepared by Ben Grow and Alan Thomas

Pennick, N (1979) *The Ancient Science of Geomancy,* Thames and Hudson, London.

Professional Association of Teachers (1989) *A Policy on Race,* PAT, Derby.

Rockport Publishers (1988) *Visual Elements: world traditional folk patterns,* Blunt and Company.

Rose, S Kamin, L J and Lewontin, R C (1984) *Not In Our Genes,* Penguin Books.

Ross, K (1989) 'See no evil' in *Times Educational Supplement,* 21st, July.

Sapir, E. (1963) *Language* Hart-Davies, London.

Schumacher E.F. (1974) *Small is Beautiful* Abacus.

Scottish Ethnic Minority Research Unit (1987) *Racial Harassment in Glasgow.*

Seager, J. and Olson, A. (1986) *Women in the World — an International Atlas,* Pluto Press Project , Pan Books, London.

Skemp, R.R. (1971) *The Psychology of Learning* Penguin Harmondsworth.

Shan, S. (1989) *Antiracist Approaches to Science: Fibre in your Diet,* Martineau Teachers' Centre, Birmingham.

SMILE material can be obtained from SMILE Centre, Isaac Newton Centre, Lancaster Road, London W11 1QS.

Smith, D.E. (1953) *History of Mathematics Vol.1 and Vol.2,* Dover.

Stern, P. et al, (1983) *Field Engineering,* Intermediate Technology Publications, London.

Strevens, P. (1974) *What is linguistic and how it may help the mathematics teacher,* an introductory paper prepared for the 1974 Conference, UNESCO, Paris.

Times Educational Supplement (1984) *Pupils know little about Third World,* 7th September.

Tirthaji, K. (1965) *Vedic Mathematics,* Motilal and Banarsidas, Delhi.

*Tools for Self-Reliance,* Netley Marsh Workshops, Southampton, SO4 2GY.

Traidcraft (1990) *People Friendly Clothing Pack.* Traidcraft Exchange, Kingsway, Gateshead, Tyne and Wear NE11 0NE.

Traidcraft (1989) *People-Friendly Clothing — campaign briefing,* (as above).

Tully, L. (1990) *Birmingham Evening Mail,* 10th March.

UNICEF (1981) *UNICEF News.*

UNICEF (1984) *Child survival: some prerequisites,* UNICEF News issue 119/1984/1.

UNICEF (1990) *The state of the world's children,* OUP, Oxford.

University of London School Examinations Board (1985) *Sexism, Discrimination and Gender Biases in GCE Examinations,* London.

University of London School Examinations Board (1986) *Cultural diversity and GCE Examinations,* ULSEB, London.

Van Dormolen, J. (1988) *Value of texts for learning mathematics for real life,* Meulenhoff Educatief, Amsterdam.

Vidal, J. *The Guardian* 15th June.

Vole, (1979) *The Little Green Book,* The Green Alliance, Wildwood House, London.

Vygotsky, (1962) *Thought and Language,* MIT Press and John Wiley, New York.

Woodrow, D. (1984) 'Cultural impacts on children learning mathematics' *Mathematics in schools* 13(5).

World Bank (1975) *World Bank Atlas.*

World Development Movement (1982) *The Tea Trade,* WDM, London.

World Studies Project (1976) *Learning for Change in World Society.*

*Young People Now* (1988), National Youth Bureau, Leicester.

Zaslavsky, C. (1979) *Africa Counts: Number and Pattern for Teachers,* Lawrence Hill, New York.

Zaslavsky, C. (1979) *Count on your fingers African style* , Harper and Row, London.

Zaslavsky, (1982) *Tic Tac Toe and other Three-in-a-row games from Ancient Egypt to the modern computer,* Harper and Row, London.

# Resource Lists

The first list gives some books and materials which will be of interest to teachers who would like to try out some of the ideas in the book. The second list gives some organisations which are able to provide material for further examples or background information of use to both teachers and students. Neither list is exhaustive, but we have found these materials and organisations helpful to us in our work.

## Books and Materials

Bell, R. and Cornelius *M. Board games around the world,* Cambridge University Press, Cambridge.

Development Education Project *Teaching development issues,* c/o Manchester Polytechnic, 801 Wilmslow Road, Didsbury, Manchester M20 8RG.

Devi, S. *Figuring: the joy of numbers,* Hodder and Stoughton, Sevenoaks, 1977.

Dodd, P. *Mathematics from around the world: a multicultural resource book* and *Puzzles; a mathematical resource book,* available from 73 Beech Grove, Whitley Bay, Tyne and Wear NE26 3PL.

El-Said, I. and Parman, A. *Geometry concepts in Islamic art,* World of Islam Festival Trust and Scorpian Publishing Ltd.; available from Jonathan Press, Colchester, 1976.

EQUALS Publications *Assessment alternatives in Mathematics,* EQUALS and the California Mathematics Council; available through Jonathan Press, Great Tey, Colchester.

Harris, M. Ed. *School, Mathematics and Work,* Falmer Press, Basingstoke, 1991.

Jones, L. Ed. *Teaching mathematics and art,* Stanley Thornes, Cheltenham.

Mathematical Association *Mathematics in a multicultural society*, Leicester, 1989.

*Mathematics in Schools* — a journal of The Mathematical Association.

*Mathematics Teaching* — A journal of The Association of Teachers of Mathematics.

Merttens, R. and Vass, J. *Sharing Maths Cultures: IMPACT (Inventing Maths for Parents and Children and Teachers)*, Falmer Press, Basingstoke.

*Multicultural Teaching*, a journal published by Trentham Press, 13/14 Trent Trading Park, Bottleslow Street, Stoke-on-Trent, ST1 3LY.

*New Internationalist*, a journal from New Internationalist, 42 Hythe Bridge Street, Oxford OX1 2EP.

OXFAM/UNICEF *Games of the world*, OXFAM.

Stern, P. et. al. (Ed.) *Field Engineering*, from an original work by Longland F., Intermediate Technology Publications, 9 King Street, London WC2E 8HW.

UNDP *Human Development Report*, One United Nations Plaza, New York NY 10017, 1990.

UNICEF-UK *State of the World's Chidren*, OUP, Oxford.

World Studies Teacher Training Centre *Global Pi: world studies in the science and maths classroom*, Unversity of York, Heslington, York YO1 5DD.

## Organisations

Anti-Apartheid Movement, 13 Mandela Street, London NW1 0DW for information about South Africa.

Applied knowledge, Dean Clough Business Park, Halifax, West Yorkshire HX3 5AX for PC Globe (database).

Association of Teachers of Mathematics working group *Bilingual Students and Maths,* Colin Penfold, Peterborough Maths Centre, Stanground College, Peterborough Road, Farcet, Peterborough PE7 3BW.

Baby Milk Action (BMAC) 6 Regent Terrace, Cambridge, CB2 1AA.

Centre for World Development Education (CWDE), Regent's College, Inner Circle, Rengent's Park, London NW1 4NS for database (using GRASS) on world statistics (UN sources).

Christian Aid, PO box 100, London SE1 7RT for information on life in many countries, aid and trade.

City of Birmingham (Community Language Unit), Marineau Teachers' Centre, Balden Road, Harborne, Birmingham for Multilingual posters and for ESG booklets.

Commission for Racial Equality, Elliot House, 10/12 Allington Street, London SE1E 5HE for information on racism in Britain.

Development Education Centre, Gillett Centre, Selly Oak Colleges, Bristol Road, Birmingham B29 6LE for a wide range of resources.

Friends of the Earth, 26/28 Underwood Street, London N1 7JQ for materials, on the environment.

Multilingual Matters Ltd., Bank House, 8a Hill Road, Clevedon, Avon BS21 7HH for books on bilingualism and multiculture.

National Anti-Racist Movement in Education, PO Box 9, Walsall, West Midlands. SW1 3SF, an organisation fighting racism in education.

New Internationalist Publications Ltd., 55 Rectory Road, Oxford, OX4 1BW for the N.I. calendar, New Internationalist journal and other publications.

One World Week, PO Box 100, London SE1 7RT, ideas for the October week.

OXFAM, 274 Banbury Road, Oxford, OX2 7DZ for many ideas and resources on development, trade and aid.

Royal Society for the Prevention of Cruelty to Animals, Causeway, Horsham, Sussex RH12 1HG.

Runnymede Trust, 37A Grays Inn Road, London WCIX 8PP for material on racism.

SMILE Centre, Isaac Newton Centre for Professional Development, Lancaster Road, London W11 1QS for resources such as Bengali Puzzle.

Traidcraft, Kingsway, Gateshead, Tyne and Wear NE11 0NE for People Frendly Clothing campaign.

UNESCO, 7 place de Fontenoy, 75700 Paris for information on world education.

UNICEF-UK, 55 Lincoln's Inn Fields, London WC2A 3NB for resources on the U.N. and children around the world.

Vegetarian Society, Parkdale, Dunham Road, Altrincham, Cheshire WA14 4QG for information on efficiency in farming and vegetarian matters.

Women into Technology Foundation, Concept 2000, 250 Farnborough Road, Farnborough, Hampshire GU14 7LU.

World Development Movement, 25 Beehive Place, London SW9 7RQ for information on trade and aid.

# INDEX

307